Inside Classrooms

The Teaching and Learning of Mathematics
in Social Context

INSIDE CLASSROOMS

THE TEACHING AND LEARNING OF MATHEMATICS IN SOCIAL CONTEXT

Maureen Lyons, Kathleen Lynch, Sean Close, Emer Sheerin and Philip Boland

INSTITUTE OF PUBLIC
ADMINISTRATION

First published 2003
by the Institute of Public Administration
57–61 Lansdowne Road
Dublin 4
Ireland

for
The Department of Education and Science

ISBN   1 902448 83 9

British Library Cataloguing in Publication Data
A catalogue record for this book is available from the British Library

Cover design by Creative Inputs, Dublin
Typeset in 10.5/12.5 Times New Roman by Computertype Ltd., Dublin
Printed by Betaprint, Dublin

Contents

Acknowledgements

Like all research, this study would not have been completed without the co-operation and support of several people. There were so many who gave generously of their time and talent to see the project through to completion that it seems best to follow the chronology of the research itself in our vote of thanks.

This study was initiated and funded by the Gender Equality Committee of the Department of Education and Science (DES). We acknowledge their generous support and encouragement throughout, in particular the support of Maureen Bohan and Hilda McHugh. Both Maureen and Hilda have been unfailing and generous in the time and attention they have given to the project, and in encouraging the research team at every stage. We also wish to express our appreciation to the mathematics inspectors in the Department of Education and Science for their interest in and commitment to the research. We acknowledge in particular the work of Doreen McMorris and Brendan O'Regan for the advice and guidance they gave us as members of the Research Advisory Committee to the project. The support of Rhona McSweeney of the recently established Gender Equality Unit of the Department of Education and Science is also gratefully acknowledged.

The Research Advisory Committee played a key role in guiding the project to completion, and we are deeply grateful to all those, including the mathematics inspectors named above, who gave so generously of their time to attend research presentations and advisory meetings. Many thanks to Leone Burton, University of Birmingham, Mairead Dunne, University of Sussex, Sheelagh Drudy, University College Dublin, Anne McNamara, Chairperson of the Irish Mathematics Teachers Association, Anne Lodge, National University of Ireland, Maynooth, John O'Donoghue, University of Limerick, Elizabeth Oldham, Trinity College Dublin and Emer Smyth, Economic and Social Research Institute.

The initial production of the Junior Certificate data was greatly assisted by the generous help and support of staff from the department, in particular by Catherine Kelly of the examinations branch in Athlone. The statistics branch of the Department of Education and Science also gave guidance and assistance in preparing the data for analysis, for which we are extremely grateful.

The research involved a series of intensive studies including the videotaping of mathematics and English classes, interviews with students, teachers, school principals and parents, and a questionnaire study with students. We are deeply indebted to the teachers and students who welcomed us into their classrooms, both during the pilot phase and the main phase of the study. We thank the school principals for the time they gave us in completing interviews about their schools, and the parents, students and teachers for talking so openly and honestly with us. We hope that we have honoured their word in what we have written.

Although we cannot name the persons involved, given the rules of confidentiality that govern our research, we would particularly like to thank those mathematics teachers who not only gave us the opportunity to videotape their lessons, but who also read draft chapters and commented on the text as it was developing. Their contribution to the research has been invaluable, not least because of the experiential wisdom that they brought to the reading of the text.

The project was facilitated not only by the support of those who had a formal role in the research, but also by those who made informal contributions at different stages. We would like to thank Leonie Warren for the contribution she made as a researcher in the fieldwork stage of the project, and Rose Dolan and Diane Birnie for the valuable contribution they made, as teachers of mathematics, in reading and commenting on the draft text. We also acknowledge the work of a number of graduate students in the Equality Studies Centre in UCD, and that of mathematics students in St. Patrick's College in Drumcondra, for the work they did in transcribing the classroom tapes. Carlos Bruen worked as a research assistant in the final phase of the study. We want to acknowledge his sterling and meticulous work in preparing the text for publication. We also appreciate the contribution made by Fergus Mulligan in editing the final draft, and the work of the IPA editors and publication staff in seeing the book through to publication.

The analysis of the various data sets for the study was a long and complicated task. We would like to thank all of those technical support staff in University College Dublin who assisted us with the analysis, and in particular the staff of the Computer Centre and the Audio Visual Centre. Our thanks also to the Library staff for their assistance at every stage of the project and to all the technical and administrative staff in the university who provided back-up and support.

As with all projects, there are people who have made an exceptional contribution to guiding and supporting the team in completing the study. In this regard, we want to acknowledge the profound generosity and support of Anne Lodge of the Education Department of NUI Maynooth, Elizabeth Oldham of TCD and Emer Smyth of the ESRI, for the time and attention they gave to the project. It was far in excess of what was expected of them as members of the Advisory Committee.

This project was completed by a multidisciplinary team involving social scientists, equality studies specialists and mathematics educators from University College Dublin and St. Patrick's College Drumcondra. It was an exciting and challenging intellectual adventure that we hope will make a significant contribution to educational debate and public policy. It could not have been completed however without the support and encouragement of our colleagues in our own departments and centres. We are especially grateful to Sara Cantillon, Patricia Gantly, Mary McEvoy and Phyllis Murphy for their generous support and assistance.

Like all major studies, the completion of this research was a truly collective effort. The not-so-visible members of that collectivity were our partners and families. We thank them sincerely for their kindness, patience and support throughout the project.

Introduction

What the book is about

Inspired by the use of video in the analysis of mathematics classrooms in the Third International Mathematics and Science Study (TIMSS) (Kawanaka et al, 1999), this book represents a unique venture in Irish educational research. With the co-operation of teachers and students, it takes a video camera into classrooms to analyse the ways in which mathematics (and some English) classes are taught in second-level schools. It also examines the relationship between teaching practices and attitudes to learning by listening to the voices of students, as well as their teachers and parents. While the primary focus of the study is on mathematics, it also offers insight into the teaching of English, highlighting similarities and differences in classroom environments.

The impetus for this study came from earlier research undertaken by the Economic and Social Research Institute (ESRI) study (Hannan, et al, 1996) on coeducation. The ESRI study indicated that certain girls in coeducational schools were underachieving in mathematics, and further research of the issue was recommended. The present study was designed to explore the inside life of coeducational and single sex classes across different types of schools. The main objective was to provide greater understanding of the pedagogical practices employed across different classes, and explore how pedagogical styles impacted on students' attitudes to, and experience of, learning mathematics. A related objective was to establish the impact that gender and social class had on the teaching and learning of mathematics in the context of different teaching styles and different tracking (streaming, banding or setting) systems.

The core part of the book is based on an intensive video study of twenty mathematics lessons and six English lessons involving second-year students in ten different second-level schools. The video studies are complemented by interviews with the students about their learning experiences; with teachers about their subject and about teaching; with principals about their schools; and with parents about schooling in general and mathematics education in particular. It is the first intensive video study of its kind to be undertaken in schools in Ireland, and one of the very few to be undertaken internationally.

In preparation for the main video study, an analysis of Junior Certificate Mathematics Examination results for 1992 to1996 was carried out. This data is also reported in the book. It sets the scene for the video-study of classrooms, highlighting important issues in relation to the relationship between the gender of students, their social class background, and the status of different types of schools.

Outline of Chapters

The opening chapter, *The Teaching and Learning of Mathematics: Gender and Related Issues,* provides a background and framework for interpreting the findings of the study. It examines major trends in national and international thinking on mathematics education, focusing in particular on recent theoretical developments and research findings relating to the teaching of the subject. This chapter also sets the study in the context of debates about how students', teachers' and parents' attitudes to school mathematics impact on learning. As a primary objective of the study was to examine the impact of gender on learning climates of mathematics classrooms, the literature in this field is given particular attention.

Using Junior Certificate Examination data, Chapter 2 examines the *Take-up and Performance in Junior Certificate Mathematics* over a five year period, 1992-96. It outlines the differences in both take-up and performance rates at each of the three levels of mathematics (Foundation, Ordinary and Higher), focusing in particular on gender and school type differences over the five-year period. The analysis of the Junior Certificate data took place before the case studies of specific schools. Knowing the national patterns in take-up and performance enabled us to make informed choices in the selection of schools and classes for the case studies.

A brief account of the research methodology is provided in Chapter 3, *The Case Studies.* Special attention is given to the rationale for using a triangulated, multi-method approach. Using data provided by school principals, a profile of the schools and classes chosen for the case studies is also presented here. A profile of the teachers of mathematics who co-operated in the research is also provided in this chapter.

Chapter 4, *Core Themes in the Teaching and Learning of Mathematics,* is the first of five chapters investigating the mathematics classroom. It is based on the analysis of the videotape transcripts of twenty mathematics lessons in ten different classrooms. The focus is on describing and analysing the dominant teaching methodologies employed across the mathematics classes, including the physical and social environment of the classroom, and on exploring the implications of these for learning mathematics.

Chapter 5, *Classroom Interaction: An In-depth Analysis*, explores in greater depth the nature and dynamics of teacher-student interactions in the context of the different pedagogical practices and climates observed in the mathematics classes. Interactions are analysed along two dimensions, in terms of who initiated them and in terms of their specific character or role. The private exchanges between the teacher and the students, or those among the students themselves, were not included in this analysis.

While there are certain normative trends in the teaching and learning environment of Irish classrooms, not all students are treated the same. Chapter 6, *Gender Differences in Classrooms,* examines the ways in which classrooms differ in terms of gender, particularly in terms of the relations between teachers and students. In so doing, it helps us understand why schools may produce different outcomes for female and male students. The chapter also examines the impact of particular gendered identities on students' attitudes to mathematics.

Both our study of the Junior Certificate data and international research had indicated clearly that gendered identities are not uni-dimensional in terms of their impact on mathematics learning. The students' social class and the track (stream, band or set) in which they are placed (and by implication, the level at which they study mathematics) also impact strongly on their learning experience. In the light of this, Chapter 7 is devoted to analysing *The Impact of Grouping and Social Class* on the learning environment in mathematics classes.

When we were designing the video study, it was decided that the research would be greatly enriched if we had some comparative data on teaching practices other than mathematics. A small number of English classes were videotaped therefore to give an indication as to whether the styles we observed in mathematics were specific to that subject. The focus of Chapter 8, *The English Classroom,* is on the teaching of English and in particular on the differences and similarities between the teaching of mathematics and English. The data provides many interesting insights into how the culture of English classrooms is different, but also similar in some ways, to that of mathematics.

To fully comprehend what was happening in classrooms, we elicited the views of the teachers and students we had observed, about their classroom experiences. We also interviewed a sub-sample of parents. Using data from questionnaires, interviews and focus groups, we explored the differences between all three groups in terms of their understanding of the learning and teaching of mathematics.

Chapter 9 is devoted to examining *Teachers' Perspectives* on teaching and learning, while we outline the *Students' Perspectives* in Chapter 10. Through the interviews and questionnaires, we also explored the attitudes of teachers and students to the subject of mathematics itself. We devoted attention, however, to listening to how teachers interpreted gender and social class differences in their students' responses to mathematics.

As one of the first studies to examine parent views on the learning process, the study provides considerable insight into how parents and schools differ in their understanding of school education and mathematics education in particular. Chapter 11, *Parent Perspectives*, shows how some parents suffer from a serious knowledge deficit on education and mathematical matters (the Outsiders) while Insiders are relatively advantaged by both their experiential and researched knowledge of the educational system.

The book closes with an analysis of the major findings in the context of international research on classroom teaching and learning. It highlights in particular the over-riding impact of traditional, procedural approaches to the teaching of mathematics. It demonstrates how these practices are driven, not only by the deeply formal view of mathematics held by teachers, but also by the constraints of a traditional examination and syllabus framework.

Overall, the study offers many insights into students' experiences of mathematics classrooms, not only in terms of pedagogical practices but also in terms of how grouping procedures, gender and social class impact on their learning. The book also demonstrates the crucial role that emotions play in learning; the sense of fear and anxiety that many students felt about 'being wrong' in a mathematics class was clearly articulated by the students at interviews. The interviews and questionnaires completed by the students also suggest that whether girls or boys like mathematics, or whether they want to pursue the subject at more advanced levels, is as much about the identity that the subject offers them, as it is about the pedagogy that is employed in the classroom.

1

The Teaching and Learning of Mathematics: Gender and Related Issues

Setting the Context

We live in a world increasingly influenced by globalisation and technological change. Within this new global order, the media, telecommunications and information technologies exercise a powerful role in social and economic development. As the mathematical sciences and related disciplines are fundamental to developing, understanding and using these technologies, we need to examine what kind of mathematics education is best for a student's future life as a citizen and worker in this 'global village'.

The impetus to research mathematics education has come not only from developments within the technological and scientific sphere. It is also generated by the wider movement both nationally and internationally to create knowledge-based economies. Improved education is increasingly regarded as a key to economic development in a global order in which cultural capital plays a defining role (OECD, 1996, 1997; Skilbeck, 1998, 2001). The twin dynamics of economic and educational globalisation have stimulated a renewed interest in research in education, especially research on mathematics and science education.

Mathematics does not only have extrinsic value however, it also has intrinsic value. It is of cultural value in its own right, irrespective of its utilitarian functions. The teaching of mathematics needs to be studied therefore, not just because it can enable society to produce more scientists or technologically skilled personnel, but also because of the integral part that teaching plays in the development of the subject itself.

In the international arena, there have been numerous studies undertaken on the teaching and learning of mathematics across countries. There are several journals devoted to mathematics education[1] and major conferences are held regularly on the subject (for a résumé of such activity, see for

1

example the Annual Proceedings of the International Group for the Psychology of Mathematics Education). There has also been a limited amount of research undertaken on mathematics education in the Republic of Ireland (Close, Kellaghan, Madaus and Airasian, 1978; Greaney and Close, 1976; Oldham, 1993, 1996, 2001; Widmer, Goulding and Oldham, 1998); and in Northern Ireland (Daly and Shuttleworth, 1997; Daly and Defty, 2000). In addition, Ireland has been party to a number of major international studies of mathematical achievement (Beaton et al., 1996; Martin et al., 1992, 2000).

In this first chapter we will examine some of the major trends in national and international thought in mathematics education. The review will examine contemporary research findings and theoretical developments relating to the teaching of mathematics generally, as well as the impact of teachers', parents' and students' attitudes on the learning of the subject. As one of the primary objectives of the study was to examine the impact of gender on the learning climates of mathematics classrooms, the literature in this field will be given particular attention. The primary purpose of the review is to provide a framework for understanding our findings in relation to the teaching and learning of mathematics in Ireland, focusing especially on mathematics education at the junior end of second-level school.

Perspectives on mathematics education

What we understand by knowledge and knowledge development in the field of mathematics is important from an educational point of view, as it influences what mathematics is included in the curriculum, how it is taught and examined, how teachers are trained to teach it, and what value is placed on achievement in mathematics by schools, students, parents and society.

As the literature on the epistemologies of mathematics and mathematics education is vast, it is not possible to review such material here. It is important however to comment briefly on the distinction between two contrasting epistemological approaches to mathematics, namely the absolutist and the relativist perspectives, as these have a profound influence on mathematics education generally (Burton, 1992, 1994a, 1994b, 1995, 1996a).

Within the absolutist tradition, mathematics is defined as an 'objective, value-free, logical, consistent and powerful knowledge-based discipline which students must accept, understand and manipulate' (Burton, 1994a: 207). The learning that takes place is 'by transmission from knowers to novices who search for certainty, singularity and clear definition from their teachers'. It is generally assessed 'by unseen pencil-and-paper tests' requiring 'knowledge and skill reproduction' (ibid). Burton (1992) suggests that a didactic approach to teaching mathematics fits easily with an absolutist epistemological framework, drawing as it does on Behaviourist learning theory and its principles of repetition and reinforcement. She suggests that the absolutist perspective has facilitated competition between learners, and a dependency between learner and teacher that does not allow an effective learning style to emerge. If teachers view their role as presenting a fixed body of knowledge to students, the effect is that students learn the 'how' rather than the 'why' of mathematics (Dossey, 1992). Burton is not alone in her critique of absolutism in mathematics. Bloor (1976, 1983), Davis and Hersch (1983), Lakatos (1976), Lerman (2000), Restivo (1985, 1992) and Thompson (1992) are among the many scholars who have critiqued the absolutist perspective.

What Burton refers to as the relativist view was 'derived by examining the connections between the discipline and those who use it, and the society within which it develops' (Burton, 1995, p. 275). The more relativist tradition 'emphasises the interaction between individuals, society and knowledge out of which mathematical meaning is created' (op cit, p. 277). In this way mathematics is seen as 'a human creation', and 'as such, is prey to the same subjectivities of individuals and cultures' (Burton, 1994b, p. 6). Within the more relativist perspective, all knowledge is regarded as culturally, historically and politically situated. Education itself is never regarded as neutral (Freire, 1972). The Relativist tradition fits more easily with a cognitive science approach to teaching and learning mathematics, including problem-based and constructivist learning. Through this approach students are encouraged to construct their own mathematical ideas and procedures by attempting to mathematise meaningful problem situations, often leading to collaboration, discussion and consensus concerning mathematics. (Kilpatrick, 1992; Dossey, 1992)

The debate between relativists and absolutists within mathematics does not stand alone. It is part of a wider debate internationally regarding the merits of positivist, and postmodernist and poststructuralist approaches to knowledge and understanding. Several major challenges to objectivism have emerged across all disciplines, but especially within the social sciences, education and cognate fields. Postmodernists, critical theorists and feminist scholars have been among the most ardent critics of positivist and absolutist epistemologies and methodologies in the social sciences generally (Bernstein, 1976, 1983; Harding, 1987, 1991; Harre, 1981; Humphries, 1997; Lentin, 1993; Reay, 1996; Smith, 1987; Stanley and Wise, 1983) and in education in particular (Giroux, 1983, 1997; Hooks,

1994; McLaren, 1986, 1994; Weiler, 1988, 1991). Mainstream positivism has also been subjected to critique from an ethical standpoint (Reason and Rowan, 1981; Reason, 1988). Positivism has not been without its defendants however. Hammersley (1992, 1995), although not subscribing to a crudely positivist view, has been among the more vocal of these within education.

Major changes have occurred in mathematics education internationally in response to these and other paradigmatic debates within the field. Mathematics educators have developed a diverse range of perspectives on the teaching of the subject, including constructivist, realistic, competency and literacy-based approaches. The strength of any one tradition varies greatly cross-culturally (Abrantes, 2001; Gravemeijer and Kindt, 2001; Romberg, 2001 and Steinbring, 2001). Ireland has remained relatively removed from such international developments however. The curriculum has retained its more abstract, formalist and comparatively conservative character (Oldham, 2001). In terms of Burton's (1994b) paradigmatic framework, it would be located in the absolutist tradition.

The Junior Certificate mathematics curriculum

Students throughout Ireland follow a national curriculum in mathematics at Junior cycle level (age 12-15 approximately). They have a choice between three levels: Foundation, Ordinary and Higher. The uptake of each level is approximately in the ratio 1:3:2 respectively. Practically all second-level students sit the Junior Certificate Mathematics Examination.

Junior Certificate mathematics is assessed by means of a terminal written examination, centrally set and marked by the Department of Education and Science (Department of Education and Science, 2000c). Students are offered a limited choice of questions to encourage full coverage of the syllabus. In the revised Junior Certificate Mathematics Examination (to be examined for the first time in 2003), the current proposal is that students should have no choice between questions so as to ensure coverage of the entire course.

Time allocated to Junior Certificate mathematics varies from school to school, but is usually four to five periods of thirty-five to forty-five minutes per week. There is increasing pressure to reduce the time allocated to any given subject due in part to the introduction of new subjects in recent years. The problem of time is exacerbated by the short length of the Irish school year in comparative terms (Oldham, 2001).

Typically, the resources used in the mathematics classroom are comprised of blackboard and chalk, or whiteboard and marker, and student textbooks. For specific topic areas teachers may make use of a graph board, or large geometrical instruments. Use of a scientific calculator has not been the norm in the Junior Cycle mathematics classroom to date. However the revised course assumes that calculators are available for appropriate use, and calculators will be permitted in examinations from 2003. While a variety of projects have been undertaken on the use of computers in the teaching of mathematics, many of them as part of the Schools IT2000 initiative (Department of Education and Science, 2000a), the use of educational technology in the mathematics classroom remains the exception rather than the rule.

Various revisions of the Junior Cycle mathematics programme have encouraged (but not required) the use of a variety of methodologies. The in-service provision that supports the revised Junior Certificate programme (implemented in September 2000) focuses on the notion of 'teaching for understanding' and on giving teachers an experience of a wide range of active methodologies and concrete materials (Junior Certificate Support Service, JCSS). It is too early to ascertain what changes, if any, will result in teachers' classroom practice from this in-service provision. Yet it is unlikely that teachers will experiment with new techniques when their students will be taking a public examination at the end of the three-year cycle where didactic teaching is known to be rewarded with good examination results (Beaton et al., 1996). If teaching work is assessed by traditional criteria, then it is illogical to expect teachers to be experimental and innovative in their approach to the subject.

Changes and Developments

During the 'new mathematics' movement of the 1960s, a major review of the Irish mathematics syllabuses at second level was undertaken, 'highlighting mathematical structures, abstraction and rigorous presentation' (Oldham, 1993). Since then, revision of the mathematics curriculum has been largely concerned with reducing curriculum overload and lessening levels of abstraction for certain cohorts of students (Oldham, 1997). At present, the curriculum is presented in terms of content rather than of process. While the objectives of Junior Cycle mathematics education include the ability to create mathematics, the appreciation of the beauty of mathematics, and an awareness of the history of mathematics, these still appear to be stated rather than examined goals (Department of Education and Science, 2000c).

Among the factors that may affect the initiation of change are the profile of the teaching body and the learning priorities of teachers. Junior Certificate mathematics teachers are usually not subject specialists in that they teach other subjects as well as mathematics (Oldham, 2001). Their interest in, or commitment to, change in mathematics education is simply unknown. What we do know however is that Irish mathematics teachers generally rank lower-order abilities (e.g. remembering formulae and procedures) more highly, and higher-order abilities (e.g. providing reasons to support conclusions, thinking creatively and using mathematics in the real world) less highly, than do teachers in many other countries (ibid). In particular, there is evidence that Irish teachers do not see the relevance of introducing students to the applications of mathematics (Beaton et al., 1996; Oldham, 1997). There is a danger therefore that teachers with such opinions may concentrate their lessons on the basics: procedures, lower-order skills, and decontextualised knowledge. On the other hand, it has been argued that such an approach can lead to diligent and focussed work, and good teacher-student interaction (ibid).

As indicated earlier, there have been very few studies of Irish mathematics education. Those undertaken have usually been part of major international studies of attainment across countries, so the primary focus has not been on understanding the dynamics of teaching and learning in mathematics classrooms *per se*. The data available suggest that mathematics classes consist of whole class expository teaching, with individual seat work (with the teacher circulating and offering assistance) and frequent short homework assignments. There is little evidence of group work, individualised work, whole class discussion or reflection. Neither is there evidence of much use of technology, including the calculator (Beaton et al., 1996; Martin et al., 1992; Martin et al., 2000; Oldham, 1993, 2001; Shiel et al., 2001).

While there has been debate in Ireland about the amount of mathematics students should learn, and what they should learn, the debate has taken place within the received wisdom of what Burton (1994b) has termed traditional or absolutist mathematics. There has been relatively little debate about the merits and demerits of different epistemological traditions within the subject of mathematics or of different pedagogical approaches to teaching the subject.

One reason why there has been so little emphasis on process or pedagogy in mathematics education, is because Irish education generally has been examination driven, particularly at second level (Points Commission, 1999). Although the Junior Certificate Examination is designed to assess students' attainments at the end of compulsory education, most Irish students do not leave school at sixteen years (Department of Education and Science, 2001). Over 80 per cent complete the Leaving Certificate (at age eighteen approximately) which is widely regarded as the desirable end to second-level education. Students' grades in the Leaving Certificate examination are used by all third-level colleges and by employers to select entrants. The focus throughout second-level education therefore is generally on preparing for the Leaving Certificate, with the Junior Certificate often being regarded as a preparation for the former (Points Commission, 1999). Therefore, even in the Junior Cycle, the emphasis is on course coverage and examination performance rather than understanding and application (Oldham, 1997). As a result, many teachers feel obliged to 'teach to the test' (Oldham, 1997), and this has implications for what happens inside classrooms.

The National Council for Curriculum and Assessment (NCCA) has recommended that assessment of Junior Certificate programmes should make use of a wide range of assessment techniques including, where appropriate, written examinations, orals, aurals, practicals and coursework (NCCA, 1999). This has not happened however, and in the majority of subjects, including mathematics, terminal written examinations are the principal modes of assessment.

Recent changes in the working conditions of teachers, most notably the proposed introduction of bench marking and quality assurance systems such as whole school evaluation, are expected to promote greater openness and accountability in teaching. The research available from the UK however does not lend great support to this hypothesis. The growth of 'bench marking', 'quality assurance' and the pressures of state examinations, not only create a stressful climate, but also operate to curtail teachers' willingness to use exploratory or innovative teaching methods (Murphy and Torrance, 1988; Hargreaves *et al*, 1996). Furthermore, the multiple roles that teachers and schools are now expected to fulfil have become increasingly complex (van Veen *et al*, 2001). While it is true that teachers are relatively autonomous in their own classrooms, in terms of the pedagogical approaches they employ, they are also subject to a range of internal as well as external controls. They experience their own role as both powerful and powerless, and this, in turn, influences their capacity and motivation to be innovative or experimental (Davies, 1996).

Realising change in teaching practice is therefore not a simple matter. It is dependent on creating a culture throughout education and society generally that is supportive of change (Abrantes, 2001). Ironically, the introduction of national comparative testing in mathematics and other subjects may have the opposite effect to what is intended in terms of promoting change. Studies such as the TIMSS tend to focus public attention on narrowly defined aspects of mathematics education, having a conservative as opposed to a revolutionary effect on both the curriculum and pedagogy of the subject (Keitel and Kilpatrick, 1998).

Pedagogical Challenges

The allegiance to traditional or absolutist approaches to mathematics education is not an exclusively Irish phenomenon. It is part of a global school mathematics tradition where teaching is didactic, and mathematics is presented as the replication of procedures demonstrated by the teacher (Brown et al., 1990; Cobb et al., 1992). Neither is the absence of change in the culture of mathematics teaching simply due to lack of research, or of attempts at reform internationally. There have been numerous strategies and programmes introduced to initiate change across different countries, yet there is a large body of evidence that there has been relatively little change in school mathematics teaching over time (Cuban, 1984; Gates, 2001; Gregg, 1995a, 1995b; Sirotnik, 1983). While teachers invoke notions of good practice to explain their work, they often do so without implementing the practices entailed (Desforges and Cockburn, 1987). The move from familiar instructional practices to new methodologies is not easily accomplished (Fennema and Nelson, 1997). There is ample evidence now of teachers modifying the impact of new practices by adapting them to fit their existing practice (Thompson, 1992).

Part of the problem of change rests with the deeply ingrained culture of schooling itself. Mass public education has a long history in Western European societies; it is a history that demonstrates a strong allegiance to 'drill and practice' for all subject teaching, not just for the teaching of mathematics (Bowles and Gintis, 1976; Coolahan, 1981; Foucault, 1977). When subject matter is pre-ordained, and performance is assessed by written terminal examinations with an established curriculum over many years, there is little incentive for teachers to be inventive in teaching. It is not sufficient to change the mindset of teachers, to focus purely on the psychology of change, when and if this can be achieved. There is also a need to examine the structural conditions of teaching and learning, the socio-political conditions within which teaching and learning takes place. Traditional conceptions of teaching and learning are not only institutionalised in the minds of teachers, students and parents, they are also institutionalised in texts, syllabi, and in the architecture of classrooms and school buildings. In many respects, subjective dispositions represent the internalised representations of objective opportunities and social structures (Bourdieu, 1977). Unless we address the wider socio-political conditions within which mathematics education takes place, we cannot realise change in classroom practice (Gates, 2001).

Realising change in education generally, and in mathematics education in particular, has been complicated by other factors that are culturally specific to Ireland. Ireland is a small country, with a very small academic community by international standards. This is as true of professionals in education, including mathematics educators, as it is of other disciplines. There has also been very little targeted funding for research on schools until recent times. The size of the academic community and the relative lack of research investment has not only meant that there is little depth in expertise, it has also meant that there is reluctance to challenge traditions when challenge can be easily interpreted in a personalised way. Challenging established practices and procedures is not easy when all of the parties are known personally to each other.

Irish education is also characterised by a high level of consensualism, something that forestalls dissent and debate about all educational matters (Lynch, 1987). The combination of the smallness of the research community, limited research opportunities and consensual politics has created a culture of silence around many educational matters. The culture of silence (or what some refer to as the culture of contentment, cf. Allen, 2000) has been reinforced in recent years with the development of social partnerships both within education, and the wider society. There is a growing reluctance to disagree or dissent from the prevailing wisdom in any sphere (Lynch, 2001). The net effect of these social developments has been that many of the major international debates about change in education have by-passed Ireland. While individual scholars have been party to the circles of debate internationally, there has been little debate or division within Ireland on educational matters. While this consensus is often regarded in a positive light in political terms, it has serious limitations in terms of realising change, especially in education. Without dissent and challenge to the established order, there is little incentive to change, even though radical change may be necessary.

Performance in mathematics

One of the few areas in which research has been undertaken on mathematics in Ireland is on attainment. Ireland has been party to several major international studies focused on performance in mathematics including the Second International Mathematics Study (SIMS) in the early 1980's; the International Assessment of Educational Progress (IAEP) studies in 1988 and in the early 1990's; the Third International Mathematics and Science Study (TIMSS) conducted by the International Association for the Evaluation of Educational Achievement (IEA) in the mid-1990's; and the Programme for International Student Assessment (PISA) study of literacy in language, mathematics and science in 2000.

The limitations of these studies need to be recognised, not least because they assess only limited aspects of the curriculum (with the exception of the PISA study which is aimed at assessing how well students can use mathematics to solve realistic problems rather than assessing school mathematics curricula). The studies are merely a snapshot of particular cohorts of students at a given time, and they have a number of inherent limitations in terms of what they can assess (Keitel and Kilpatrick, 1998). Nonetheless, they do give some indication as to the relative attainment levels of given sets of students, in particular subjects, at a given time.

In the International Assessments of Educational Progress (IAEP I in 1988 and IAEP II in the early 1990's), Irish students performed around the international average level. In the mid-1990's, the performance of fourth class students (nine-year olds) on the TIMSS was significantly higher than the international average, while the mean scores for second year (second level) students (fourteen-year olds) were not significantly different from the international average.

Oldham suggests some possible reasons for the relative improvement in Irish students' performance which occurred in spite of the fact that there had been no significant curriculum changes or teaching innovation. The mathematical content of IAEP I was not well matched to the Irish curriculum (although this was not the case for IAEP II). In addition, some students participating in IAEP I were the last cohort to be following an old curriculum while others were the first to be studying a revised curriculum. In contrast, the TIMSS study was well suited to the Irish curriculum, as it did not emphasise problem solving or context-specific mathematics. Oldham also suggests that the greater level of innovation that was occurring in other countries between IAEP II and TIMSS may have been counterproductive in terms of performing well in the more traditional-type tests included in TIMSS. Ironically in many respects, by minimising curriculum revision and preserving the traditional teaching approach, Ireland out-performed other comparable countries that participated in TIMSS.

The most recent international study comparing the performance of Irish students with those in OECD countries is the Programme for International Student Assessment (PISA) study (Shiel et al., 2001). While the major focus of this study was on reading, it also examined the basic competencies of fifteen-year-olds in mathematical and scientific literacy. Only two areas of mathematical literacy were assessed however (Change and Growth, and Shape and Space; these incorporated aspects of measurement, algebra, functions, geometry and statistics). The perform-ance of Irish students in mathematics was at the international average level, with Irish students being ranked fifteenth among the twenty-seven countries involved. The performance of high achieving Irish students was low however, while the low achievers did quite well in comparative terms (Sheil et al., 2001). Performance in mathematics was considerably below that in reading where Irish students recorded the fifth highest means score, and a significantly higher score than the international average: only one country (Finland) had a significantly higher mean reading score. Attainment in mathematics was also below that in science, where the mean score for Irish students was significantly higher than the international average (ibid).

Gender and performance in mathematics

Gender differences in educational attainment have been a major subject of educational research in recent years. While research in the 1970's and 1980's focused on girls' underachievement relative to boys, the focus recently has been on boys' underachievements, especially in language (Arnot et al., 1998). Several recent major studies have questioned claims regarding the gender 'gap' in performance, recognising an increasing homogenisation in performance between gender groups (Harker, 2000; Arnot et al., 1998; Gorard et al., 2001).

A comprehensive study was carried out in Wales by Gorard, Rees and Salisbury (2001), examining gender attainment differentials over a six-year period (1992-1997). This study is particularly important as it uses a complete national data set and is inclusive of all students at every level of assessment from Key Stage 1 (age 7) up to A-Level stage. It seriously challenges common assumptions regarding the widening gender gap in performance in national examinations (in favour of girls). While Gorard et al. (ibid) did identify the persistence of gender differences in performance in English, they found that gender differences in mathematics at GCSE level were 'close to neutral', although somewhat more boys achieved the highest grades (A*). No gender gaps were found for all grades below this. At the A-Level stage, there were no gender-related achievement gaps for any grade in mathematics. Neither is gender of much significance in explaining differences in performance in the sciences, where there is just a small achievement gap in favour of boys (especially at the higher grades). As with mathematics, gender differences in science performance have been decreasing over time.

In summary, the work of Gorard et al. shows that the standard view of a 'problem' regarding differential performance between boys and girls is misconceived. Gender 'gaps' at high levels of achievement are not growing over time, and importantly, do not exist at all in mathematics and the sciences.

Similarly, an English study based on national data found no major gender differences in performance in mathematics or science at the three key stages of age 7, 11 and 14 (Arnot et al., 1998). At GCSE level, there were no major gender differences in performance, although boys did receive proportionately higher top grades. As is common across many countries, including Ireland, Arnot et al. (ibid) found that girls' grades in English and languages were generally higher than those of boys.

In line with patterns internationally (Arnot et al., 1998; Gorard et al., 2001; Harker, 2000), gender differences in mathematical attainment have been largely eliminated in Ireland in recent years. While girls achieve higher grade point averages in public examinations overall, there are no major gender differences in mathematics performance in public examinations, although boys do still receive a slightly higher proportion of A grades in Higher level papers. (Department of Education and Science, 1999, 2001; Hannan et al., 1996). Interestingly, the number of girls taking Higher level papers in mathematics has risen significantly over the last fifteen years. The number of girls taking Higher papers at Junior Certificate levels exceeded that of boys in 2000, although the numbers of girls taking Higher papers at Leaving Certificate level was still somewhat lower than that of boys (Department of Education and Science, 2001). Although the PISA study is a more limited test of mathematical attainments than public examinations (given it focused on only two areas of mathematics and was confined to fifteen year-olds), it did find significant gender differences in mathematical performance between girls and boys, to the advantage of boys, at the higher levels of attainment (Sheil et al., 2001).

Other studies have examined gender differences in performance across single-sex and coeducational schools. Using a national data set for Ireland, Hannan et al. (1996) found that most of the differences in performance in the Junior Certificate between coeducational and single-sex schools were due to differences in social class background, and differences in the attainment levels of different cohorts of students at intake. Harker (2000) also found that when ability and background is controlled for, there are few significant gender differences in mathematics and science, and no major differences in the performance of girls attending single-sex or co-educational schools in New Zealand.

What the latest studies suggest therefore is that gender may not be as important a variable in explaining performance differentials in schools as it once was, particularly in the field of mathematics. Where major differences exist, they are increasingly linked to social class background rather than gender. Evidence from the PISA study also suggests that social class background may be an important factor in explaining differences in performance in Ireland. The authors found the socio-economic status of parents to be significantly linked to performance in reading, mathematical and scientific literacy (Sheil et al., 2001).

Gender issues in the teaching and learning of mathematics

In the 1970's and much of the 1980's, debates relating to gender differences in mathematics were grounded in a liberal discourse of deficits and assimilation (Leder, 2001). It was assumed that women were unable to achieve as well as men in mathematics because of lack of opportunity, social barriers and biased instructional methods. The objective was to assimilate women into mathematics in male terms. 'Male (white and western) norms of performance, standards, participation levels, and approach[es] to work were generally accepted uncritically as optimal and to be attained by all students. When failing to reach these, females were considered deficient... perceived as a problem in mathematics' (ibid, p. 47). The development of new modes of feminist discourse in the 1980's and 1990's, in particular the rise of radical feminist thinking, critiquing much of the foundational thinking in epistemology and ethics (Gilligan, 1982; Harding, 1987, 1991; Smith, 1987) created a different context for examining the position of women in mathematics. Feminist perspectives on understanding gained credibility and began to challenge dominant discourses within all disciplines. When combined with the rise of postmodernism, with its strong challenge to positivism in particular, feminist analysis made it increasingly clear that female interests had to be considered not only in determining how mathematics was taught, but also in determining the content of the mathematics curriculum (Kaiser and Rogers, 1995). Such concerns arose not only from the problematising of the content and pedagogy of subjects generally, but also from a growing critical analysis of the deep structured power relations between women and men in the construction of knowledge in the first instance (Harding, 1991). What also became clear, especially from the work of socialist feminists (Barrett, 1980; Beechey, 1987; Eisenstein, 1979; Phillips, 1987) is that women were not homogenous. Social class, ethnicity, race, disability and other status differences created divisions between women that had profound implications for their experience of education (Arnot and Weiner, 1993; David, 1993; Mahony and Zmroczek, 1997).

Within all traditions of feminism in education however, an overriding concern has been the issue of power relations and their implications for teaching and learning. Nowhere has this been more evident than in the analysis of classroom interaction.

Gender issues in classrooms

Although 42 per cent of second-level students in Ireland attend single sex schools, with half of girls attending such schools, the majority of students, both nationally and internationally, attend coeducational schools. The growth in the development of coeducational schools has stimulated an interest in their outcomes for girls, especially in Ireland where coeducation was not the norm at second level until relatively recently.

One of the first questions to be addressed in research has been the impact of coeducation on performance. Both national and international studies suggest that, when we control for background variables such as differences in intake, social class and resources, there is no significant difference in the performance of girls and boys in single sex or coeducational schools (Arnot et al., 1998; Hannan et al., 1996; Harker, 2000). There is evidence however, that school experience differs across gender groups, both within coeducational schools, and between single sex schools (Hannan et al., 1996; Lynch and Lodge, 2002). One of the most persistent questions considered in research focuses on why boys and girls experience school differently (Murphy and Gipps, 1996; Fennema, 1996a, 1996b).

One of the problems to be faced in analysing classrooms is that the majority of interactions in class involve complex exchanges of information at speeds which do not allow teachers to monitor or study their own behaviour (Good and Brophy, 2000). As a result, most teachers are unable to describe the dynamics of their classroom interactions (She, 2000). What we do know however, even if teachers cannot explain why it happens, is that students in the same classroom, with the same teacher, studying the same material, can experience very different educational environments. In broad terms, students are either 'interaction-rich' or 'interaction-poor' (Omvig, 1989). We also know from a large number of classroom interaction studies that boys are more likely to be in the 'interaction–rich' category while girls tend to be more 'interaction-poor' (Howe, 1997). While boys are reprimanded more often than girls, they contribute more than girls to whole class interaction, and they receive more feedback from teachers on what they contribute (Drudy and Uí Catháin, 1999; Younger et al., 1999).

Research on mathematics classrooms has also found gender-differentiated patterns of teacher interaction favouring boys (Leder, 1989; Leder and Fennema, 1990). Leder and Fennema found that teachers interact more with boys, praise and scold boys more frequently than girls, and call on boys more often to answer questions. Toale et al. (1995) also found that boys received more attention in mathematics classes through questioning, having work corrected and getting help from the teacher.

Not all boys in every classroom are dominant or receive more teacher attention, however, and not all girls remain silent or invisible in the classroom. A number of studies have shown that a few verbally active students tend to dominate or monopolize classroom interactions (Jones and

Gerig, 1994; Jones, 1990; Tobin, 1988). Tobin (1988) found that such students, whom he termed 'target students', tend to be high-achieving and male, and that the same target students tended to dominate in consecutive years of their schooling. In their study of Irish classrooms, one third of which were coeducational, Lynch and Lodge (2002) also found that public interactions in both coeducational and single sex classes are dominated by a relatively small number of students. While those who dominate were found to be disproportionately male, not all coeducational classes were dominated by males. There were also a small number of coeducational classes that were female dominated. Moreover, the majority of public interactions in coeducational classes were gender balanced, although mathematics classes (seven of which were observed) were less gender balanced than a number of other subjects including science and language classes.

Understanding male dominance in classrooms
One of the principal reasons why teachers give boys more attention in class is because of their need to maintain control during lessons (Mahony, 1983; Smith and Glynn, 1990). Irish research confirms these findings: Drudy and Uí Catháin (1999) found that the reasons put forward by teachers for gender imbalance in the classroom centred on behaviour. Their classroom observations confirmed that boys demanded more attention and were disruptive, while girls were relatively quieter and more passive. It would appear therefore that it is the threat that boys pose to the orderly running of the class that predisposes teachers to focus more attention on them. There is a fear that at least some boys will not remain involved, or will attempt to disrupt the class unless they are receiving teacher attention (Younger et al., 1999). Tobin's (1988, 1993) studies suggest however, that it may not be only disruptive students who get more teacher attention. Both those who were good academically and those who are disruptive got more teacher attention.

Male domination of coeducational classes has also been explained in terms of the pedagogical style of the teacher, in particular the teacher's acceptance of gendered patterns of 'calling out' answers in class. Taber's (1992) research on public interactions in physics classes suggested that boys got more attention in class, not because teachers initiated more interactions with boys, but rather because boys called out answers in an unsolicited manner more frequently than girls. Kelly (1988) also found that while girls seemed to be willing to take equal part in lessons, usually by raising their hands to answer a question, they were often not allowed to do so. Kelly suggests that the reason this happened was because boys had a greater tendency to call out, or to answer open questions, and that this tendency was not checked by teachers. H.C. She's (2000) study on a biology teacher's classroom behaviour showed how gender differences in the classroom situation were reinforced when no action was taken by the teacher to control the calling out of answers by more assertive male students.

Given what we know about the importance of psychic rewards in teaching, it is not entirely surprising perhaps that teachers pay attention to those who are most demanding, or who participate spontaneously. In a major study of 5000 teachers in Canada, Lortie (1975) found that the only rewards that teachers received on a daily basis from teaching were psychic rewards: the sense of personal fulfilment achieved with seeing individual students learning or actively participating in class. Working in isolation from other adults, teachers had to rely on feedback from students to give them a sense of achievement. Students who were most outstanding, for whatever reason, gave teachers their greatest challenge and their greatest reward. More recent research lends confirmation to Lortie's findings: Tobin (1988) found that teachers regard 'target' students as more beneficial to them than other students as they enable them to maintain the lesson momentum and content coverage.

While these studies help us understand why more demanding and participative students receive more attention, they do not explain why it is boys who are the most likely to be 'calling out' answers, or who are disruptive in a way that commands a disproportionate amount of the teacher's time.

The importance of teacher attitudes

It is widely accepted that the expectations, beliefs and attitudes of mathematics teachers have a substantial influence on classroom practice (McCleod, 1992; Ruffell, Mason and Allen, 1998; Thompson, 1992). Student attitudes are also considered to have a considerable bearing on their school achievements (Leder, 1992; Ponte et al., 1992).

However, other studies have highlighted inconsistencies between teacher beliefs and actual teaching practices. Research by Raymond (1997) and Gregg (1995a) present a more complicated view of the relationship between mathematics teachers' beliefs and their classroom practices. In Raymond's study, a teacher, interviewed and observed in her classroom, was found to have very traditional views on the nature of mathematics, while holding more non-traditional views about the learning and teaching of the subject. When this teacher's class was observed however, her instructional decisions were more in line with the traditional model of teaching. The inconsistency between the teacher's professed commitment to non-traditional methods and her classroom practices was explained in terms of time constraints, scarcity of resources, concerns regarding standardised testing and concerns regarding student behaviour. The teacher claimed that traditional methods were more efficient and required fewer resources.

Gregg (1995a) found that teachers felt they had to coerce the students to engage with mathematics by telling them it would help them to learn to reason and help them in real life. Yet, the claim that mathematics was relevant appeared to be belied by the school mathematics tradition with its emphasis on memorising formulae, procedures, etc. Teachers coped with such contradictions in different ways. Students were asked to accept ideas and facts rather than engage in discussion regarding the meaning of terms. Teachers set homework and tests to help students remember and to assess student understanding; they explained students' difficulties with the subject matter in terms of their given capacities, thereby eschewing responsibility for their achievement. It would seem that, when working in the context of traditional examinations, teachers coped with the contradiction between relevance and proceduralism by reinforcing the very proceduralist approaches that caused difficulties in the first instance.

It is evident therefore that there is no perfect correlation between beliefs and actions. Moreover, there is evidence that what people think and feel about mathematics is not stable and consistent across all contexts or situations. Most surveys of attitudes are taken at one point in time and in a given context. The same issues may be viewed quite differently in a different context (Gellert, 2001).

Teacher attitudes on gender issues

Fennema et al. (1990) found that teachers' beliefs about girls and boys in mathematics were different. They perceived boys as their best students. They attributed effort and ability as reasons for success (or failure) differently: the success or failure of boys in mathematics was attributed to ability whereas girls' achievements were attributed to effort. Teachers also believed that boys exhibited more autonomous learning behaviours, seeing them as more competitive, logical and adventurous than girls, and more likely to volunteer answers, to be more independent in mathematics and to enjoy the subject more than girls. However, they also point out that little is known regarding the impact of these teachers' beliefs on learning patterns among girls and boys.

While it is clear that there is no perfect correlation between attitudes and action, or between attitudes of teachers and the learning outcomes of students, there is a real danger that stereotypical views of ability and effort may impact adversely on students' general perception of the subject of mathematics. Teachers who hold strongly stereotypical views may feel they have little control over the eventual outcomes of their students' mathematics education, and may unconsciously communicate their stereotypical views to students. Given the evidence of the differential attention given to girls and boys in mathematics classes (and in classrooms generally), it does seem entirely plausible that teacher attitudes may have some bearing on the outcomes. Even when teachers are aware of gender issues and believe that they are treating students equally, the evidence suggests that this is not the case. Younger et al. (1999) found that the perceptions held by teachers, that they did not give differential treatment to girls and boys in the classroom, was not borne out by the observational evidence which revealed that boys received more attention than girls. There is a considerable body of evidence to show that boys are more 'salient' in teachers' minds, that teachers react to pressure from students, and that they tend to receive more pressure from boys (Fennema, 1996a).

Student attitudes to mathematics

To locate responsibility for gender differentiated classroom practices with teachers is to oversimplify the nature of social life. Pedagogical practices are undoubtedly influenced by students' own attitudes and values, which in turn, are influenced by the gendered assumptions of society at large (Martin, 1996). Schools are, in many respects, a microcosm of society (Robinson, 1992). Teachers and students carry into school cultural assumptions as to what is gender appropriate behaviour, and what are gender appropriate subject choices (Hannan et al., 1983; Kelly, 1985a).

In our society the cultural code that is most celebrated for boys is one that emphasises dominance, both of other boys and of girls (Connell, 1995; Kimmel and Messner, 1997; Moane, 1999; Lynch and Lodge, 2002), while co-operation, caring, and passivity remain highly prized, albeit increasingly contested, feminine values (ibid). In so far as schools and teachers are unable or unwilling to contest these cultural codes, they may provide contexts in which gender-differentiated practices can be perpetuated, practices that may have adverse effects on learning (Murphy and Gipps, 1996). In terms of mathematics in particular, Fennema (1996a) suggests that doing advanced-level mathematical problem solving requires girls (and boys) to be independent, active, questioning and rule-breaking. Yet, for girls to behave in this way is to step outside typically socialised ways of behaviour.

There are other cultural codes that predispose girls to succeed in schools relative to boys. Research with GCSE students in the UK found that it is possible for girls to work hard and still be accepted by their peers, whilst

boys were under greater pressure to conform to a 'cool', masculine image. Boys were ridiculed by their peers for working hard in a way that did not apply to girls (Warrington et al., 2000).

Francis (1999) analysed classroom behaviour and found that the 'laddish' behaviour of boys (which included not working hard) in class was regarded positively by both girls and boys. Laddish behaviour was constructed as desirable not only within male friendship groups, but also for attracting girls. She claims that certain traits, such as humour, defiance, strength and competition are constructed as male by both sexes and are defined as desirable by both men and women (Francis, 2000).

If boys are defining themselves as 'cool' and not working (at least in public), and accepting of laddish behaviour in class, then it is easy to see how their academic success might be adversely affected by their interaction style. Thus, even if the boys do dominate pubic interaction in class, their dominance may be offset by other cultural mores that are antithetical to achievement.

Help seeking by students in the classroom is seen by many as an important strategy for learning and success in school (Arbreton, 1993; Karabenick and Knapp, 1991; McCaslin and Good, 1996; Nelson Le-Gall, 1981). Interesting gender differences have also been found in this area, indicating that although boys may be more vocal in class, they are less likely than girls to ask for, and benefit from, such help (Ryan et al. 1998). Ryan et al. suggest that the patterns of help seeking reflect boys' unwillingness to present themselves as dependent in class rather than indicating assertiveness on the part of girls.

Gender differences in perceptions of performance and abilities

Gender differences in attitudes to work in class are but one of the areas in which girls and boys differ, however they also differ in their perceptions of different subjects and in their perceptions of their own abilities. Bornholt et al. (1994) examined gender differences in Australian students' perceptions of performance and ability in mathematics and English. While they found no gender differences in achievement in either subject, they did find significant gender differences in perceptions of performance and general ability in the subjects. Boys overestimated their performance in both the mathematics and English tests, while girls were more realistic in their self-appraisal. These findings broadly concur with Irish research findings where girls have been found to have a lower academic self image than boys even at comparable levels of performance (Hannan et al., 1983; 1996).

Bornholdt et al. (1994) also examined gender differences in perception of abilities. They found that students adhered to quite essentialist views of their abilities in different subjects, views that were gender stereotypical in many respects: girls saw themselves as having 'natural talent' in English, while more boys were likely to perceive themselves as having 'natural talent' in mathematics.

In contrast to these findings, however, studies by Francis (2000) and Leder and Forgasz (2000) suggest that students' perceptions of ability at certain subjects are no longer as gender stereotyped as they were in the past. Francis found that the majority of students constructed ability at various subjects as unrelated to gender, claiming they had more to do with individual differences and preferences. Francis also found a blurring of traditional subject preferences between girls and boys: girls' favourite subjects were not necessarily in arts, while boys were not necessarily science-related.

Leder's research (2001) confirms Francis' findings regarding the breaking down of gender stereotyped attitudes to different subjects. In a study of attitudes to mathematics in Australia, Leder found that high school students 'now consider boys more likely than girls to give up when they find a problem too challenging ... to find mathematics difficult ... and to need additional help. Girls were considered more likely than boys to enjoy mathematics ... and [to] find mathematics interesting' (ibid, pp. 1-51).

While the aforementioned studies do suggest that change may be occurring, nonetheless, both studies were based on relatively small samples. There is a danger in generalising from such small samples to national populations. There is also a danger that such studies may deflect attention from gender inequalities and differences (Volman and Ten Dam, 1998; Holland et al, 1998). There are still gender differences in subject choices that are strongly stereotyped along the arts/science/technology continuum both at second and third level (Department of Education and Science, 2000b; Clancy, 2001). Even if girls are doing well at mathematics or even showing a liking for mathematics and related subjects, they are still opting out of careers that are exclusively technology-related in particular.

Girls opting out
There is a considerable body of research suggesting that girls do not feel confident in their own ability to do mathematics, and that this may be a reason why they opt out of the subject. (Pedro et al., 1981; Fennema, 1980; Fennema and Tartre, 1985; Eccles, 1989; Jones and Smart, 1995a; Seegers and Boekaerts, 1996). Even among those women who pursue mathematics-related careers, there is evidence that they lack confidence in the field relative to their male peers (Becker, 1990; Mura, 1987). Whether

girls' lack of confidence in mathematics is learned in class or not is a subject of debate (Dweck et al. 1978).

Some studies suggest however that it may not be lack of confidence that deters women from mathematics. They claim women opt out of mathematics as they do not want to stand out from their peers (Leder, 1980), or to be seen as 'square' or 'boring' by their school friends (Jones and Jones, 1989). Jones and Smart (1995a) suggest however that a further reason may be that girls tend to see mathematics as remote and unrelated to their concerns. It is seen as an asocial and impersonal subject, whereas women who have been strongly socialised in their moral and personal development tend to be focused on both the personal and the social (Gilligan, 1982)

The claim that women may be detached from mathematics because of its perceived detached and impersonal character is a view that is widely held by feminists outside the mathematics education field. Harding (1991) claims that because science, technology and related disciplines are presented as being overwhelmingly male-dominated in terms of questions researched, leading scholars, examples and illustrations, world views, and ways of working, women are alienated from the disciplines and their cognate worlds of employment. While there may be no conscious act by those who control the discipline of mathematics to exclude women, or no sexist behaviour, nonetheless, an accumulation of small differences in teacher behaviours, organisation and instructional practices, make up a pattern which appears to favour males. Peterson and Fennema (1985) and Fennema (1996a) suggest that the view that mathematics is a male preserve may be destructive for both females and males. Fennema (1996a) suggests that women distance themselves from mathematics because they regard the way that the subject is currently taught and learned restricts their lives rather than enriches them.

Social class and mathematics education

While gender differences in the experience of mathematics have been a persistent, albeit minority, interest in mathematics education for a long time (Leder, 2001), the same is not true of the issues of social class, ethnicity, disabilities or other differences. Consequently, parties to the debate about gender issues in mathematics education have frequently treated girls as a homogenous group, even though there is an extensive body of research indicating that neither girls nor boys are homogenous; each is stratified by social class, ethnic, racial and other differences (Arnot, 2002; Ballard, 1999; Connolly, 1998; Epstein, 1994; Mac An Ghaill, 1994). Within the sociology of education alone, there is probably no theme that has been more researched than social class differences (Lynch, 2000). There are however a growing number of studies that recognise the importance of social class differences in the experience of mathematics education (Boaler, 1997a; Cooper and Dunne, 1999). There is also a welcome recognition of the importance of constructs of 'ability' for participation and achievement in mathematics (Boaler, 1997b; Dunne, 1994). Within an Irish context, the PISA study of literacy in reading, mathematics and science has also recognised the relevance of social class background for attainment. (Shiel et al., 2001).

Recognising the interface between social class, gender and other differences is important in education generally, and in mathematics in particular, as it enables us to understand differences in attainment and participation in education in all their complexities. It precludes a narrow essentialism in either the gendered or the classed accounts of educational experience.

Conclusion

Mathematics education is being challenged currently by major debates both inside and outside of the discipline, debates about the nature of knowledge and the appropriateness of particular pedagogical styles. Discussions about the appropriateness of relativist versus absolutist epistemologies in mathematics education parallel debates within a variety of other disciplines regarding the merits and demerits of post-modernist, post-structuralist and critical perspectives versus positivist paradigms. Whether one subscribes to the more objectivist view of knowledge or not, one cannot but recognise that it is being seriously challenged from a variety of intellectual positions. The implications of this challenge for the teaching of particular subjects is yet to be fully understood. However, it does suggest that there are no certainties in pedagogy, no more than there are in the substance of the subjects themselves. The different traditions that have emerged within mathematics education are indicative of the change and uncertainty that characterises the epistemological debates across the disciplines, e.g. radical and social constructivism, problem-based learning, realistic mathematics and mathematical literacy movements.

Despite the fact that there are great debates in mathematics education regarding the desirability of change and adopting different approaches to mathematics education, there is also evidence that teachers and schools adopt the labels of reform but not the practices advocated (Romberg, 2001, pp. 1-182). The dominant global school mathematics tradition is one in which teaching is didactic, and mathematics is presented as the replication of procedures demonstrated by the teacher (Brown et al., 1990; Cobb et al.,

1992). However, this approach to teaching is increasingly seen as dysfunctional in educational terms. There is a growing recognition that mathematics education takes place in a social context, and the experience of the subject is mediated through the interactional experience in the classroom and the personal histories that students bring to their learning (Boaler, 1997a; Brown, Collins and Duguid, 1989; Cobb, 1994; Watson, 1998).

Boaler (2000) found that students do not just learn methods and processes in mathematics classrooms, they 'learn to be mathematics learners'. Students' learning of mathematical knowledge cannot be separated from their interactional engagement in the classroom. Yet, the dominant school practices in mathematics that students experienced in Boaler's study were memorisation, reproduction of procedures, and individualised work. Such approaches to mathematics teaching emphasised the meaningless nature of the subject to the students; it was seen as having a limited role in situations outside the mathematics classroom (ibid).

One area in which change is occurring in practice however, is in the area of gender and attainment. There is growing evidence that gender differentials are on the decline in mathematics at all levels both internationally and in Ireland. Although girls and boys are performing similarly within mathematics and cognate disciplines, girls are still relatively absent from mathematics-related professions, especially engineering where only 24 per cent of university entrants are female, with 12 per cent in the technological sector (Clancy, 2001, pp. 31-32). It appears that girls are opting out of mathematics-related professions rather than being refused entry due to lack of qualifications. The question that has to be addressed here is as follows – is schooling, especially mathematics education, contributing to this pattern by giving girls an experience of mathematics which presents it as irrelevant to their lives? Is it contributing to the elimination of girls from mathematics and related professions, especially given the growing realisation that women's ways of obtaining and valuing knowledge may be different to that of men (Gilligan, 1982; Harding, 1991; Kelly, 1985a, 1985b; Nussbaum, 1995)?

Notes

[1] Among the journals are the following: Journal for Research in Mathematics Education, Educational Studies in Mathematics, Journal of Mathematical Behaviour, Journal of Mathematical Education in Science and Technology and Mathematics Education Research Journal. In addition, several general educational and social scientific journals carry papers on mathematics education.

2

Take-up and Performance
in Junior Certificate Mathematics

Introduction

In the study of coeducation undertaken by the Economic and Social Research Institute (ESRI) in the mid-1990s, one of the major findings was that: 'Being in a co-ed. school has significant and substantial negative effects on maths performance among girls, a difference of over half a grade from their single-sex counterparts' (Hannan et al. 1996, p. 141). The authors claimed that this appeared to be a 'pure' coeducational effect as 'girls in all types of coeducational schools have lower grades than their single-sex counterparts' (ibid). It was not clear from the study however, to what extent the lower attainment of girls in coeducational schools was a function of the differences in the levels of mathematics (Foundation, Ordinary and Higher) being taken in single-sex compared with coeducational schools.[1] The authors suggested that further research was necessary to explore this issue.

In the light of this, the research team decided to analyse gender differences in attainment between school types[2] in the Junior Certificate examinations over a five-year period. The research focused in particular on the differences in both take-up rates of different levels of mathematics (Higher, Ordinary and Foundation) across schools, and on the differences in attainment rates *within* each level for different types of schools. It was hoped that such an analysis would indicate whether the differences in the performance of girls in coeducational and single-sex schools persisted over time, and whether they were related to the differences between school types in the take-up rates in Higher, Ordinary and Foundation level mathematics. The period chosen for investigation was 1992 to 1996 as the examination data from these years was the most recent available when the study was planned in 1997/8. The analysis of the national examination data took place prior to the case studies in the schools, as it was believed that the findings from the national data would give a good indication as to what were the most significant factors that needed to be explored in the case studies.

The study of Junior Certificate mathematics 1992-1996

Mathematics is one of three subjects in the Junior Certificate curriculum that may be taken at Foundation, Ordinary and Higher levels (Irish and English are the other two). All other subjects are differentiated into Ordinary and Higher levels. Of all subjects, mathematics has the lowest take-up at the Higher level (36 per cent), followed by Irish at 40 per cent. By contrast, several other subjects attract large numbers of Higher level candidates including Geography (78 per cent), History (74 per cent), Science (69 per cent), Business Studies (68 per cent) and English (61 per cent). Of the three subjects that may be taken at Foundation level, mathematics has the highest take-up (13 per cent) at this level, ahead of Irish (10 per cent) and English (4 per cent) (Junior Certificate Examination Data, 1996).

This chapter is based on an analysis of Junior Certificate mathematics examination data[3] over a five-year period (1992-6). It examines differences in the take-up of, and performance in, mathematics at Foundation, Ordinary and Higher levels, principally by gender and school type.

The chapter is divided into three sections. The first section sets the context for the discussion that follows by examining gender differences in the distribution of students across the different types of schools. Using both school-level and individual-level data, section two presents findings in relation to the take-up of Junior Certificate mathematics and considers differences in the take-up of Foundation, Ordinary and Higher mathematics by school type and gender. Performance in mathematics is discussed in section three; the three levels are considered separately in relation to differences by gender and school type. A discussion of the findings is presented in the conclusion.

Student composition by school type and gender

As the analysis of the gender composition of schools over the five years did not reveal any major differences across school types, we used the most recent data set available at the time of analysis, that for 1996, to indicate the patterns in gender composition in different school types (Table 2.1).

Almost two thirds (63 per cent) of Junior Certificate students attend secondary schools. Within the secondary sector, twice as many students attend single-sex compared with coeducational schools (42 per cent and 21 per cent). Less than one quarter of all students (22 per cent) attend vocational schools or community colleges, while 12 per cent are in community schools and 3 per cent are in comprehensives.

Table 2.1 Distribution of Junior Certificate students by School Type and Gender: 1996

| | Percentage | | | | | |
	Scoed	SSS	VCC	COMP	CS	Total
Females	19.1	50.5	17.3	2.4	10.7	100 (33,323)
Males	22.4	34.2	27.0	2.7	13.7	100 (34,094)
Total	20.8	42.2	22.2	2.6	12.2	100 (67,417)

Key: Scoed: Secondary Coeducational; SSS: Secondary single-sex; VCC: Vocational schools and Community Colleges; COMP: Comprehensive; CS: Community School

As can be seen from Table 2.1, almost 58 per cent of all Junior Certificate students attended coeducational schools in 1996. In gender terms, however, substantially fewer females than males attended coeducational schools (50 per cent and 66 per cent, respectively). Within the coeducational sector, males outnumbered females in all school types. The gender disparity was greatest in vocational schools and community colleges where 61 per cent were male. In community schools 57 per cent were male, in secondary coeducational schools, 55 per cent were male, while 54 per cent of students in comprehensive schools were male.

Schools are not just divided in terms of gender, or whether they are secondary, vocational, community or comprehensive, they are also divided in terms of whether they are designated disadvantaged or not[4]. In addition, within the secondary sector, schools are classified as either fee-paying or free scheme (non-fee). All community, comprehensive and vocational schools and colleges are non fee-paying.

In 1996, 6 per cent of all Junior Certificate students attended fee-paying secondary schools. Two thirds of the fee-paying schools attended were single-sex while one third were coeducational secondary schools. The gender differences in participation in fee-paying education is slight although more boys than girls attend fee-paying schools. (Table A2.2).

Over a quarter (26 per cent) of all second-level schools, which catered for 28 per cent of all students, were classified as disadvantaged at the time of the study. There were slightly more males than females in designated disadvantaged schools (Table A2.3). Vocational schools and community colleges, community schools and comprehensives are over-represented in the designated-disadvantaged category, while the opposite applies to secondary schools. The difference is most striking between vocational schools and community colleges, and coeducational secondary schools: 43 per cent of the students in vocational schools and community colleges are in designated-disadvantaged schools while just 18 per cent of the students in coeducational secondary schools are in disadvantaged schools.

While there are no major gender differences in the overall distribution of students across designated-disadvantaged schools, there are slightly more boys than girls in such schools.

As the base line data on second-level schools does not provide any information on the social class or socio-economic background of students, we asked the ESRI to undertake a re-analysis of the national data they collected on schools in 1994[5] for their study *Coeducation and Gender Equality* (Hannan et al. 1996) on a social class basis. They provided us with a breakdown of the social class profile of Junior Certificate students across different school types, broken down by gender (Table 2.2). Overall, the results confirm that secondary schools are more middle class in composition than vocational, community or comprehensive schools and colleges. Almost half of students in secondary schools come from upper middle and middle-class backgrounds, compared with one in four in vocational schools and community colleges, and one in three in community and comprehensive schools. Conversely, single-sex and coeducational secondary schools have a lower proportion of students from working class backgrounds (31 per cent and 33 per cent respectively) compared with vocational schools and community colleges, where in particular, 55 per cent of whom were from working class backgrounds.

Table 2.2 Social Class Profile of Junior Certificate Students: School Type and Gender Differences

Source: ESRI, National Survey on Coeducation and Single-sex Schooling, 1994 – Special tabulation

| | Percentage by School Type | | | | | | | | | | | | | | |
| | Scoed | | | SSS | | | VCC | | | CS/Comp | | | Total | | |
	Girls	Boys	All	Girls	Boys	All	Girls	Boys	All	Girls	Boys	All	Girls	Boys	All
UMC	17	23	20	19	23	21	5	8	7	11	9	10	15	17	16
MC	26	28	27	28	27	28	18	17	18	25	26	25	25	24	25
LMC	22	19	21	22	18	20	19	21	20	20	22	21	21	20	21
UWC	18	17	18	20	19	19	33	33	33	29	24	26	22	23	23
WC	17	13	15	11	13	12	25	21	22	15	19	18	17	16	17
Total %	100	100	100	100	100	100	100	100	100	100	100	100	100	100	100
n	1501	1141	2642	513	456	969	484	750	1234	384	478	862	2884	2827	5707

Social Class Key: UMC: Upper Middle Class; MC: Middle Class; LMC: Lower Middle Class; UWC: Upper Working Class/Skilled Manual; WC: Working Class/Semi-skilled and Unskilled Manual.
School Type Key: Scoed: Secondary Coeducational; SSS: Secondary single-sex; VCC: Vocational schools and Community Colleges; COMP: Comprehensive; CS: Community School.

In terms of the social class background, there are some differences in the profile of female and male students across school types. In coeducational secondary schools, male students are more likely to come from a middle, or upper middle-class background (51 per cent) than female students (43 per cent), while female students (35 per cent) are somewhat more likely to be working class than male students (30 per cent). Girls in vocational schools and community colleges are also slightly more likely to be working class (58 per cent) than their male peers (54 per cent). Girls and boys in community and comprehensive schools are almost identical in terms of social class background, while those in single-sex schools are also very alike in terms of social class.

While it is not possible to generalise from the ESRI data set to the present study, it does give a good indication of the social class profile of Junior Cycle students in different school types in the mid-year of the period under investigation, 1994. It indicates particularly that any generalisations about school type must be interpreted in the light of the differences in social class intake across school types, and the known resource advantages and disadvantages attached to class. Secondary schools generally, and single-sex secondary schools in particular, are much more middle-class in intake than other school types, especially more so than vocational schools and community colleges. Both girls and boys in single-sex schools are twice as likely to be middle-class compared with girls and boys in vocational schools and community colleges.

Gender differences in the take-up of mathematics at each level

The first part of the analysis focuses on the overall pattern of take-up of mathematics at the three levels: Foundation, Ordinary and Higher. We also examine the extent to which take-up of mathematics varies between different school types, between fee-paying and non-fee-paying schools, and between designated-disadvantaged and non-disadvantaged schools. As our analysis showed very little change between 1992 and 1996 in the patterns of take-up rates in mathematics, we have used the most recent (1996) school-level data[6] to demonstrate the differences between schools.

Overall, an examination of the 1996 Junior Certificate examination data showed that most schools (79 per cent) provided mathematics at the three levels (Figure 2.1). In a further 14 per cent of schools, take-up of mathematics was limited to Higher and Ordinary levels. In all, Higher level mathematics was offered in the vast majority (93 per cent) of schools. In the remaining 7 per cent, take-up was mainly restricted to a combination of Foundation and Ordinary levels (6 per cent), while in 1 per cent of schools, students only took Foundation level mathematics for the Junior Certificate.

*Figure 2.1 Take-up of Mathematics by Level, 1996 (Base: 745
schools)*

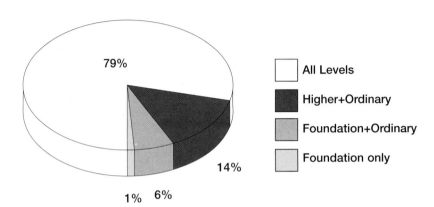

Differences in take-up rates across school types

When the take-up rates for Higher level mathematics are analysed from
1992 to 1996, they show that about one third of the students took
mathematics at the Higher level over the five-year period (Table 2.3).
However, there are important differences between school types in the take-
up of Higher level mathematics with more than twice the percentage
taking Higher level mathematics in secondary schools (either coeducational or single-sex secondary) compared with vocational schools and
community colleges. While the proportion of girls taking Higher level
mathematics was slightly greater than that of boys in the community,
comprehensive and vocational sectors, the reverse was true in the
secondary sector where more boys took Higher level mathematics,
especially in the single-sex sector.

*Table 2.3 Student take-up of Higher Mathematics by School Type and
Gender: Average rates for 1992-1996*

	Average per cent (1992-1996)					
	Scoed	SSS	VCC	COMP	CS	All
Females	36.5	38.0	19.8	34.6	28.7	33.7
Males	37.2	44.5	15.5	33.9	25.3	32.7
Total	36.9	40.8	17.2	34.3	26.8	33.2

Key: Scoed: Secondary Coeducational; SSS: Secondary single-sex; VCC: Vocational
schools and Community Colleges; COMP: Comprehensive; CS: Community School.

In most Irish schools (64 per cent) less than 40 per cent of the students take Higher level mathematics. There were forty-nine schools (7 per cent) where nobody took the Higher level paper in 1996 (Table 2.4). The patterns for 1992 to 1995 were the same as for 1996. Table 2.4 also shows that a disproportionately high number of vocational schools and community colleges do not offer mathematics at Higher level. One in five of these schools had no student taking Higher level mathematics in 1996, while a further 43 per cent had 20 per cent or fewer of their Junior Certificate students taking Higher level mathematics. These findings should however, be interpreted, in light of the fact that vocational schools have the highest proportion of designated disadvantaged schools of all school types (43 per cent)[7]. One of the criteria for getting such a designation is having a relatively large cohort of students who are socio-economically and educationally disadvantaged.

Table 2.4: Differences across types of schools in the take-up of Junior Certificate Higher Mathematics 1996

	Secondary schools			Other second-level schools			
	SSS Girls	SSS Boys	Scoed	VCC	COMP	CS	Total
	%	%	%	%	%	%	% (n)
Nobody	0	2	1	20	0	0	7 (49)
1 to 20 per cent	12	7	10	43	20	31	21 (161)
21-40 per cent	34	30	50	27	40	56	36 (267)
41-60 per cent	43	40	33	9	40	13	28 (209)
61-80 per cent	10	17	6	1	0	0	7 (52)
81-100 per cent	1	4	0	0	0	0	1 (7)
Total (n)	(166)	(142)	(136)	(225)	(15)	(61)	(745)
%	100	100	100	100	100	100	100

Key: SSS Girls: Secondary single-sex girls; SSS Boys: Secondary single-sex boys; Scoed: Secondary Coeducational; VCC: Vocational schools and Community Colleges; COMP: Comprehensive; CS: Community School.

A relatively high proportion of community schools (31 per cent) also had 20 per cent or fewer students taking Higher level mathematics, while just 9 per cent of boys' schools, 12 per cent of girls' and 11 per cent of coeducational secondary schools had 20 per cent or fewer students taking higher level papers.

Single-sex schools were also the most likely to have a clear majority (60 per cent or more) taking Higher level mathematics examinations. However, even in their case, just 11 per cent of girls' schools and 21 per cent of boys' schools had over 60 per cent of students taking Higher level mathematics. Only 1 per cent of vocational schools and none of the community or comprehensive schools had over 60 per cent of students taking Higher level mathematics examinations.

The disparity between schools is even greater when one compares fee-paying schools with other school types: while over 40 per cent of students took Higher level papers in most (85 per cent) fee-paying schools, less than one third of all other schools (32 per cent) had more than 40 per cent of their students taking Higher level examinations. The difference in Higher level take-up rates between designated disadvantaged schools and others was even greater than that between fee-paying and others: while 44 per cent of schools that were not designated disadvantaged had over 40 per cent of students doing Higher level examinations, only 12 per cent of schools that were designated disadvantaged had this rate of take-up (Table A2.4).

Vocational schools and community colleges had the highest level of take-up of Foundation mathematics: in a quarter of vocational schools and community colleges, more than 40 per cent of Junior Cycle students were taking Foundation level examinations while this was true in 4 per cent or less of all other school types (Table 2.5).

Table 2.5: Take-up of Junior Certificate Foundation mathematics by school type, 1996 (Base: second-level schools)

	Secondary schools			Other second-level schools			Total
	SSS Girls	SSS Boys	Scoed	VCC	COMP	CS	
	%	%	%	%	%	%	% (n)
Nobody	18	27	15	7	13	0	14 (107)
1 to 20 per cent	71	65	76	40	74	72	61 (459)
21-40 per cent	8	6	7	28	13	24	15 (110)
41-60 per cent	3	1	1	18	0	2	7 (50)
61-80 per cent	0	1	0	4	0	2	2 (12)
81-100 per cent	0	0	1	3	0	0	1 (7)
Total (n)	166	142	136	225	15	61	745
%	100	100	100	100	100	100	100

Key: SSS Girls: Secondary single-sex girls; SSS Boys: Secondary single-sex boys; Scoed: Secondary Coeducational; VCC: Vocational schools and Community Colleges; COMP: Comprehensives; CS: Community Schools.

Given the high concentration of disadvantaged schools in the vocational and community college sector, it is not surprising to find that there was a relatively large number taking Foundation mathematics in disadvantaged schools relative to other school types: in over one fifth (21 per cent) of disadvantaged schools, 40 per cent or more of the students were taking Foundation level examinations while this was true in 5 per cent or less of other schools. There was no fee-paying school with 40 per cent or more taking Foundation level examinations (Table A2.5).

Concluding comments

What is most notable from the analysis of take-up rates is the difference across school types in the take-up of Higher, Ordinary and Foundation level mathematics. While there is a disparity in the take-up of different levels of mathematics between vocational schools and colleges and secondary schools generally (with community and comprehensive schools occupying an interim position between the two), the differences are most pronounced between designated disadvantaged schools and other school types. The most socially selective schools, fee-paying secondary schools, have by far the highest take-up rates in Higher level mathematics and the lowest rate of take-up at Foundation level. The reverse is true among those schools that are least socially selective, most especially designated disadvantaged schools, of which a very large number are in the vocational and community college sector.

Given the heavy concentration of coeducation in vocational schools and colleges (51 per cent of all coeducational schools are vocational schools or community colleges, (Department of Education and Science, 2000b)) and the relatively low level of take-up in Higher level mathematics within such schools (63 per cent had 20 per cent or less taking Higher level papers, Table 2.4), it is easy to see how performance in coeducational schools generally would appear to be lower than that in single-sex schools. The results of schools with high concentrations of students taking Higher level courses look favourable when compared to schools with low concentra-tions of students taking Higher level examinations when results are computed on a single hierarchical scale with Higher level courses being awarded higher points. Whether it is appropriate to compare schools in this way is open to debate. Students in schools in which a Higher level course is not on offer, or where few students are encouraged or allowed to take the Higher level course, cannot be expected to get comparable results to students in schools where Higher level is the norm for a large minority or majority of the students. Why so few students are taking Higher level courses in certain schools, especially in vocational schools and colleges (in 20 per cent of which there were no students taking higher level papers) is a question that needs however to be addressed. While the pattern of low or no take-up in Higher level mathematics is most visible in the vocational sector, with 20 per cent or fewer of the students taking Higher level papers in 63 per cent of these schools, it is not a pattern exclusive to this type of school. In 31 per cent of community schools, 20 per cent of comprehensives and almost 11 per cent of secondary coeducational schools, 20 per cent or fewer of the students were doing Higher level mathematics.

Overall therefore, it would appear that differences in take-up rates of different levels of mathematics between coeducational and single-sex schools, is not so much related to their coeducational status as it is to the social class composition of their school population, and the tradition of the school. The schools with the most disadvantaged students are the ones in which there is the highest take up of Foundation and Ordinary mathematics, and these also tend to be disproportionately vocational schools and community colleges.

Gender Differences in Take-up Rates

While the discussion so far has concentrated on differences between schools, in this section we analyse the differences in patterns of take-up between the individuals within different types of schools. Given the focus of the study, the analysis centres on differences in the proportion of females and males taking mathematics at Higher and Foundation levels *within* particular school types.

The findings in Figures 2.2 to 2.4 show gender differences in the take-up of Junior Certificate mathematics for the two years, 1992 and 1996[8]. Half of all students took Ordinary level mathematics in 1992 and 1996, although slightly more females than males took Ordinary level papers in both years. While the percentage of females taking Ordinary mathematics declined slightly over the five years, the proportion of males increased slightly.

Figure 2.2 Take-up of Ordinary mathematics by gender, 1992 and 1996

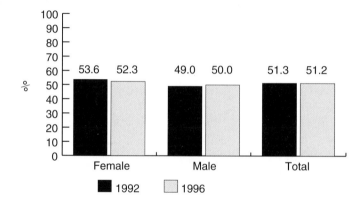

Over the five-year period, a steady increase occurred in the proportion of students taking Higher level mathematics, from 30 per cent in 1992 to 36 per cent in 1996 (Figure 2.3). While an equal proportion of girls and boys took Higher level examinations in 1992 (30 per cent), the proportion of girls taking Higher level mathematics (37 per cent) exceeded that of boys (35 per cent) in 1996. The relatively higher participation rate of girls in Higher mathematics continued to the end of the millenium. In 1999, 51 per cent of those taking Higher level mathematics examinations at the Junior Certificate level were girls (Department of Education and Science, 2000b).

Figure 2.3 Take-up of Higher Mathematics by Gender, 1992 and 1996

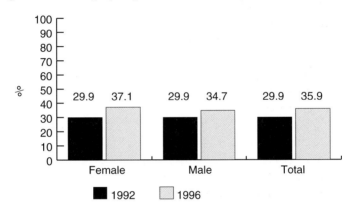

Foundation level mathematics is the least chosen option of the three levels in mathematics, with just 13 per cent of students taking this level in 1996 (Figure 2.4). This represents a decrease from the 1992 take-up rate of

Figure 2.4 Take-up of Foundation Mathematics by Gender, 1992 and 1996

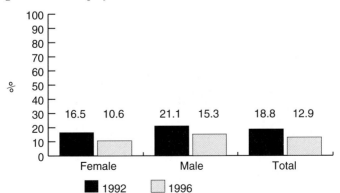

19 per cent (the 1999 data shows that the take-up rate was still at 13 per cent, ibid). A gender analysis of the 1992 and 1996 figures revealed a higher representation of boys taking foundation level mathematics. In 1996, for example, 15 per cent of males took foundation compared with 11 per cent of females. This gender pattern has persisted since 1996 (ibid).

The next part of the analysis involves an examination of how the take-up of Higher and Foundation level mathematics varies by school type and gender. As the gender patterns across school types did not vary across the five years, the analysis here is based on the 1996 figures, the most recent examination data available for this study (Figure 2.5).

Overall, the take-up of Higher mathematics is substantially higher than the average (36 per cent) in single-sex secondary schools (44 per cent), and marginally higher than average in coeducational secondary schools (40 per cent) and comprehensives (38 per cent). By contrast, take-up of Higher level mathematics in vocational schools and community colleges is approximately half the average rate (20 per cent). Community schools also rank somewhat below the average, with a take-up rate of 29 per cent (Figure 2.5).

Figure 2.5. Take-up of Higher Mathematics by School Type and Gender: 1996

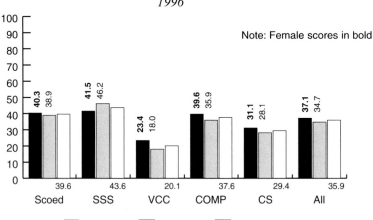

Although there are no major gender differences in the take-up of higher mathematics, there are very significant differences across school types. Boys in single-sex secondary schools are the most likely to take Higher level mathematics, either compared with girls in this sector, or compared with either gender in the other school types. The differences between males and females within the secondary sector are moderate (46 per cent and 39 per cent for males in single-sex and coeducational schools respectively, compared with 42 per cent and 40 per cent for females in single-sex and coeducational schools respectively). However, if the rates for males in single-sex schools are compared with those for either males or females in vocational schools and community colleges, the differences are considerable (ibid). Boys in single-sex schools are 2.5 times more likely than boys in vocational schools and community colleges to do Higher level mathematics and almost twice as likely as girls in these schools.

Girls in the single-sex sector are less likely than boys in this sector to take Higher level mathematics. In other school types, girls are *more* likely than boys to take mathematics at Higher level although the differences are relatively small in all cases (Figure 2.5).

Girls in single-sex schools, secondary coeducational and comprehensive schools are twice as likely to do Higher mathematics as boys in vocational schools and community colleges, and more than 1.5 times more likely to do them than girls in vocational schools and community colleges (ibid).

The analysis of the take-up rates for Foundation level mathematics is presented in Table A2.6. Overall, the take-up of Foundation level mathematics is substantially higher in vocational schools and community colleges compared with all other school types. The take-up in this sector is almost double the average rate (25 per cent compared with 13 per cent). Otherwise, what is most notable is the substantially lower take-up in the secondary sectors compared with the non-secondary sectors.

With the exception of single-sex secondary schools, girls are less likely than boys to take up Foundation level mathematics in all school types. The gender gap is quite substantial in secondary coeducational schools, vocational school and community colleges, and in community schools.

Overall therefore, the greatest gender differences in the take-up rates of different levels of mathematics is between boys in single-sex schools and boys in vocational schools and community colleges, followed by that between girls in single-sex schools and boys (and to a somewhat lesser degree, girls) in vocational and community colleges. Both girls and boys in coeducational secondary schools, and those in comprehensive schools, also, have twice as high a rate of participation in Higher level mathematics than boys in vocational schools and community colleges, and a much higher rate than that of girls in such schools and colleges. Girls and boys in community schools also have a 50 per cent higher rate of take-up in Higher level mathematics than girls and boys in vocational schools and community colleges.

Girls have a 30 per cent lower take-up rate in Foundation level mathematics than boys nationally, although girls in single-sex schools are slightly more likely than boys in single-sex schools to take Foundation mathematics. The reverse is true in all the coeducational schools.

It would appear therefore that, while the gender composition of the school does impact on the take-up of different levels of mathematics, the most notable differences are between schools with the large concentrations of students from disadvantaged working class background, 43 per cent of which are vocational schools and community colleges. In the majority of vocational schools and community colleges generally (63 per cent), and of designated disadvantaged schools (58 per cent), one fifth or fewer of the students are taking Higher level mathematics (Tables 2.4 and A2.4).

Differences between school types must be interpreted with caution however, as there is evidence from the Hannan et al. study (1996) that there are differences in attainment between students attending different school types, with secondary schools having a disproportionately higher number of students who achieved highly on tests of verbal reasoning and numerical skill[9]. The rank order of average attainment levels from the highest to the lowest in their study was as follows: boys' secondary schools, coeducational secondary schools, girls' secondary schools, community and comprehensive schools, and vocational schools and community colleges. A measure of the proportion of lower attaining students within each school was computed[10], and it was found that 18 per cent of students overall fell into this category. Almost one third of students in vocational schools and community colleges, and 27 per cent of those in community and comprehensive schools had low attainment scores compared with 10 per cent of boys and 14 per cent of girls in single-sex schools (ibid, pp. 84-87). What the data suggest therefore is that what can appear to be a school effect may be an intake effect. It is very likely that higher proportions of students in secondary schools are taking Higher level papers because these schools have a higher intake of the high attaining students in the first instance.

However, as Hannan et al.'s study did not have a test of students' attainment *prior to* second-level entry, even the test of so-called ability (in reality a test of attainment) used in that study (it was based on the entire Junior Cycle cohort in the study) does not tell us what the differences were between students *prior to* entering second-level schools. As there is no national test of attainment prior to second-level entry, there is no definitive evidence on the attainment differences between entrants to different second-level schools. In the light of this, we can only make informed estimates as to the precise differences between students in different types of schools: the available evidence does suggest that there are very significant differences and that these are to the advantage of secondary schools in particular. Whatever the extent of the differences in attainment between students across school types at entry or at Junior Certificate level, the findings raise serious questions as to how disparities in attainment arise, and why they are so evidently related to social class background.

Performance in Junior Certificate mathematics: school type and gender differences

Table 2.6 shows that the average grade obtained by students in all levels in mathematics approximated to Grade C[11] over the five years from 1992 to 1996. The average grade obtained in foundation is slightly lower than that obtained in the other levels. There are no notable gender differences in the average scores in relation to Foundation, Ordinary or Higher level mathematics, although girls' scores are marginally higher than boys' scores.

Table 2.6: Gender Differences in Attainment in Junior Certificate Mathematics: Foundation, Ordinary and Higher Examinations

	Average Mean Scores (1992-1996)		
	Females	Males	Overall Average
Foundation	3.94	3.86	3.90
Ordinary	4.16	4.07	4.12
Higher	4.16	4.15	4.15

We also examined performance in mathematics by school type (Table 2.7). Within a given level of mathematics, students in single-sex schools score higher than those in vocational schools and community colleges in particular. The greatest difference is between the performance of girls in single-sex school and those in vocational schools and community colleges at both Ordinary and Higher levels, where the differences reached almost half a grade. On average, girls in single-sex schools achieved over 10 per cent higher grades in both Higher and Ordinary level mathematics from 1992 to 1996.

Gender differences *within* school type are minor at all levels, although girls in single-sex schools have slightly higher scores than boys for each level within the single-sex sector. Boys in community schools have slightly higher scores than girls over the five-year period.

Differences in mean scores between the fee-paying and non fee-paying sectors follows a slightly different pattern. (Figures A2.1 to A2.3). Irrespective of level, students in the fee-paying sector consistently achieved higher mean scores in mathematics than those in the non-fee paying sector. The size of the differences that apply can be seen by comparing the overall lowest and highest mean scores. In Foundation level mathematics, there is a difference of a grade between the scores of girls in the coeducational free scheme, vocational, community and comprehensive schools, and those of girls in fee-paying coeducational schools to the advantage of the latter. In both Higher and Ordinary mathematics, there is a difference of approximately half a grade between the lowest and highest mean scores. Vocational schools and community colleges achieved the lowest scores at both levels, and single-sex secondary schools the highest scores (Figures A2.2 and A2.3).

Table 2.7 Gender Differences in Mathematics Attainment across School Types. Average mean scores for 1992-1996: Foundation, Ordinary and Higher

	School Type					
	Scoed	SSS	VCC	COMP	CS	Total
Foundation						
Females	3.73	3.96	3.69	3.80	3.52	3.79
Males	3.78	3.83	3.66	3.56	3.70	3.71
Total	*3.76*	*3.91*	*3.67*	*3.65*	*3.64*	*3.74*
Ordinary						
Females	4.28	4.40	3.95	3.98	3.93	4.23
Males	4.23	4.24	3.98	4.04	4.04	4.13
Total	*4.25*	*4.33*	*3.97*	*4.01*	*3.99*	*4.18*
Higher						
Females	3.92	4.14	3.75	3.91	3.86	4.03
Males	3.96	4.11	3.74	4.07	3.89	4.01
Total	*3.94*	*4.13*	*3.74*	*3.99*	*3.88*	*4.02*

Key: Scoed: Secondary Coeducational; SSS: Secondary single-sex; VCC: Vocational schools and Community Colleges; COMP: Comprehensives; CS: Community schools.

An examination of gender differences *within* these school sectors showed that female and male scores were very similar. This applied to Foundation, Ordinary and Higher mathematics. Girls in single-sex fee-paying and in free scheme secondary schools did slightly better than boys in similar schools, at both Higher and Ordinary levels. The reverse was true for both levels of the examination in all other school types, with the exception of Ordinary level mathematics in free scheme coeducational secondary schools where girls had slightly higher grades than boys. All the gender differences within sectors are small, especially in the Higher level courses, and especially when compared with the differences across designated disadvantaged and other schools, or between fee-paying and other schools.

We also examined differences in the mean scores in Foundation, Ordinary and Higher level mathematics for designated-disadvantaged and other schools (Figures A2.4 to A2.6). The overall findings for each of the three levels show that mean scores in the non-disadvantaged schools are consistently higher than scores in disadvantaged schools. For Foundation and Ordinary level mathematics, the lowest scores are found in designated-disadvantaged comprehensive schools and the highest scores in non designated-disadvantaged single-sex secondary schools. The lowest scores for Higher level mathematics are found in designated-disadvantaged vocational schools and community colleges, and the highest scores in non designated-disadvantaged single-sex secondary schools. Differences between the lowest and highest scores are quite substantial: they amount to over a half-grade for all three levels.

There were some differences however, between different types of designated disadvantaged schools in Ordinary level grades, with girls in disadvantaged secondary coeducational and single-sex schools scoring half a grade above girls in disadvantaged comprehensive and community schools in particular (Figure A2.5).

Excelling and performing poorly in mathematics

To examine the differences between types of schools, it was decided to examine the patterns of achievement at both grade A, and grade E or lower levels. The third measure was a measure of reasonable achievement, grade C or above[12].

A profile of those who excelled (grade A) in the Junior Certificate examination in Foundation, Ordinary and Higher level mathematics over the 1992 to 1996 period is presented in Figures A2.7 to A2.9. It is clear that the overall proportion achieving this grade fluctuated quite substantially from year to year[13]. The proportion awarded grade A at Higher level in 1996 (8 per cent) was only half of that of 1994 (16 per cent). At Ordinary level, while 13 per cent got a grade A in 1996, only 7 per cent got this grade in 1994.

Over the five years, boys were slightly more likely to excel than girls in both Higher and Foundation level mathematics (except for 1996). In Ordinary level mathematics, girls either performed marginally better or on a par with boys (since 1993). We can conclude, therefore, that although boys consistently achieved a slightly higher proportion of A grades in Higher and Foundation level mathematics from 1992 to 1996, girls and boys received approximately an equal number of A grades at Ordinary level.

The proportion of students awarded grade A varies considerably across school types and by level of subject. Students in single-sex schools received the highest proportion of A grades at both Higher (10 per cent) and Ordinary level (15 per cent). Comprehensive schools were those closest to single-sex schools in terms of A grades awarded at Higher level (9 per cent), while students in secondary coeducational schools were closest to them at Ordinary level (13 per cent). At Foundation level, there were no differences across school types, in terms of the A grades awarded, although comprehensive schools got slightly more (4 per cent) than other school types (3 per cent) (Table 2.8).

Table 2.8 School Type and Gender Differences in Percentage Grade A awarded in Mathematics at Foundation, Ordinary and Higher level (1996)*

	Percentage					
	Scoed	SSS	VCC	COMP	CS	Total
Foundation						
Females	3	4	3	5	1	3
Males	3	3	3	3	5	3
Total	3	3	3	4	3	3
Ordinary						
Females	14	16	8	11	9	13
Males	13	13	10	10	11	12
Total	13	15	9	10	10	13
Higher						
Females	5	8	4	7	6	7
Males	7	11	5	11	7	9
Total	6	10	4	9	6	8

Key: Scoed: Secondary Coeducational; SSS: Secondary single-sex; VCC: Vocational schools and community colleges; COMP: Comprehensive; CS: Community School
*Data for 1992-1995 showed the same trends

There were also gender differences in the proportion of A grades awarded: more males were awarded A grades in Higher level mathematics across all school types, with males in single-sex and comprehensive schools getting the highest proportion of A grades (11 per cent). The comparable figures for girls in single-sex and comprehensive schools were 8 per cent and 7 per cent respectively. The greatest disparity in A grades awarded was between boys in single-sex schools and girls in vocational schools: while 11 per cent of boys in the single-sex schools got Higher level A grades, only 4 per cent of girls in vocational schools and community colleges got A grades. As pointed out above (Table 2.2 and on page 28), the gender findings need to be interpreted in the light of the social class profile of the schools and their general attainment scores: boys in single-sex schools are the second most likely to be middle-class (boys in coeducational secondary schools are slightly more middle-class) while girls in vocational schools and community colleges are the most likely to be working class. Single-sex boys' schools also had the lowest proportion of students with low general attainment scores in the Junior Certificate classes while vocational schools had the highest proportion.

Gender differences between schools are not confined to secondary and vocational schools. There was also a considerable disparity between girls and boys *within* comprehensive schools: 7 per cent of girls got A grades on Higher examinations compared with 11 per cent of boys. Equally, within the single-sex sector, considerably more boys (11 per cent) than girls (8 per cent) got A grades. Gender disparities are reversed at Ordinary level with girls in single-sex schools getting most (16 per cent), followed by girls in coeducational secondary schools (14 per cent). Girls in both single-sex and comprehensive schools got more A grades at this level than boys in these school types.

There is also a considerable disparity between fee-paying and all other schools in the proportion of A grades awarded at both Higher and Ordinary levels (Table A2.7). At Higher level, the greatest disparity is between boys in single-sex fee-paying schools (14 per cent of whom got A grades) and girls in vocational, community and comprehensive schools and community colleges (5 per cent of whom got A grades). At Ordinary level it is girls in single-sex fee-paying schools who got most A grades and girls in vocational, community and comprehensive schools and community colleges who got least. What is interesting to note is that slightly more boys (14 per cent) in fee-paying schools got A grades at Higher level than girls in such schools (10 per cent).

We must enter a caveat here about these differences in performance across school types. There is a widespread use of grinds by students undertaking public examinations. As grinds are relatively expensive, it is highly probable that students from more economically advantaged backgrounds are disproportionately more likely to have taken them, thereby boosting their grades. There is some research evidence to support the contention that it is the more economically advantaged students that have the highest take-up rates for grinds (Lynch and O'Riordan, 1998; Lynch and Lodge, 2002).

When designated disadvantaged schools are compared with other schools, the greatest disparity in the proportion of A grades awarded is between boys in non-disadvantaged single-sex schools and girls in designated disadvantaged vocational schools and community colleges

(Table A2.8). While 12 per cent of boys in the former schools got A grades at Higher level, only 1 per cent of girls got A grades at higher level in the vocational schools and community colleges (and 3 per cent of boys). At Ordinary level, the gender disparities in the proportion of A grades awarded are not as great between designated disadvantaged and non-disadvantaged schools. In this case, it is girls who get most A grades across most school types, but not in vocational schools and community colleges or in designated disadvantaged community schools (Table A2.8).

The proportion of students performing very poorly (Grade E or less) in the Junior Certificate mathematics examination are presented for the years 1992 to 1996 in Figures A2.10 to A2.12. Although there is some variation over the five-year period, between 2 per cent and 12 per cent of students are awarded grade E or less in the Junior Certificate mathematics examination each year. Although gender differences within each level and year are slight, it is notable that males consistently perform more poorly than females.

The proportion of students performing poorly is shown to differ quite substantially between secondary and other schools (Tables A2.9 to A2.11). Most notably, the proportion of students performing poorly is considerably higher in vocational schools and community colleges as it is in single-sex secondary schools (Table A2.9).

Discussion

Although mathematics is a core subject for the Junior Certificate examination, there is considerable variation in the take-up of the subject at different levels. While take-up rates in all subjects vary at Higher and Ordinary level, the take up rate in Higher level mathematics is much lower than in most other major subjects. In 1996, just 36 per cent took Higher level mathematics (an increase from 30 per cent in 1992) compared with 61 per cent taking Higher level English and 69 per cent taking Higher level science. The take-up rate for Higher level mathematics was still 36 per cent in 1999 (Department of Education and Science, 2000b).

Over the five year period of the study (1992 to 1996), mathematics had the lowest take-up at the Higher level and the highest take-up at Foundation level of the three subjects which are divided into three levels. While the majority of schools (79 per cent) were shown to have examined mathematics at all three levels in 1996, in 20 per cent of schools only Ordinary and Foundation level mathematics were taken for the Junior Certificate examination, while in 1 per cent of schools only Foundation level mathematics was examined at Junior Certificate level.

Although boys and girls were equally likely to take Higher level mathematics in 1992, girls were slightly more likely to take the Higher level course in 1996, a pattern that has continued into the new millennium (Department of Education and Science, 2000b).

The low take-up of Higher level mathematics was shown to be a feature of vocational schools and community colleges, and designated disadvantaged schools especially, with a heavy overlap between the two. On the other hand, schools where a high percentage of students were studying Higher level mathematics were typically single-sex secondary schools, with boys' schools in the fee-paying sector being the most likely to offer the Higher level course.

Boys in single-sex secondary schools were shown to be more likely to take Higher level mathematics, either compared with girls in this sector, or students of either gender in the other school types. While differences between males and females within the secondary sector were moderate, those between males in single-sex schools, and males and females in vocational schools and community colleges were considerable. The take-up of Foundation level mathematics was especially high in vocational schools and community colleges.

In terms of performance, an examination of mean scores showed that students in vocational schools and community colleges achieved the lowest mean scores, while students in single-sex secondary school achieved the highest scores at Foundation, Ordinary and Higher levels. The differences were noticeable and consistent: students in secondary schools were awarded just over a quarter of a grade higher scores in the Foundation examination, and a little over one third of a grade higher scores in both the Higher and Ordinary level papers than those in other school types.

Differentiating schools by fee-paying and non-fee-paying, and designated-disadvantaged and non-designated disadvantaged, revealed some notable differences. Schools in the fee-paying and non designated-disadvantaged sectors consistently achieved higher mean scores in mathematics than those in the non fee-paying sector (with differences of over a half to one whole grade differentiating between those at the top and bottom across school types). An examination of gender differences *within* these school sectors showed that female and male grades were very similar.

An examination of gender differences between designated-disadvantaged and non-designated disadvantaged schools showed that female and male scores were very similar within each level, although girls in single-sex schools performed slightly better than boys in both designated-disadvantaged and non-designated disadvantaged single-sex schools. Girls in designated-disadvantaged (coeducational) community and comprehensive schools performed relatively poorly compared with other schools, especially compared with designated-disadvantaged single-sex girls' schools in Ordinary mathematics. In Higher mathematics, girls in designated-disadvantaged single-sex schools achieved a half a grade higher score than girls in designated-disadvantaged vocational schools and community colleges. Girls in designated-disadvantaged coeducational secondary schools also had higher scores than girls in vocational schools and colleges, and than girls in designated-disadvantaged comprehensive and community schools, although the differences were not as pronounced.

An examination of the proportion achieving an A grade or grade E or less reveals a similar pattern. Irrespective of level, schools in the single-sex secondary sector achieve the greatest share of the highest grade while the opposite applies to vocational schools and community colleges. Once again, however, one needs to remember that these grade differences across school types may well be boosted by the level of uptake in mathematics grinds for the Junior Certificate.

In gender terms, although boys consistently achieve a slightly higher proportion of A grades in Higher level mathematics, girls and boys are performing fairly equally at the upper end of the academic spectrum. The opposite applies in relation to poor performance. Here boys consistently perform more poorly than girls, although the differences are slight. An examination of the achievement of a grade C or above by gender shows that girls consistently do better than their male peers; again, however, the differences are small.

In general, the fact that one in five vocational and community schools do not have students taking Higher level mathematics has important implications for students' choices further on in their education. Specifically, the option of taking Higher level mathematics at senior cycle is usually contingent on having studied the subject at this level at junior cycle. The choice of Foundation mathematics at junior cycle, in particular, is likely to limit options both in terms of further educational and vocational choices. On a broader level, because attainment in mathematics is used to allocate students to classes within their year group, placement in a Foundation or Ordinary level class for this subject is likely to have implications for the student's placement in other subjects as well.

While the gender differences in performance are relatively minor within given levels of Junior Certificate mathematics, there are still some differences in performance. Although girls are now slightly more likely to take Higher level mathematics examinations at Junior Certificate level, boys are still more likely to get A grades at higher levels. This is especially true of boys in single-sex secondary schools and of boys in comprehensive schools. Girls are more likely to get A grades at Ordinary level and there is no difference at Foundation level.

In terms of overall performance in Junior Certificate mathematics, girls in single-sex schools achieved the highest scores across all three levels of mathematics between 1992 and 1996. Girls and boys in vocational schools and community colleges got the lowest scores in the Higher level examinations, while girls in community schools got the lowest scores in both Ordinary and Foundation level examinations. The gender differences 'within' each school type are generally very small however.

Differences in performance therefore are much more notable across school types than across gender groups, with more middle class schools having the higher rates of attainment, and more working class schools having lower rates. Such findings raise questions as to how such differences are generated and perpetuated in the first instance. This is a major subject of our case studies.

APPENDIX TO CHAPTER 2

Table A2.1: Allocation of points to mathematics

Grade	Level		
	Foundation	Ordinary	Higher
A	6	6	6
B	5	5	5
C	4	4	4
D	3	3	3
E	2	2	2
F	1	1	1
No Grade	0	0	0

Table A2.2: Distribution of Junior Certificate students across free scheme and fee-paying, single-sex and coeducational secondary schools: 1996 data

	School Type					
	Scoed Fee	Scoed Free	SSS Fee	SSS Free	Other	Total
Females	1.7	17.5	3.4	47.1	30.4	100.0
Males	2.8	19.6	3.8	30.4	43.4	100.0
Total	2.2	18.6	3.6	38.6	37.0	100.0

Key: Scoed FEE: Secondary Coeducational fee-paying; Scoed FREE: Secondary Coeducational free-scheme; SSS FEE: Secondary single-sex fee-paying; SSS FREE: Secondary single-sex free-scheme.

Table A2.3: The proportion of students across school types that are in designated disadvantaged schools: 1996 data

	School Type					
	Scoed	SSS	VCC	COMP	CS	Total
Females	16.0	23.5	40.2	38.5	41.5	27.2
Males	19.9	18.9	44.8	33.3	38.3	29.2
Total	18.2	21.6	43.0	35.7	39.7	28.2

Key: Scoed: Secondary Coeducational; SSS: Secondary single-sex; VCC: Vocational schools and Community Colleges; COMP: Comprehensive; CS: Community Schools.

Table A2.4: Take-up of Junior Certificate Higher mathematics non-fee vs. fee-paying and designated-disadvantaged (DD) vs. non-designated disadvantaged (NDD), 1996 (Base: all second level schools)

	Non-fee vs. Fee-paying Schools		DD vs. NDD Schools		Total
	Non-fee %	Fee-paying %	DD %	NDD %	Schools % (n)
Nobody	7	0	12	5	7 (49)
1-20 per cent	23	2	46	13	21 (161)
21-40 per cent	37	13	30	38	36 (267)
41-60 per cent	27	39	11	34	28 (209)
61-80 per cent	5	38	1	9	7 (52)
81-100 per cent	0	8	0	1	1 (7)
Total (n)	693	52	196	549	(745)
%	100	100	100	100	100

Table A2.5: Take-up of Junior Certificate Foundation mathematics non-fee vs. fee-paying and designated-disadvantaged (DD) vs. non-designated disadvantaged (NDD), 1996 (Base: all second level schools)

	Non-fee vs. Fee-paying Schools		DD vs. NDD Schools		Total
	Non-fee %	Fee-paying %	DD %	NDD %	Schools % (n)
Nobody	12	44	4	18	14
1-20 per cent	62	52	49	66	61
21-40 per cent	16	4	26	11	15
41-60 per cent	7	0	14	4	7
61-80 per cent	2	0	4	1	2
81-100 per cent	1	0	3	0	1
Total (n)	693	52	196	549	745
%	100	100	100	100	100

Table A2.6 Take-up of Foundation mathematics by school type and gender: 1996

	Percentage					
	Scoed	SSS	VCC	COMP	CS	All
Females	6.5	8.6	19.8	8.3	12.9	10.6
Males	11.0	7.1	28.6	11.5	19.3	15.3
Total	8.8	7.9	25.2	10.0	16.5	13.0

Key: Scoed: Secondary Coeducational; SSS: Secondary single-sex; VCC: Vocational schools and community colleges; COMP: Comprehensive; CS: Community Schools.

Table A2.7 Percentage obtaining grade A in mathematics by fee-paying vs. free-scheme, and school type and gender: 1996 Data

	School Type (fee-paying vs. free-scheme)				
	Scoed FEE	Scoed FREE	SSS FEE	SSS FREE	VCC/CS/COMP FREE
Foundation					
Females	23	2	0	4	2
Males	8	3	11	2	3
Total	14	2	5	3	3
Ordinary					
Females	15	13	24	16	9
Males	19	12	15	13	10
Total	17	13	20	15	10
Higher					
Females	6	5	10	8	5
Males	7	8	14	11	6
Total	7	6	12	9	6

Key: Scoed FEE: Secondary Coeducational fee-paying; Scoed FREE: Secondary Coeducational free-scheme; SSS FEE: Secondary single-sex fee-paying; SSS FREE: Secondary single-sex free-scheme; VCC/CS/COMP FREE: Vocational schools and community colleges, community schools and comprehensive free-scheme.

Table A2.8 Percentage obtaining Grade A in mathematics: differences by gender and designated-disadvantaged status: 1996 Data

	School Type (Designated Disadvantaged Status vs. Non-Designated Disadvantaged Status)									
	Scoed		SSS		VCC		COMP		CS	
	DD	NDD	DD	NDD	DD	NDD	DD	NDD	DD	NDD
Foundation										
Females	1	4	3	4	2	5	4	5	0	1
Males	4	3	2	3	2	3	2	3	4	5
Total	3	3	2	4	2	4	3	4	3	4
Ordinary										
Females	12	14	13	17	6	9	5	15	5	13
Males	11	13	10	14	8	11	4	12	7	13
Total	12	14	12	16	7	11	5	14	6	13
Higher										
Females	4	5	5	9	1	5	2	9	5	6
Males	5	8	9	12	3	5	11	11	6	7
Total	5	6	7	10	2	5	6	10	6	7

Key: ScoedDD: Secondary Coeducational designated-disadvantaged; ScoedNDD: Secondary Coeducational non designated-disadvantaged; SSSDD: Secondary single-sex designated-disadvantaged; SSSNDD: Secondary single-sex non designated-disadvantaged; VCCDD: Vocational schools and community colleges designated-disadvantaged; VCCNDD: Vocational schools and community colleges non designated-disadvantaged; CompDD: Comprehensive designated-disadvantaged; CompNDD: Comprehensive non designated-disadvantaged; CSDD: Community school designated-disadvantaged; CSNDD: Community school non designated-disadvantaged

Table A2.9 Percentage performing poorly (grade E or lower) in mathematics by school type and gender: 1996 Data

	School Type					
	Scoed	SSS	VCC	COMP	CS	Total
Foundation						
Females	10	6	10	9	14	9
Males	6	9	12	13	12	11
Total	8	7	11	12	13	10
Ordinary						
Females	7	5	10	11	12	7
Males	8	8	11	11	11	9
Total	7	6	11	11	12	8
Higher						
Females	7	4	11	10	9	6
Males	9	8	11	7	9	9
Total	8	6	11	9	9	7

Key: Scoed: Secondary Coeducational; SSS: Secondary Single-sex; VCC: Vocational schools and community colleges; COMP: Comprehensive; CS: Community Schools.

Table A2.10 Percentage performing poorly (grade E or lower) in mathematics by fee-paying vs. free-scheme school type and gender: 1996 Data

	School Type (fee-paying vs. free-scheme)				
	Scoed FEE	Scoed FREE	SSS FEE	SSS FREE	VCC/CS/ COMP FREE
Foundation					
Females	4	11	6	6	11
Males	3	7	7	9	12
Total	3	8	7	7	12
Ordinary					
Females	3	7	1	5	11
Males	3	8	5	8	11
Total	3	8	3	6	11
Higher					
Females	6	7	3	4	10
Males	6	9	5	8	10
Total	6	8	4	6	10

Key: Scoed FEE: Secondary Coeducational fee-paying; Scoed FREE: Secondary Coeducational free-scheme; SSS FEE: Secondary single-sex fee-paying; SSS FREE: Secondary single-sex free-scheme; VCC/CS/COMP FREE: Vocational schools and community colleges, community school and comprehensive free-scheme.

Table A2.11: Percentage performing poorly (grade E or lower) in mathematics by designated-disadvantage status compared to all other schools and gender: 1996 Data

	School Type (Designated Disadvantaged Status vs. Non-Designated Disadvantaged Status)									
	Scoed		SSS		VCC		COMP		CS	
	DD	NDD	DD	NDD	DD	NDD	DD	NDD	DD	NDD
Foundation										
Females	11	10	8	4	10	9	11	8	17	10
Males	8	6	7	9	13	11	17	10	16	9
Total	9	7	8	6	12	10	14	10	16	9
Ordinary										
Females	9	6	6	4	14	8	14	8	17	8
Males	11	7	10	7	14	9	22	5	17	8
Total	10	7	8	5	14	9	18	7	17	8
Higher										
Females	9	6	5	4	16	9	21	5	14	6
Males	14	8	12	7	13	11	12	6	16	6
Total	11	7	8	6	14	10	17	5	15	6

Key: ScoedDD: Secondary Coeducational designated-disadvantaged; ScoedNDD: Secondary Coeducational non designated-disadvantaged; SSSDD: Secondary single-sex designated-disadvantaged; SSSNDD: Secondary single-sex non designated-disadvantaged; VCCDD: Vocational schools and community colleges designated-disadvantaged; VCCNDD: Vocational schools and community colleges non designated-disadvantaged; CompDD: Comprehensive designated-disadvantaged; CompNDD: Comprehensive non designated-disadvantaged; CSDD: Community school designated-disadvantaged; CSNDD: Community school non designated-disadvantaged

Table A2.12 Percentage obtaining grade C and above in mathematics by school type and gender: 1996 Data

	School Type					
	Scoed	SSS	VCC	COMP	CS	Total
Foundation						
Females	60	69	57	62	49	62
Males	61	64	56	51	56	58
Total	60	67	56	55	54	59
Ordinary						
Females	76	79	65	64	64	72
Males	74	74	66	68	69	71
Total	75	77	65	66	67	72
Higher						
Females	65	74	59	66	63	69
Males	66	70	58	68	62	67
Total	66	72	58	67	63	68

Key: Scoed: Secondary Coeducational; SSS: Secondary Single-sex; VCC: Vocational schools and community colleges; COMP: Comprehensive; CS: Community Schools.

Table A2.13 Percentage obtaining grade C and above by fee-paying vs. free-scheme school type and gender: 1996 Data

	School Type (fee-paying vs. free-scheme)				
	Scoed FEE	Scoed FREE	SSS FEE	SSS FREE	VCC/CS/ COMP FREE
Foundation					
Females	93	57	71	69	55
Males	87	59	75	64	56
Total	89	58	73	67	56
Ordinary					
Females	86	75	91	78	65
Males	84	73	81	74	67
Total	85	74	87	77	66
Higher					
Females	65	65	81	73	61
Males	70	65	77	69	61
Total	68	65	79	71	61

Key: Scoed FEE: Secondary Coeducational fee-paying; Scoed FREE: Secondary Coeducational free-scheme; SSS FEE: Secondary single-sex fee-paying; SSS FREE: Secondary single-sex free-scheme; VCC/CS/COMP FREE: Vocational schools and community colleges, community school and comprehensive free-scheme.

Table A2.14 Percentage obtaining grade C and above in mathematics by designated-disadvantage compared to other school types and gender: 1996 Data

	Designated Disadvantaged compared to other school types									
	Scoed		SSS		VCC		COMP		CS	
	DD	NDD	DD	NDD	DD	NDD	DD	NDD	DD	NDD
Foundation										
Females	60	60	65	73	53	62	61	62	46	54
Males	53	64	67	62	55	57	36	64	51	61
Total	55	62	65	68	55	58	45	63	49	59
Ordinary										
Females	69	77	75	80	59	69	55	70	55	71
Males	68	76	68	76	62	69	54	75	60	74
Total	69	76	72	79	60	69	55	73	58	73
Higher										
Females	62	66	71	74	52	61	61	68	52	68
Males	57	67	65	71	52	60	62	70	54	66
Total	60	66	68	73	52	61	61	69	53	67

Key: ScoedDD: Secondary Coeducational designated-disadvantaged; ScoedNDD: Secondary Coeducational non designated-disadvantaged; SSSDD: Secondary single-sex designated-disadvantaged; SSSNDD: Secondary single-sex non designated-disadvantaged; VCCDD: Vocational schools and community colleges designated-disadvantaged; VCCNDD: Vocational schools and community colleges non designated-disadvantaged; CompDD: Comprehensive designated-disadvantaged; CompNDD: Comprehensive non designated-disadvantaged; CSDD: Community school designated-disadvantaged; CSNDD: Community school non designated-disadvantaged.

Figure A2.1: Mean scores for Foundation level mathematics by school type and gender, 1996.

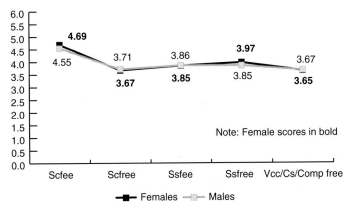

Key – Figures A2.1 to A2.3: *Scfee*: Secondary Coeducational fee-paying; *Scfree*: Secondary coed free-scheme; *Ssfee*: Secondary single-sex fee-paying; *Ssfree*: Secondary single-sex free-scheme; *Vcc/cs/comp free*: Vocational schools and community colleges, community schools and comprehensives.

Figure A2.2: Mean scores for Higher level mathematics by school type and gender, 1996

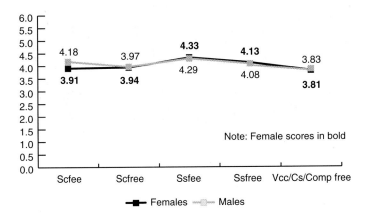

Figure A2.3: Mean scores for Ordinary level mathematics by school type and gender, 1996

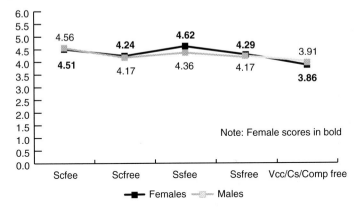

Figure A2.4: Foundation level mathematics mean scores by designated disadvantaged compared with other school types, 1996 Data

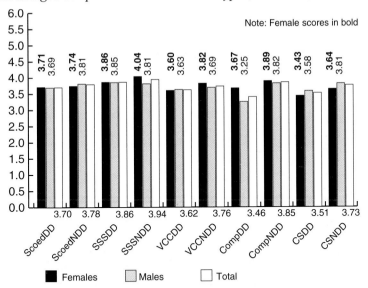

Key – Figures A2.4 to A2.6: ScoedDD: Secondary Coeducational designated-disadvantaged; ScoedNDD: Secondary Coeducational non designated-disadvantaged; SSSDD: Secondary single-sex designated-disadvantaged; SSSNDD: Secondary single-sex non designated-disadvantaged; VCCDD: Vocational schools and community colleges designated-disadvantaged; VCCNDD: Vocational schools and community colleges non designated-disadvantaged; CompDD: Comprehensive designated-disadvantaged; CompNDD: Comprehensive non designated-disadvantaged; CSDD: Community school designated-disadvantaged; CSNDD: Community school non designated-disadvantaged.

Figure A2.5: Ordinary level mathematics mean scores by designated disadvantaged compared with other school types, 1996 Data

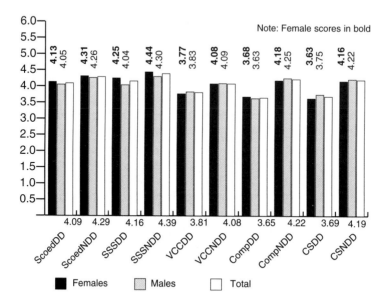

Figure A2.6: Higher level mathematics mean scores by designated disadvantaged compared with other school types, 1996 Data

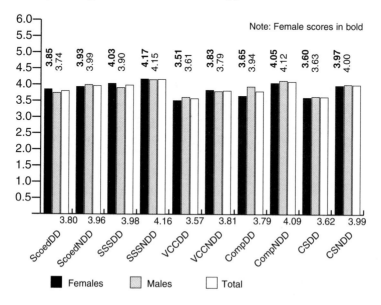

Figure A2.7: Percentage achieving grade A in Foundation mathematics, 1992 to 1996.

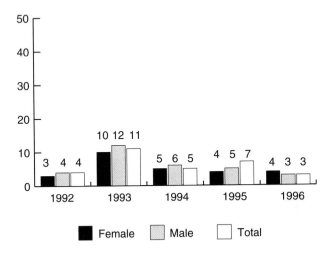

Figure A2.8: Percentage achieving grade A in Higher mathematics, 1992 to 1996.

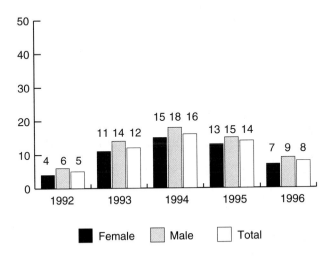

Figure A2.9: Percentage achieving grade A in Ordinary mathematics, 1992 to 1996.

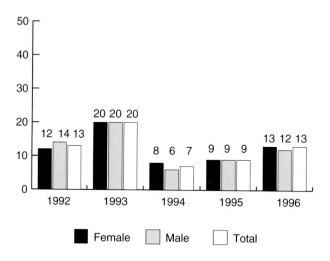

Figure A2.10: Percentage performing poorly in Foundation level mathematics by gender, 1992–6.

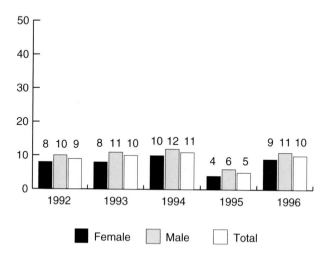

Figure A2.11: Percentage performing poorly in Higher level mathematics by gender, 1992–6.

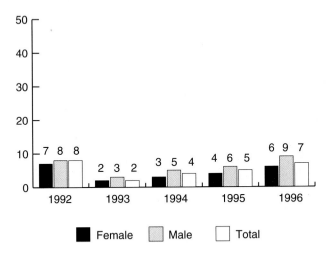

Figure A2.12: Percentage performing poorly in Ordinary level mathematics by gender, 1992–6.

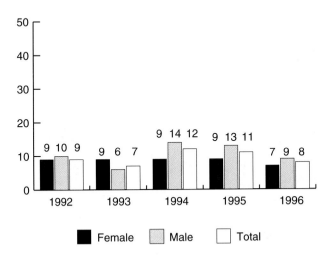

Figure A2.13: Percentage achieving a grade C or above in Higher level mathematics by gender, 1992–6.

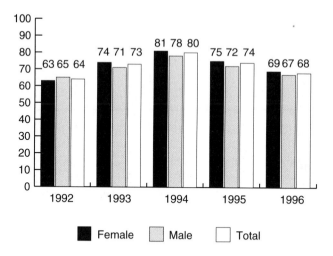

Figure A2.14: Percentage achieving a grade C or above in Foundation level mathematics by gender, 1992–6.

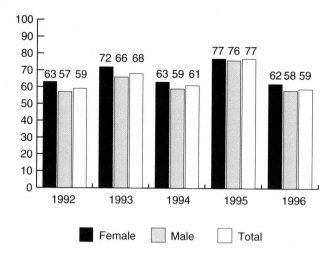

Figure A2.15: Percentage achieving a grade C or above in Ordinary level mathematics by gender, 1992–6.

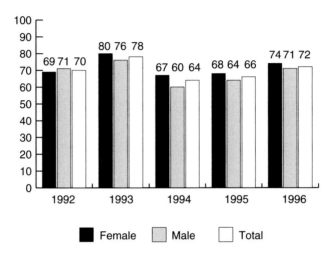

Notes

[1]In the ESRI study, a single scale based on all three grades of mathematics was computed for each school. Higher level papers got the top score ranging from 12 points for an A grade to 7 points for a D grade. An A grade in Ordinary level was awarded 7 points also, while a D in Ordinary level was worth 4 points. The Foundation course was graded from 4 points for an A grade to 1 point for a D (Hannan et al. 1996, p. 262). The inevitable effect of this scaling system was that schools where most students took Higher examinations were bound to have a higher score than those in which most took Ordinary or Foundation level examinations. Given the bias built into the ESRI scale against schools that did not offer Higher level courses, we devised an alternative scale for each level, in which an A grade was given 6 and an F grade was given 1 for each of the three levels in mathematics. An NG grade was given 0. Performance across schools was compared for each level separately (see Table A2.1).

[2] There is a range of different school types at second level. Secondary schools comprise 58 per cent of all schools; these schools were set up by a variety of religious and a few non-religious bodies and organisations. They are traditionally the most academic schools, and also traditionally the most selective in terms of both academic and social intake. Although no schools can select on the basis of entrance tests since the mid-1990's, in practice there is still selection albeit using more discrete criteria (Lynch and Lodge, 2002). Vocational schools and community colleges are under the jurisdiction of vocational education committees. These schools were established under the Vocational Education Act of 1930 and were originally designed to be engaged only in vocational education and training. They were known originally as vocational schools or technical schools but many changed their name, and their management structure, to become community colleges in the 1990's. Vocational schools were not allowed to prepare students for the Leaving Certificate examination until the early

1970's. Not surprisingly therefore, they did not attract the more academically ambitious students in the past, although this changed when they were able to offer the full complement of Leaving Certificate courses some thirty years ago. The vocational schools and community colleges are generally coeducational, unlike secondary schools, of which two thirds are single sex. Vocational schools have traditionally been more working class in intake than all other school types. Comprehensive schools were established from the 1960's onwards and were inspired by similar initiatives in the UK. They have a management structure that comprises representatives of the Department of Education and Science, the vocational education committee and the religious bodies engaged in the schools. They are either Catholic or Protestant in ethos. Community schools were established in the 1970's under Deeds of Trust. They are similar to comprehensives in management structure although the religious bodies involved in running them are generally Roman Catholic while the Department of Education and Science is not as directly involved. Both the community and comprehensive schools can offer the full complement of second-level subjects. They are generally coeducational schools. While most of the early community and comprehensive schools were built on green field sites, in the 1990's a growing number of community schools have resulted from amalgamations of secondary and vocational schools or of other school combinations. Even some of the recently created community colleges have resulted from the amalgamation of secondary and vocational schools. In terms of intake, both the community and comprehensive schools occupy an interim position between vocational/community colleges and secondary schools.

[3] The Junior Certificate examination data comprises a record of results (grade achieved within each subject level) for each candidate. In addition, each record contains a code identifying the school attended by each student. The following school-level information was identified and entered into the data base for all candidates:
(1) school type: secondary, vocational schools and community colleges, community schools and comprehensive schools;
(2) gender composition: single-sex or coeducational;
(3) fee-paying or free-scheme;
(4) designated-disadvantaged or non designated-disadvantaged.

[4] Over one quarter (26 per cent) of all schools are designated disadvantaged. This designation is based on an assessment of the proportion of socially, economically and educationally disadvantaged students in the school. The criteria for assessing each form of disadvantage are laid down by the Department of Education and Science: they include levels of educational attainment in the schools, proportion of families on low incomes, numbers who are welfare dependent, have medical cards, etc.

[5] As 1994 was the mid-year of our five year study (1992 to 1996), it provided a useful benchmark for estimating the social class profile of the students in different school types.

[6] The individual-level Junior Certificate examination data were aggregated by the school variable, to produce school-level data.

[7] The corresponding figures for the proportion of other school types having designated disadvantaged status are as follows: Community Schools (40 per cent), Comprehensives (36 per cent), Secondary single-sex (22 per cent) and Secondary Coed (18 per cent).

[8] We do not report the findings for the intervening three years, as the patterns do not vary to any significant degree from those in 1992 and 1996.

[9] In order to obtain a measure of ability, the Department of Education and Science's Psychological Service administered Differential Aptitude Tests (DATS) to almost 5,000 of the Junior Cert students surveyed. These tests comprised assessments of competence in verbal reasoning and numerical skill. The summed score of both tests was used as an indicator of general academic ability (VRNA) in the ESRI study (Hannan et al., 1996).

[10] Defined as the proportion of students within each school type falling more than one standard deviation below the aggregate mean VRNA (Verbal Reasoning/Numerical skill) score.

[11] Grades 'A' to 'NG' are marked 6 to 0 within each level (Table A2.1). This means that a difference of 1 between scores equals a whole grade difference. Other differences are *pro rata*.

[12] While the results of the patterns for the C or higher grades are not discussed in the text, tables reporting the results of this analysis are included in the Appendix (Figures A2.13 to A2.15 and Tables A2.12 to A2.14).

[13] There are a number of reasons why this could have happened, including changes in marking schemes from year to year and changes in tasks the students were required to undertake in the examinations.

3

The Case Studies

Introduction

The study of take-up and attainment in Junior Certificate mathematics indicated that while there were certain gender differences in take-up and attainment rates between girls and boys, these differences were relatively minor when compared with differences across school types. The greatest differences in take-up patterns and attainment were not those between girls and boys *within* school types, but between both girls and boys *across* school types. Vocational schools and community colleges, which are generally coeducational schools, also tend to be more working class in intake than other school types (Table 2.2). Both girls and boys in these schools were less likely to take Higher level mathematics than their peers in other types of schools, including coeducational secondary schools[1] (Tables 2.3, 2.4). While differences in performance, within each level of mathematics, did not vary greatly across school types, they did vary somewhat. Single sex schools generally, and girls' schools in particular, had the highest average rates of attainment in the Junior Cycle examinations of all groups (Table 2.7).

What the analysis of Junior Certificate data suggested, therefore, was that gender differences were strongly related to school-type differences, which, in turn, were closely related to social class differences. In choosing the case study schools, therefore, we were mindful of the importance of school-type and social class, as well as gender differences. While we chose schools that were representative of schools nationally, we chose a disproportionately larger number of both high and low achieving schools to help understand differences in take-up and performance, and to establish how gender and school type[2] impacted on students' experience of learning mathematics.

Choosing the Schools and Classes for the Case Studies

The aim of the case studies was to engage in an in-depth analysis of the teaching and learning of mathematics. In the context of this overriding objective, the study was designed to examine the perspectives of mathematics teachers, of students and of parents on the teaching and learning of mathematics. Arising from the findings of our analysis of the Junior Certificate data, a further objective of the case studies was to analyse how the students' gender, social class background, the type of school they attended, and class group in which they were placed, impacted on their learning of mathematics.

The study was designed as a co-operative inquiry based on the general principles of co-operative and emancipatory research (Heron, 1981; Humphries and Truman, 1994; Humphries, 1997; Oliver, 1992). Because of this, the process of choosing case study schools took several months and involved a wide range of consultations with all the relevant management bodies, teacher unions and the Mathematics Teachers Association of Ireland. One of the first tasks was to make a presentation to the Mathematics Teachers Association at their annual general meeting in 1997. We held subsequent meetings with interested mathematics teachers as to the objectives of the study and the methodologies we should employ. We held discussions with the mathematics inspectorate in the Department of Education and Science and with experts in the field of mathematics education both in Ireland and internationally. In addition, a research advisory committee was established to guide the study. It comprised representatives of mathematics teachers in Ireland, mathematics educators and researchers, social scientists with research expertise on education, representatives of the Department of Education and Science mathematics inspectorate, and two leading international experts on the subject of mathematics education. The Gender Equality Committee of the Department of Education and Science, who funded the study, were also represented on the advisory committee.

Given the complex nature of the issues to be addressed, and in particular the need to gain insight into the teaching of mathematics in classrooms, a triangular approach to the research subject was adopted. A triangular approach is employed when a subject is complex and is not readily understood by employing a single research methodology (Seale, 1998). It involves using a range of research strategies to elicit different perspectives on a single phenomenon. In our case, it involved listening to the views of students, teachers and parents on the teaching and learning of mathematics as well as video-taping the classroom teaching of the subject. The use of a multi-faceted methodological approach enabled us to study the complex interface between the teaching and learning of mathematics from a range of different standpoints. By listening to all the major education partners, students, teachers and parents, and by observing teachers teaching and by recording their work on video, we were able go gain a holistic understanding of how the subject is taught and how learning takes place.

We were well placed, therefore, to understand whether boys and girls, and students from different social backgrounds, had different experiences of learning mathematics.[3]

Guided by insights gained from the TIMSS videotape study of mathematics classrooms (Kawanka et al., 1999), a small pilot study was undertaken prior to the main study. The pilot study involved the videotaping of six mathematics classes in three schools. The classes were both coeducational and single sex. In addition, pilot interviews were undertaken with both teachers and students. Both primary and second-level schools were involved in the pilot study as it was thought that a small study of the teaching and learning of mathematics at primary level would enhance our understanding of teaching and learning at second level. After the pilot study, it was decided to focus exclusively on second-level schools, largely because it would have been impossible to make any meaningful statement about the teaching of mathematics at primary level without engaging in an equally in-depth study to that planned for second-level. It was not possible to complete such an intensive study of primary-level mathematics within the time and resources available.

The research instruments were refined after the pilot study. Apart from the decision to focus exclusively on second-level mathematics, the most significant change after the pilot was the decision to use a second digital video recorder to observe the classes for the main study. In the pilot study we had used only one camera focused mostly on the students. The limitation of this was that it was not possible to record all teacher responses, especially non-verbal responses and initiatives. It also meant that if we focused the camera on the teacher, we had no video record (although we did have an audio record) of the students in the class at that moment. With the second digital camera, we were able to observe both the students and the teacher simultaneously. Having a second camera also minimised the disruption to the class, as we did not have to move around during the lesson.

There were ten schools chosen for the main case studies, a profile of which is presented in Table 3.1. Six of the schools were secondary, three were vocational/community colleges, and one was a community school. Five of the schools were coeducational, three of which were vocational/community colleges, one was a community school and one was a secondary school. Of the five single-sex schools, two were boys' schools and three were girls' schools. There were two fee-paying schools in the study, one boys' school and one girls' school (both secondary) and four designated disadvantaged schools, two of which were vocational/community colleges and two of which were secondary schools, one girls' school and one boys' school.

Table 3.1 *Case-study schools: distribution by type, gender composition, status, size, geographical location and grouping procedure*

Case-study schools	School type*	Gender composition**	Status		Size *****	Location	Class group
			Fee- ***	DD versus NDD ****			
Barrow (SSG F)	S	SSG	FP	NDD	MEDIUM	City	Top Set
Nore (SSG Fr)	S	SSG	FS	NDD	MEDIUM	City	Mixed
Suir (SSG Fr D)	S	SSG	FS	DD	VERY LARGE	Town	Bottom Band
Liffey (SSB Fr D)	S	SSB	FS	DD	SMALL	City	Top Stream
Lee (SSB F)	S	SSB	FP	NDD	MEDIUM	City	Mixed
Lagan (SC Fr)	S	COED	FS	NDD	MEDIUM	Town	Top Band
Errigal (CS Fr)	CS	COED	FS	NDD	LARGE	Town	Middle Band
Mourne(VCC Fr D)	VCC	COED	FS	DD	LARGE	City	Bottom Band
Blackstairs (VCC Fr D)	VCC	COED	FS	DD	LARGE	Small Town	Top Stream
Nephin (VCC Fr)	VCC	COED	FS	NDD	MEDIUM	City	Bottom Band

Key:
* S = Secondary; CS = Community School; VCC = Vocational/Community College;
** SSG = Single-Sex Girls; SSB = Single-Sex Boys; SC = Secondary coeducational; COED = Coeducational;
*** FP = Fee-Paying; FS = Free-Scheme (where free-scheme represents non-fee paying status);
**** DD = Designated Disadvantage Status; NDD = Non Disadvantage Status;
***** Small = <300; Medium = 301-600; Large = 601-800; Very Large = 801+.

The case study schools were strategically chosen, not only to represent different school types, but also to enable us to understand why there were differences across schools in terms of both take-up rates for different levels of mathematics as well as differences in performance. As the greatest difference in take-up rates for different levels of mathematics was between fee-paying secondary schools and vocational schools and community colleges, both of these types of schools were over-represented in the case studies relative to their representation nationally: two of the ten schools we studied were fee-paying, although just 7 per cent of schools nationally are of this type; four of the ten schools were disadvantaged, although only 26 per cent of schools nationally are disadvantaged.

The method for choosing the schools was based on a combination of criteria. While it was essential that schools were representative of different types of schools, and in particular that they would enable us to understand key differences related to gender and social background, they were also chosen on the basis of their regional location, and the type of grouping system that they operated (we needed to have schools using different methods of grouping students so that we could examine the learning experiences in different tracks or streams). Finally, it was necessary to choose schools and classes where principals, teachers and students were interested and willing to be part of the research project.

The soliciting of schools and classes took place through a series of advertisements in educational newsletters and newspapers and by making direct contact with the relevant bodies representing schools and teachers. A list of forty-seven schools was eventually drawn up in which teachers had volunteered to be part of the study, and in which principals had also agreed that they could participate. These schools were willing also to seek the permission and co-operation of students. It was from this list that the final ten schools were selected.

Classes within schools were chosen from among the second year students of the Junior Cycle. The reason for focusing on Junior Cycle mathematics was because the ESRI study (Hannan et al., 1996) had identified significant gender differences at this stage across school types that they believed needed further research investigation. In addition, second year students seemed an appropriate research group, as they had covered a good deal of the Junior Cycle syllabus but were not undertaking examinations during the course of the study. The fact that they were not examination classes meant that school principals, teachers and students were more likely to have time to participate in the study.

Having chosen the schools and year of classes, we then systematically chose classes at the top, bottom and middle streams or tracks across the schools. The objective was to ensure that we observed the teaching of

mathematics at different levels. We knew from existing research that high
track students were generally taking the Higher level course, while mixed
classes varied, with some being taught Higher, others being taught
Ordinary and some being taught both Higher and Ordinary. Lower tracks
or streams generally follow either the Ordinary mathematics syllabus or, in
some cases, the Foundation level course (Hannan et al.1996; Lynch, 1989;
Lynch and Lodge, 2002).

Table 3.2 Case study schools: grouping practices in the Junior Cycle

Schools	1st Year	2nd Year	Junior Cert Year
Barrow (SSG F)	Mixed	Mixed, Set for Irish and mathematics	Mixed, Set for Irish and mathematics
Nore (SSG Fr)	Mixed	Mixed	Mixed
Suir (SSG Fr D)	Banded	Banded	Streamed for mathematics
Liffey (SSB Fr D)	Streamed	Streamed	Streamed
Lee (SSB F)	Mixed	Mixed	Mixed
Lagan (SC Fr)	Banded	Banded	Banded
Errigal (CS Fr)	Mixed, Banded for Irish, English, mathematics, French, German	Banded	Banded
Mourne (VCC Fr D)	Mixed, Banded for Irish, English, mathematics	Banded	Banded
Blackstairs (VCC Fr D)	Mixed	Streamed	Streamed
Nephin (VCC Fr)	Mixed, Banded for Core Subjects	Banded	Banded

Key: SSG F: Secondary girls', fee-paying; SSG Fr: Secondary girls', free scheme; SSG
Fr D: Secondary girls', free scheme designated disadvantaged; SSB Fr D: Secondary
boys', free scheme designated disadvantaged; SSB F: Secondary boys', fee paying; SC
Fr: Secondary coed, free scheme; CS Fr: Community school, free scheme; VCC Fr D:
Vocational/Community college, free scheme designated disadvantaged; VCC Fr:
Vocational/Community college, free scheme (where free-scheme represents non fee-
paying status).

There were three mixed classes[4], three top streams/ bands/sets, three
defined as bottom bands, and one class that was a middle band.However,
as can be seen from Table 3.2, the schools varied their grouping procedures
from year to year. The most notable change is from mixed classes in first
year to a more hierarchical ordering of tracks in second and third year.

Researching the Mathematics Classes and English Classes

When permission was obtained from the school principals, teachers and students in the ten classes to participate in the study, the design of the research instruments got under way.

After extensive consultations with teachers and the research advisory group, it was agreed that it would be desirable to have some measure of students' attainment in mathematics at the outset of the study. To determine this we devised a short test in mathematics based on the released items of the TIMSS study. Forty items were selected in all; these examined students' competency in mathematical skills that were appropriate to their age and Junior Certificate status. The test was administered to students in the ten classes after the teacher had obtained their consent at a previous lesson. It provided us with useful background data on students' skills in mathematics, and enabled us to determine what level of competence students had in the different classes at the time the study was being undertaken. The overall national mean for the forty items chosen from the TIMSS for this study is 62 per cent (25 out of a possible 40).

To research students' experience of learning mathematics, a threefold research strategy was devised. First, it was agreed that the best method for recording information on teaching was to videotape the classes. With the agreement of the ten mathematics teachers and their students, each of the chosen mathematics classes were videotaped twice, at intervals several weeks apart. While it was appreciated that videotaping was intrusive, research from the TIMSS study had suggested that videotaping was a very valuable research tool for understanding how mathematics was actually taught in classrooms. (Stigler and Heibert, 1999). Therefore, to counter some of the bias built into the video observation, classes were videotaped on two separate occasions. Contrary to expectations, we did not find that the videotape interfered greatly with the flow of the lesson. Following the initial interest in the mechanics of the video itself, the classes settled down to a normal lesson routine, especially in the second lesson. Our focus group interviews with students after the observations suggested that being videotaped was not unusual for students as many of them had been videotaped before in their homes and at social gatherings. Moreover, we used small digital cameras, one focused on the teacher and the other on the students, and these were not particularly intrusive.

In the analysis of the video material we were guided by the procedures utilised in the TIMSS study (Stigler and Heibert, 1999). When the video material was collected, the tapes were coded and viewed by all the research team, both individually and collectively. After the initial viewings, the tapes were transcribed in full on to hard copy and analysed systematically in terms of their public discourse and interactions. The analysis focused on the style of teaching, language content, teacher-student interaction patterns, and gender differences in interaction flows. Initial interpretations were read and re-read by the research team, and were presented to the research advisory committee on four separate occasions. In the light of their comments and further viewing of the material, interpretations were revised and edited further. Coding systems based on key themes were devised and a content analysis of these was undertaken systematically for all classes. The teachers who had been videotaped, and who had expressed an interest in continuing dialogue with us about the study, were also invited to read our interpretations of the video material. Their comments and reservations were taken into account in the final analysis. In addition, a senior mathematics teacher, who was not involved in the study, read the entire manuscript to check it for authenticity prior to publication.

Students were also asked to complete a detailed questionnaire about their experience of learning mathematics, and to provide other relevant personal background information. Much of the focus of the questionnaire was on students' attitudes to, and experience of, learning mathematics. Details of the research instruments devised for measuring attitudes, and examining students' experiences of mathematics are presented in Chapter 10 below. As with all aspects of the study, students were informed in advance that they need not fill out the questionnaires and a small number chose not to do so: of the 250 students in the ten classes, 237 filled out the questionnaires.

On the basis of a preliminary analysis of both the videotapes and questionnaires, a number of students from each of the ten classes were asked to take part in a short focus group discussion about their experience of learning mathematics, focusing especially on their current class experience. We chose students who were both high and low participants in class, as well as students who were getting high grades and lower grades. There were equal numbers of girls and boys. In all, eighteen focus group interviews were undertaken with an average of four students in each. The questionnaire data was analysed using the SPSS software programme while the interviews were transcribed in full and rigorously analysed, using software applications where relevant. As with the classroom material, a coding scheme for analysing key themes was drawn up and each interview was analysed within that frame.

Although the main focus of the study was on mathematics, it was believed that it would be useful to video a small number of English classes in the case-study schools, with the same groups of students if possible. Like mathematics, English is a core subject for almost all second-level students. It was important to know if the style of teaching that operated in mathematics operated also in another core subject. Although time and resources did not enable us to investigate English teaching in any depth, the data we collected did enable us to make some basic comparisons between the teaching of English and mathematics to second year students.

While grouping practices did not allow us to videotape identical groups of students, we were able to videotape some of the same students in English classes that we had observed in mathematics. Five English classes were videotaped, and of this, three were in single sex classes and two were in coeducational classes. These were coded and analysed the same way as the mathematics lessons, but not in as much depth. A more detailed discussion of the classes and findings in relation to the teaching of English is presented in Chapter 8.

Teachers and Parents

How students approach the learning of mathematics and how they learn is not just influenced by their views and interests in the subject, it is also strongly determined by the attitudes of their parents and teachers. Because of this, we undertook intensive interviews with the ten mathematics teachers.[5] The objective was to explore their views on the teaching of mathematics in particular. The teachers also filled out a short questionnaire giving their professional profiles and general views on the subject of mathematics. A detailed profile of individual teachers is not included here to preserve the anonymity of those who participated[6].

We also decided to interview a small subset of the parents of students that we had observed. We asked the parents of students from each of the ten schools if it was possible to interview them, stressing that we did not need, nor had we time, to interview them all. Our target was to interview a few, three or four parents, from each class to ascertain their views on the teaching and learning of mathematics. We eventually interviewed twenty-eight parents of students across the ten schools. The findings from these interviews are reported in Chapter 11.

General profile of the schools

Table 3.1 above provides a general profile of the ten schools in the study. Of the ten, six were secondary schools, three were community colleges and one was a community school. Five of the six secondary schools were single-sex, three being single-sex girls' schools while two were boys' schools. Two of the ten schools were fee-paying while four were designated-disadvantaged.

In terms of size, one of the schools was very large with over 800 students, and one was small with less than 300 students. Of the remainder, four were classified as medium (between 301-600) while three were classified as large (601-800). Six of the schools were located in the Dublin or the greater Dublin area. Of the four schools outside of these areas, two were located in medium-sized towns and two others were in small towns.

Coeducational Schools – Origin and Gender Distribution

Table 3.3 provides a profile of the coeducational schools in terms of their origin, their present status, and the gender distribution within the school. What is clear from this is that boys were in the majority in three of the five schools. The only school in which girls were in the majority was the one that was originally a girls' school but became a coeducational school some years previously.

Table 3.3 Coeducational case-study schools: origin by present school type and gender distribution

School	Origin of school	Present school type	Gender		Ratio m-f
			Male %	Female %	
Lagan (SC Fr)	Girls only	Coed Secondary	46	54	0.85
Errigal (CS Fr)	Amalgamation	Greenfield	53	47	1.12
Mourne(VCC Fr D)	Greenfield	Greenfield	50	50	1.0
Blackstairs (VCC Fr D)	Greenfield	Greenfield	56	44	1.27
Nephin (VCC Fr)	Greenfield	Greenfield	57	43	1.32

As can be seen from this table, three of the five schools were established as coeducational schools. One of the five schools was formed through amalgamation and one broadened its intake to include students of the opposite sex.

Social-Class Background of Students in Case Study Schools

Table 3.4 shows that a slight majority of the students were from middle-class backgrounds (52.4 per cent), with just under half (47.6 per cent) from working-class backgrounds. When social class is considered across the single-sex and coeducational sectors, we can see that over three quarters of students in the single sex schools are from a middle-class background while just over one third of students attending the coeducational schools are from middle-class backgrounds. The table also shows that there is a major difference between the case study schools in terms of the proportion of students from upper middle-class backgrounds in attendance: over

Table 3.4: Case-study schools: social class* background of students in observed mathematics classes

School	Upper middle class	Middle class	Lower middle class	Total middle class	Upper working class and skilled manual	Working class semi-skilled and unskilled	Total working class	% (n)	Class organisation: streamed or mixed
Barrow (SSG F)	76.0	12.0	8.0	96.0	4.0	0	4.0	100 (25)	Streamed-Top
Nore (SSG Fr)	0	38.1	28.6	66.7	33.0	0	33.3	100 (21)	Mixed
Suir (SSG Fr D)	0	10.0	10.0	20.0	40.0	40.0	80.0	100 (10)	Streamed-Bottom
Liffey (SSB Fr D)	0	9.5	14.3	23.8	42.9	33.3	76.2	100 (21)	Streamed-Top
Lee (SSB F)	72.0	24.0	4.0	100.0	0	0	0	100 (25)	Mixed
Average SS	36.3	19.6	12.7	79.4	20.6	0	20.6	100 (102)	
Lagan (SC Fr)	6.9	41.4	13.8	62.1	34.5	3.5	37.9	100 (29)	Streamed-Top
Errigal (CS Fr)	0	4.5	9.1	13.6	68.2	18.2	86.4	100 (22)	Streamed-Middle
Mourne(VCC Fr D)	0	5.9	17.6	23.5	11.8	64.7	76.5	100 (17)	Streamed-Bottom
Blackstairs (VCC Fr D)	0	18.8	15.6	34.4	34.4	31.3	65.6	100 (32)	Streamed-Top
Nephin (VCC Fr)	0	0	37.5	37.5	50.0	12.5	62.5	100 (8)	Streamed-Bottom
Average COED	1.9	19.4	15.7	37.0	45.4	17.6	63.0	100 (108)	
Overall Average	18.6	19.5	14.3	52.4	33.3	14.3	47.6	100 (210)	

*The social class profile of students was compiled using the standard Central Statisitics Office procedure devised from the 1996 Census, Principal Socio-economic Results, Dublin: Stationery Office.

Key: SSG F: Secondary girls', fee-paying; SSG Fr: Secondary girls', free scheme; SSG Fr D: Secondary girls', free scheme designated disadvantaged; SSB F: Secondary boys', fee paying; SSB Fr D: Secondary boys', free scheme designated disadvantaged; SC Fr: Secondary coed, free scheme; CS Fr: Community school, free scheme; VCC Fr D: Vocational/Community college, free scheme designated disadvantaged; VCC Fr: Vocational/Community college, free scheme (where free-scheme represents non fee-paying status).

36 per cent of students attending single-sex schools were upper middle-class compared with only 2 per cent of those in coeducational schools.

Case Study Classes: Mathematical Profile

A profile of the grades achieved by students in each of the ten classes in the TIMSS-related test is presented in Table 3.5 below. It is evident from this table that there is a considerable disparity in the attainment level of the students in mathematics at the time the study was undertaken. The highest scores were in Barrow, a girls' fee-paying school, where the students were in the top set for mathematics and 72 per cent achieved an A or B grade. The students in a top stream in Lagan had the next highest grades where 60 per cent were awarded an A or a B, followed by a top band in Blackstairs (a designated disadvantaged community college) where 51.6 per cent got an A or B grade. It is interesting to note that although almost all the students in Barrow and over 60 per cent of those in Lagan were middle-class, two thirds of students in Blackstairs were working class.

The lowest scores were in the low streams with 90 per cent of the students in the girls' school in Suir, and over two thirds of those in Mourne, getting an E or lower grade. Both schools were designated disadvantaged.

The relatively low rates of mathematical attainment of the students observed in Mourne and in Suir were reflected in their Junior Certificate examinations. No students from the classes in Suir or Mourne took the Higher level paper, while 31 per cent of those in Suir and 26 per cent of those in Mourne took Foundation level examinations (Table A3.1)[7]. School-level data on the take-up of different levels of mathematics in the ten schools three years prior to the case studies (1996) show that the patterns we observed in the case study classes were typical of the overall patterns in some schools but not in others. This arises from the fact that in some schools the classes we observed were not typical of that school, in others they were more typical. In Suir (SSG Fr) for example, we observed a bottom stream class in a school that had several higher stream classes doing Higher and Ordinary level mathematics. Thus, while the Junior Certificate take-up rates for Suir for 1996 show that 44 per cent took Higher level examinations, none of the students in the class we observed took Higher level. In Mourne (VCC Fr D) and Liffey (SSB Fr D) however, the patterns of take-up for Higher level mathematics in the classes we observed seemed to be quite typical of whole-school patterns. In Mourne, none of the students we observed took Higher level mathematics while just 3 per cent of the whole cohort took Higher level in 1996; in Liffey, almost 17 per cent of the students we observed took the Higher level paper, while

Table 3.5: Case-study schools: performance in TIMSS-related test*

School	Mean Score on TIMSS-related test	Grades					Group position	% Working class in the group %
		A %	B %	C %	D %	E or lower %		
Barrow (SSG F)	29.8	16.0	56.0	24.0	4.0	0.0	Top Set	4.0
Nore (SSG Fr)	21.9	4.2	20.8	29.2	25.0	20.8	Mixed	33.3
Suir (SSG Fr D)	13.2	0.0	0.0	0.0	10.0	90.0	Bottom Band	80.0
Liffey (SSB Fr D)	24.4	9.1	27.3	22.7	36.4	4.5	Top Stream	76.2
Lee (SSB F)	25.6	11.5	26.9	23.1	38.5	0.0	Mixed	0.0
Lagan (SC Fr)	28.5	16.0	44.0	28.0	8.0	4.0	Top Band	37.9
Errigal (CS Fr)	18.1	0.0	0.0	33.3	29.7	37.0	Middle Band	86.4
Mourne (VCC Fr D)	13.3	0.0	0.0	0.0	33.3	66.7	Bottom Band	76.5
Blackstairs (VCC Fr D)	27.2	12.9	38.7	29.0	19.4	0.0	Top Stream	65.6
Nephin (VCC Fr)	16.5	0.0	0.0	10.0	70.0	20.0	Bottom Band	62.5

*The national mean for second year students in second-level schools is twenty-five out of a possible forty.

no student in the school took the Higher level paper in 1996 (Tables 3.1, 3.2).

Profile of the Individual Case Study Schools and Classes

Before presenting the findings from the case studies, it is important to present a brief profile of the individual classes and their schools. In the following pages a pen picture of each of the case study schools is presented, including a resume of their stated educational philosophy.

The Girls' Schools

Barrow

Barrow is a single-sex, girls', fee-paying school, run by a Roman Catholic religious order. It is a large school situated in a city. The prospectus for the school emphasised the importance of educating the whole person, focusing on formation of character and spiritual values. The school stressed the importance of equipping the girls to fulfil their certain future roles within 'marriage, parenthood and careers'. It also emphasised the importance of educating students for dealing with leisure time, and stressed the need to develop leadership skills. The school operated very strict regulations regarding uniform, punctuality and general manners.

Almost all of the second year students in Barrow were from middle-class backgrounds, with over three-quarters of the twenty-five girls in the class from upper middle-class backgrounds (Table 3.4).

Within the Junior Cycle, the school had mixed classes for all subjects with the exception of Irish and mathematics, both of which were set by level of attainment. The class we observed in Barrow was the top set for mathematics in second year. All of the students expected to be taking the Higher level mathematics paper for the Junior Certificate Examination. The mean score achieved by the class on the TIMSS-related test was 29.8 (out of a possible 40), which was the highest score of all ten schools. All of the girls passed the test, while twenty-four of the twenty-five attained a grade C or higher, with 4 attaining grade A (Table 3.5). In their Summer Test of 1999 (at the end of second year) all of the students attained a grade C or higher, while ten attained grade A.

The core subjects in Barrow were Irish, English, mathematics, history, geography, science and civil, social and political education (CSPE). As with all secondary schools, physical education (PE) and religious education (RE) are part of the core curriculum but are not examined. Other subjects, on offer in Barrow included French, Spanish, business studies, art and choir. None of the subjects available at Barrow were taught at Foundation level for the Junior Certificate.

All of the girls we observed were taking at least one modern language and science. Over three quarters were studying science at the Higher level. Just over one quarter of the students were doing an arts and humanities subject, such as art or music. Practical subjects such as home economics or metal technology, metalwork or technical graphics were not on offer in this school (Table A3.3).

Nore

Nore is also a single-sex girls' school, located in a city and run by a Catholic religious order. It is a free-scheme school and does not charge fees. It is categorised as a large school, having over 500 students. The ethos of this school centres on the all-round development of the individual, emphasising the importance of relationships and respect among staff and students. Nore also has strict regulations regarding uniform, the wearing of make-up and jewellery and general behaviour. However, the development of good working relationships is emphasised over discipline in the school.

Overall, the school had students from quite a wide range of backgrounds in social class terms. More than half of the second-year students were from a working-class background (60 per cent), with the remainder being either from middle-class (20 per cent) or lower middle-class (20 per cent) backgrounds. In the class we observed, two thirds were from middle-class backgrounds (Table 3.4).

The school used a mixed system of grouping for all classes throughout the Junior Cycle (Table 3.2). Almost 60 per cent of the girls in the observed class in Nore expected to take the Higher level paper in the Junior Certificate mathematics examination. Just over one third reported that they expected to sit the Ordinary level in the examination, while a minority (4 per cent) expected to do mathematics at Foundation level (Table A3.1).

The mean score achieved by the students in Nore on the TIMSS-related test was 21.9 (out of a possible 40), which ranked it sixth among the case-study schools. Over one fifth of the class got a grade E or lower on the test. Six of the twenty-four girls got grade D, while the remainder were awarded a grade C or higher. Just one of the class group attained a grade A in this test (Table 3.5). The broad range of mathematical competency in the class was also evident in their summer test of 1999: scores ranged from four grade A's and six grade E's or lower in the higher paper.

The core subjects in Nore were Irish, English, mathematics, history, geography, CSPE, RE and PE. Other subjects provided were science, French, German, home economics, business studies, art, music, classics and computer studies. Three of the subjects, Irish, English and mathematics, were taught at Foundation, Ordinary and Higher levels.

The majority of girls we observed were taking one modern language (96 per cent) for the Junior Certificate Examination. Three quarters were studying science, of which just over one third were taking the subject at the Higher level. Over half of the students in the class were taking home economics, while other practical subjects such as metal technology, metalwork and technical graphics were not on offer. Almost two thirds of the girls were studying at least one of the arts and humanities subjects (art, craft and design or music) (Table A3.3).

Suir

Suir was the third single-sex girls' school in the study. It is owned and managed by a Catholic religious order and is situated in a large town. It is a free-scheme school and is a designated-disadvantaged school. The educational philosophy of the school emphasises the holistic development of students, and the accommodation of the diverse needs of the student group. The principal of Suir emphasised the importance of gearing education programmes in the schools towards the disadvantaged; she also mentioned the importance of team work and extra-curricular activities.

The social class intake in Suir is quite wide, although almost two thirds of the second year students were from a middle-class background. The class we observed in Suir was a bottom stream group. Of the ten girls in the class, eight were from working-class backgrounds.

The class in Suir achieved the lowest mean score among the ten schools (13.2) on the TIMSS-related test. Nine of the ten girls got a grade E or lower on the test and one girl attained a grade D (Table 3.5). In the Junior Certificate Examination, of those taking the Foundation level (two students) one attained a grade C and one a grade D. Of the remaining eight students (all of whom took the Ordinary level paper), the results were evenly divided between a grade C and grade D).

Suir was one of four of our ten case-study schools to have completed the Junior Certificate Examination during the course of the field work. Comparing students' expectations of expected level of mathematics to be taken in the exam with the actual level taken, we can see that almost 70 per cent of the girls had expected and eventually took the Ordinary level paper. Fifteen per cent expected to take the Higher level paper but none of the class did and although only 15 per cent expected to do Foundation level mathematics in the examination, almost one third (31 per cent) of the class were examined at this level (Table A3.1).

All of the students took at least one modern language and all were studying science, of which just over one third were studying for the Higher level paper. Almost two thirds were taking at least one arts and humanities subject. Of the practical subjects, 46 per cent were taking home economics and 31 per cent were taking either metal technology/metalwork or technical graphics (Table A3.3).

Students in Suir were banded for the first two years of the Junior Cycle and streamed for mathematics in the Junior Certificate year (Table 3.2). The core subjects in Suir were Irish, English, mathematics, history, geography, science, French, art, music, CSPE, choral singing, computer science, physical education and religious education. Other subjects provided by Suir were German, home economics, business studies, technology, art, and RSE. Just Irish, English and mathematics were provided at Foundation level.

The Boys' Schools

Liffey

Liffey is a single-sex boys' school located in a city. It is a free-scheme, designated-disadvantaged school. The principal claimed that a major objective of the school was to encourage parents to take an active part in school life. There was a high drop-out rate traditionally in Liffey. However, the principal highlighted a new plan for improving performance, encouraging students to attend third level education, and a move away from an 'obsession' with monitoring student behaviour.

Most students in Liffey were from the immediate vicinity of the school and all students in second year in Liffey were from working-class backgrounds. The class we observed in Liffey was a top stream (Table 3.1). More than three quarters (76 per cent) of the boys in the class were from working-class backgrounds.

Liffey ranked fifth among the ten schools on the TIMSS-related test with a mean score of 24.4 out of a possible 40 (Table 3.5). Just one of the twenty-three boys sitting the test in this class achieved a grade E or lower; thirteen of the boys attained a grade C or higher, two of which attained a grade A.

The students in Liffey had also completed their Junior Certificate during the course of the study. While most of the top-stream group (71 per cent) expected to take the higher mathematics paper in the Junior Certificate, just 17 per cent actually took this paper in the examination in 2000. While only 4 per cent of the class reported that they would take the Foundation level paper, 12 per cent of the class were examined on this course. The remainder of the class group, 70 per cent, took mathematics at Ordinary level, despite just one quarter of the class reporting that they would do so (Table A3.1).

Of the three people sitting the Higher paper, one got an E and the remaining two got either a grade C or D. Sixteen students in the class sat the Ordinary paper in mathematics; one of these got an E, four attained a grade D while the remainder were awarded either a grade C (eight students) or B (three students). Of the three boys taking the Foundation paper, just one attained a grade B and two a grade C, while one student had left the school prior to the Junior Certificate exam.

The school used a streaming policy and students were streamed from the moment they entered first year. The core subjects in Liffey were Irish, English, mathematics, history, geography, woodwork, CSPE, PE, RE and RSE. Other subjects provided were science, French, home economics, business studies, art and computers. Foundation level was taught in Irish, English and mathematics in this school.

All of the boys in this class were taking at least one modern language and the vast majority (97 per cent) were studying an arts and humanities subject (art, craft, design or music). Just 4 per cent of the class were taking science, none of whom were studying it at Higher level. Just under one third (31 per cent) were taking either metal technology/metalwork/ technical graphics, while home economics was not on offer in Liffey (Table A3.3).

Lee

Lee is a single-sex boys', fee-paying school located in a city. The school is owned and managed by a Roman Catholic religious order. The educational philosophy focuses on the development of the whole person and students are encouraged to work in the service of others. There is also a strong commitment to academic excellence.

All of the second year students in Lee were from middle-class backgrounds, with almost one third from upper middle-class backgrounds. Almost three quarters of the class we observed were from upper-middle class backgrounds.

The mean score on the TIMSS-related test for the boys in Lee was the fourth highest among the schools (25.6 out of a possible 40). Ten of the twenty-six boys sitting the test were awarded a grade D. Just three of the class attained a grade A, while the remaining thirteen boys received either a grade B or grade C (Table 3.5). The summer test results for the class showed that seven boys were awarded an E or lower, six students got grade D, four attained a grade A and the remaining nine got either grades B or C.

All of the boys expected to take the Higher level paper in the Junior Certificate mathematics examination (Table A3.1). All of the boys were taking at least one modern language subject and were studying science; 96 per cent were taking Higher level science. Over half of the class were studying an arts and humanities subject and the majority (92 per cent) were taking either metal technology, metalwork or technical graphics (Table A3.3).

Lee employs a mixed system of grouping throughout the Junior Cycle. The core subjects in the school were Irish, English, mathematics, history, geography, science, French, music, Latin, PE, RE, RSE, and CSPE. Other subjects provided were German, art and Greek. All subjects were taught at Higher level only.

The Coeducational Schools

Lagan

Lagan is a coeducational secondary school located in a small town. It is a free-scheme school. The educational philosophy of the school centres on the development of the individual, in particular, focusing on relationships, respect and instilling a sense of responsibility in individual students. Lagan was originally a girls' school and became coeducational during the 1980s.

The social class intake is mixed in Lagan with 65 per cent of second year students from middle-class backgrounds. The class we observed was a top-stream group and of the twenty-nine students in the class, almost two thirds were from middle-class backgrounds.

The class in Lagan achieved a mean TIMSS-related score of 28.5 (out of a possible 40) which was the second highest of the ten schools. Just one of the twenty-five students sitting the test was awarded a grade E or lower, two students attained a grade D and the remaining twenty-two attained a grade C or higher, four of which were awarded a grade A (Table 3.5).

Almost all the class (97 per cent) expected to take the Higher level mathematics paper in the Junior Certificate Examination: all of the girls in the class and 93 per cent of the boys felt they would take the Higher level. Nobody expected to take Foundation level mathematics and 7 per cent of the girls and 3 per cent of boys expected to take mathematics at Ordinary level (Table A3.1).

All of the class in Lagan were taking at least one modern language and all were studying science. Almost half of those taking science were studying the subject at the Higher level. Looking at this in gender terms, almost two thirds (65 per cent) of females and just under one third (29 per cent) of boys were studying science at Higher level. Almost two thirds of the class were taking either art, craft and design or music, which accounted for 82 per cent of girls and 43 per cent of boys. Looking at the practical subjects in Lagan, almost one third of the class were taking home economics – 47 per cent of the girls in the class and just 14 per cent of the boys. Just under one third were taking metal technology/metalwork/-

technical graphics, and this included half of the boys and just 11 per cent of the girls (Table A3.3).

The school employs a banding system for the first three years of the Junior Cycle. The core subjects in Lagan were Irish, English, mathematics, history, geography, science, French, German, CSPE, RE, RSE and PE. Other subjects provided in Lagan were woodwork, technical graphics, art and music. Foundation level is taught in Irish and mathematics only.

Errigal

Errigal is a free-scheme coeducational, community school. It is a large school and is situated in a small town. Errigal was built as a community school arising from the amalgamation of three schools. The school claimed its principal objective was to improve students educationally, socially and morally. There is also a strong emphasis on religious education. In addition, the school stressed the importance of developing mutual respect among students, and between students and staff. It also emphasised the importance of developing the potential of each individual.

The majority of the second year students were from working-class backgrounds, with 25 per cent from lower middle-class and 10 per cent from middle-class backgrounds. The observed class in Errigal was a middle-stream group. Of the twenty-five students in the class, 86 per cent were from working-class backgrounds (Table 3.4).

The mean score achieved by the class on the TIMSS-related test was 18.1 (out of a possible 40), which was the fourth lowest score among the ten schools (Table 3.5). Ten of the twenty-seven students sitting the test got grade E or lower and the remainder achieved either grade C or grade D.

All of the boys and just 65 per cent of the girls expected to take Higher level mathematics for the Junior Certificate Examination, accounting for three quarters of the whole class. The rest of the girls in the class reported that they would take Ordinary level mathematics. Nobody in the class said they would take the Foundation level paper (Table A3.1).

All of the girls and 78 per cent of the boys were studying at least one modern language. All of the class were taking science: two thirds of the girls in the class, and all of the boys were taking this subject at the Higher level. Turning to practical subjects, 80 per cent of the girls were taking home economics, while none of the boys had opted for this subject. On the other hand, all of the boys and just 25 per cent of the girls were taking metal technology, metalwork or technical graphics (Table A3.3).

Errigal employs a banding system to group students for certain subjects up to the Junior Certificate year. The core subjects in the school were Irish, English, mathematics, science, CSPE, RE and PE. Other subjects included history, geography, French, German, home economics, business studies, metalwork, woodwork, technical graphics, art and music. Irish, English and mathematics were taught at Foundation as well as Higher and Ordinary level.

Mourne

Mourne is a coeducational vocational community college, situated in a city and is designated-disadvantaged. The philosophy of Mourne is strongly influenced by the location of the school, which is in an extremely disadvantaged area. One of the main objectives of the school (as stated by the principal) is 'to expose children to education for as long as they can hold them'. A core element in their philosophy was to ensure that the staff responded to the needs of the children and families in the area; the principal hoped the school would generally raise expectations regarding education in the area.

All of the second year students were from working-class backgrounds, with almost 30 per cent primarily dependent on social welfare. The observed class was a bottom stream and almost all of the eighteen students were from working-class backgrounds (Table 3.4).

This class scored a below average score of 13.3 out of a possible 40 in the TIMSS-related mathematics test. This was the second lowest score among our case-study schools. Two thirds of the eighteen students sitting the test got a grade E or lower, while the remainder attained a grade D (Table 3.5).

Mourne was one of our four schools to have completed the Junior Certificate Examination during the course of the study. When students' expectations, regarding the level of mathematics they would take, were compared with the actual level taken, there was a wide disparity. While no students expected to take Foundation level, 26 per cent actually took this paper (30 per cent of the girls and 22 per cent of the boys). Also, 26 per cent of the class (33 per cent of the girls and 20 per cent of the boys) expected to take the Higher level paper, but none did. Expectations for the Ordinary level paper appeared more realistic with 70 per cent of the girls and 78 per cent of boys actually taking this paper (Table A3.1).

Less than one third of the students in the class were studying a modern language: just 22 per cent of the girls and 40 per cent of the boys. All of the students were taking science: over half of the girls and less than one third of the boys were studying the subject at Higher level, accounting for 42 per cent of the whole class. With regard to practical subjects, one third of the girls and just 10 per cent of the boys were taking home economics, while one third of the girls and almost three quarters of the boys were studying metal technology, metalwork or technical graphics (Table A3.3).

A system of banding was used in Mourne in the Junior Certificate year. The core subjects were Irish, English, mathematics, history, geography, science, French, CSPE, PE, RE and RSE. Other subjects on offer in Mourne were home economics, business studies, materials technology (metal/woodwork), technical graphics, art and music. Irish, English, mathematics and science were taught at Foundation as well as Higher and Ordinary level.

Blackstairs

Blackstairs is a coeducational vocational community college situated in a rural area. It is a designated-disadvantaged school. There was no written or stated philosophy articulated for the school, or no prospectus.

The majority of the second year students were from working-class backgrounds. The class we observed in Blackstairs was a top stream. Of the thirty-two students, two thirds were from working-class backgrounds (Table 3.4).

The average mean score on the TIMSS-related test was 27.2 (out of a possible 40), which was the third highest among the ten schools (Table 3.5). All of the girls and 94 per cent of the boys expected to take the Higher level mathematics paper for the Junior Certificate. The remainder of the boys (6 per cent) expected to take Ordinary level mathematics. None of the class reported that they would take mathematics at Foundation level (Table A3.1).

All of the girls and just over half of the boys were taking at least one modern language (accounting for 77 per cent of the class). All of the students were taking science: 42 per cent of the boys and of the girls were studying the subject at Higher level. A small minority were taking art or music. Three quarters of the girls and just 6 per cent of the boys were studying home economics, while 88 per cent of boys and just 12 per cent of girls were taking metal technology, metalwork or technical graphics (Table A3.3).

Blackstairs used streaming to group students in the second and third years of the Junior Cycle. The core subjects in the school were Irish, English, mathematics, history, geography and science. Other subjects provided were French, German, home economics, business studies, metalwork, woodwork, technical graphics, technology, art, music, CSPE, PE, RE, RSE and computer studies. Irish, English and mathematics were taught at all three levels.

Nephin

Nephin is a coeducational vocational community college, free-scheme school located in a city.

The social class intake is varied with approximately 40 per cent of second year students from working-class backgrounds, 40 per cent from lower middle-class backgrounds and roughly 10 per cent from middle-class backgrounds. The class we observed was a bottom stream group of students, almost two thirds of whom were from working-class backgrounds (Table 3.4).

In the TIMSS-related test, no student got an A or B grade in Nephin, 10 per cent got a C grade, 70 per cent got a D and 20 per cent got an E or lower grade. The average mean score on the TIMSS-related test was 16.5 out of a possible 40 (Table 3.5).

Nephin was one of the schools to have completed their Junior Certificate Examination. Comparing expected level of mathematics to be taken with actual level taken, we can see that all of the students expected to take the Ordinary level paper. In the examination, just one third of the girls and 57 per cent of the boys actually took this paper. While nobody expected to take the Foundation level paper, two thirds of the girls and 43 per cent of the boys actually sat this paper in the exam. None of the students either expected to sit, nor eventually sat, the Higher level paper (Table A3.1).

All of the girls in the class and just 14 per cent of the boys were taking a modern language. All of the class were studying science, but just one third of the girls and almost three quarters of the boys were taking science at the Higher level. Turning to the practical subjects, two thirds of the girls and 27 per cent of the boys were taking home economics, while just one third of the girls and 86 per cent of boys were taking metal technology, metalwork or technical graphics (Table A3.3).

Nephin employs a banding system of student allocation in the Junior Certificate year. The core subjects in the school were Irish, English, mathematics, history, geography, science, PE, RE and CSPE. Other subjects provided were French, home economics, business studies, metalwork, technical graphics and art. Irish, English and mathematics were taught at all three levels.

Conclusion

The case studies undertaken to analyse the teaching and learning of mathematics were intensive and wide ranging. Not only were twenty mathematics classes videotaped and analysed in depth, the students observed in these classes were subsequently surveyed and interviewed about their learning experience.

To complement the mathematics study, a small video study of English classes, with as many of the same students as possible, was completed in five of the ten case study schools.

Each of the mathematics teachers observed, and a small sample of observed students' parents, were interviewed about their perspectives on the teaching and learning of mathematics. A triangulated view of the research problem was obtained by dialoguing with all the main parties to the learning process, namely students, teachers and parents.

The study employed a co-operative mode of research inquiry with teachers in particular, and to a lesser degree with students. In so far as time and resources permitted, we operated a dialogue with the case study teachers as to the authenticity of our interpretations of their classroom teaching.

The account of our findings from the case studies is presented in Chapters 4 to 11.

Appendix to Chapter 3

Table A3.1: *Case-study schools that had completed the Junior Certificate: actual level of mathematics taken* (in parentheses) compared with students' expectation regarding participation.*

School	Foundation %			Ordinary %			Higher %		
	F	M	T	F	M	T	F	M	T
Barrow (SSG F)	0	–	0	0	–	0	100	–	100
Nore (SSG Fr)	4.2	–	4.2	37.5	–	37.5	58.3	–	58.3
Suir (SSG Fr D)	15.4	–	15.4	69.2	–	69.2	15.4	–	15.4
	(30.8)		(30.8)	(69.2)		(69.2)	(0)		(0)
Liffey (SSB Fr D)	–	4.2	4.2	–	25.0	25.0	–	70.8	70.8
		(12.2)	(12.2)		(70.1)	(70.1)		(16.7)	(16.7)
Lee (SSB F)	–	0	0	–	0	0	–	100.0	100.0
Total SS			3.6			21.4			75.0
Lagan (SC Fr)	0	0	0	0	7.1	3.2	100	92.9	96.8
Errigal (CS Fr)	0	0	0	35.0	0	24.1	65.0	100	75.9
Mourne (VCC Fr D)	0	22.2	0	56.6	80.0	68.4	33.4	20.0	26.3
	(30.0)	(22.2)	(26.3)	(70.0)	(77.8)	(73.7)	(0)	(0)	(0)
Blackstairs (VCC Fr D)	0	0	0	0	5.9	2.9	100	94.1	97.1
Nephin (VCC Fr)	0	0	0	100	100	100	0	0	0
	(66.7)	(43.0)	(50.0)	(33.3)	(57.1)	(50.0)	(0)	(0)	(0)
Total COED			0			26.2			73.8

* Junior Certificate results were only available for four of the ten case study schools.

Key: SSG F: Secondary girls', fee-paying; SSG Fr: Secondary girls', free scheme; SSG Fr D: Secondary girls', free scheme designated disadvantaged; SSB Fr D: Secondary boys', free scheme designated disadvantaged; SSB F: Secondary boys', fee paying; SC Fr: Secondary coed, free scheme; CS Fr: Community school, free scheme; VCC Fr D: Vocational/Community college, free scheme designated disadvantaged; VCC Fr: Vocational/Community college, free scheme (where free-scheme represents non fee-paying status).

Table A3.2 Case-study schools: level of mathematics taken in Junior Certificate Examination by the entire year cohort in the school, 1996

School	Foundation %			Ordinary %			Higher %		
	F	M	T	F	M	T	F	M	T
Barrow (SSG F)	0	–	0	30	–	30	70	–	70
Nore (SSG Fr)	2	–	2	44	–	44	54	–	54
Suir (SSG Fr D)	6	–	6	50	–	50	44	–	44
Liffey (SSB Fr D)	–	33	33	–	67	67	–		0
Lee (SSB F)	–		0	–	3	3	–	97	97
Lagan (SC Fr)	6	9	8	51	59	55	43	32	37
Errigal (CS Fr)	12	24	19	55	70	63	33	6	18
Mourne (VCC Fr D)	50	60	56	50	35	41	0	5	3
Blackstairs (VCC Fr D)	7	24	17	61	68	64	32	8	19
Nephin (VCC Fr)	7	14	12	74	66	69	19	20	19

Table A3.3: Case-study schools: school types and gender differences in subject choice for the Junior Certificate Examination

	% studying at least 1 modern language (French, German or Spanish)			% studying at least 1 arts and humanities subject (art, craft and design or music)			% studying home economics			% studying at least 1 practical subject (metal technology, metalwork or technical graphics)			% studying science at any level			% studying higher level science			% Gender distribution (coeducational schools)	
	F	M	T	F	M	T	F	M	T	F	M	T	F	M	T	F	M	T	F	M
Barrow (SSG F)	100	–	100	26.9	–	26.9	0	–	0	0	–	0	100	–	100	76.9	–	76.9		
Nore (SSG Fr)	95.8	–	95.8	60.9	–	60.9	58.3	–	58.3	–	–	–	75.0	–	75.0	37.5	–	37.5		
Suir (SSG Fr D)	100	–	100	61.5	–	61.5	46.2	–	46.2	30.8	–	30.8	100	–	100	38.5	–	38.5		
Liffey (SSB Fr D)	–	100	100	–	96.5	96.5	–	–	–	–	30.8	30.8	–	4.0	4.0	–	–	–		
Lee (SSB F)	–	100	100	–	57.7	57.7	–	–	–	–	92.0	92.0	–	100	100	–	96.2	96.2		
Lagan (SC Fr)	100	100	100	82.4	42.9	64.5	47.1	14.3	32.3	11.8	50.0	29.0	100	100	100	64.7	28.6	48.4	54	46
Errigal (CS Fr)	100	77.8	93.1	85.0	44.4	75.4	80.0	0	55.2	25.0	100	48.3	100	100	100	65.0	66.7	65.5	47	53
Mourne (VCC Fr D)	22.2	40.0	31.6	55.6	10.0	31.6	33.3	10.0	21.1	33.3	70.0	52.6	100	100	100	55.6	30.0	42.1	50	50
Blackstairs (VCC Fr D)	100	52.9	76.5	11.8	5.9	8.8	76.5	5.9	41.2	11.8	88.2	50.0	100	100	100	41.2	41.2	41.2	44	56
Nephin (VCC Fr)	100	14.3	40.0	66.7	57.1	60.0	66.7	28.6	40.0	33.3	85.7	70.0	100	100	100	33.3	71.4	60.0	43	57
TOTAL	93.8	79.6	87.3	53.9	50.9	52.5	48.1	5.6	28.7	13.3	62.0	35.6	95.3	77.8	87.3	55.0	46.3	51.1	51.5	49.5

Notes

[1] Coeducational secondary schools are very similar to single sex secondary schools in terms of social class profile, although the boys in such schools are somewhat more middle class in background than girls . Girls in vocational schools and community colleges are also slightly less likely to be middle class than their male peers, and more likely to be working class, while both gender groups in the community and comprehensive sectors have similar class profiles (Table 2.2). What this data suggests therefore is that girls in coeducational schools are somewhat more likely to be working class than boys.

[2] While we knew the gender profile of schools and their official status in terms of school type, we had no way of measuring the social class profile of students taking the Junior Certificate courses in 1998 and 1999 (the years we were collecting the data). To address this problem we used designated disadvantaged status and fee-paying status as proxy measures of social class. The analysis of both the 1994 data provided by the ESRI, and information available from the Department of Education and Science regarding the classification of schools, indicated clearly that schools designated disadvantaged had high proportions of students from working class backgrounds, while fee-paying schools were largely catering for upper middle class students. Non-feepaying secondary schools, and community and comprehensive schools occupied an interim position between the fee-paying and disadvantaged sectors, as did non-disadvantaged vocational schools and community colleges although the latter had a higher working class intake than the former.

[3] Given the wide range of research instruments used it was not possible to incorporate them into the present text. They are available on the Equality Studies website at www.ucd.ie/~esc/.

[4] So-called *Mixed-Ability Grouping* refers to the practice of allocating students to classes across all subjects so that there is a range of different attainment levels in all classes. *Banding* refers to the practice of dividing students into broad 'ability' bands with two or three mixed classes in each. It is a form of streaming in larger schools where numbers allow schools to stratify students into top, middle and lower bands. Students are mixed within each band, but not between bands. Although banding is formally a less stratified system than streaming, in our study we found that some teachers used the terms interchangeably, often referring to the bottom or top band as the bottom or top stream respectively. *Streaming* is a method of assigning students hierarchically to classes on some overall assessment of general attainment. The streamed classes are used as the teaching units for all subjects. *Setting* is a practice whereby students are grouped into streams or tracks according to their attainment in a given subject; at Junior level it is quite common for schools to set students for mathematics and Irish, and sometimes English. Occasionally throughout the text we refer to the different groups (whether they are called bands, sets or streams) as *tracks* as it is a relatively generic and neutral word and is inclusive of different types of grouping.

[5] We also undertook interviews with each of the school principals about the school's educational policies and philosophies.

[6] The mathematics teachers who participated were very experienced with most (seven of the ten) having twenty or more years of service, while all but one had taught the subject at Leaving Certificate level. In addition, all the teachers had a Higher Diploma in Education, two had master's degrees, while three more had other postgraduate educational qualifications. Eight of the teachers had studied mathematics for their basic degree, while two had read mathematics only in the first year of their degree. Six of the teachers had done mathematics as part of their science degree, while three had taken it as a subject in an arts degree; there was one person who studied mathematics in a commerce degree. Four of the teachers were men and six were women; three were under forty years of age, four were between forty and fifty, while three others were over fifty years of age.

[7] Unfortunately Junior Certificate results were only available for four of the ten case study classes. This happened because of the timing of the study. The classes that we observed in the early part of the study had completed their Junior Certificate Examination and had obtained their results by the end of the data collection period, thereby enabling us to record their results in time for analysis. The Junior Certificate Examination results of the classes we videotaped later in the study were not available in time for us to analyse them. We did ask the schools to forward the results after the study was completed, but this did not happen for a variety of reasons, including pressures on teachers' and principals' time and changes of staff.

4

Core Themes in the
Teaching and Learning
of Mathematics

Introduction

This chapter is the first of five chapters examining the mathematics classroom. The focus here is on the common themes in mathematics lessons, in particular on classroom interactions in terms of dominant pedagogical practices.

Chapter 5 elaborates on the core themes investigated in Chapter 4, presenting a more in-depth analysis of the dynamics of classroom interactions. The subsequent two chapters (6 and 7) examine differences in pedagogical practices in the teaching of mathematics arising from gender, social class and grouping practices. Throughout the discussion, the analysis is confined to the public interaction that took place in the lessons between the teacher and the students.

Overall, the findings suggest a high level of uniformity in terms of how mathematics lessons are organised and presented in second level schools. The majority of the lessons largely comprised teacher demonstration and student practice (Table 4.1). Demonstration of mathematics consisted of a combination of verbal explanations and written demonstration, typically using either a blackboard or whiteboard. In one of the ten schools, Nore (SSG Fr), the teacher used an overhead projector with pre-prepared overheads. In most cases, demonstration was based on exercises or examples from the textbook and included teacher-led question-and-answer sessions and reviews. In Table 4.1, revision appears as a separate category from demonstration. In reality, the revision lessons mostly involved demonstration and the demonstration practices observed were identical to those observed in the other lessons where new material was presented. For clarification purposes, the categories are separated to distinguish new from revision material.

Student practice consisted of students practising the methods demonstrated by the teacher. Typically this work was set by the teacher (in the

Table 4.1: Time allocated to pedagogical activities in mathematics lessons

School	Lesson number	Lesson aims	Demonstration (new material) Total	(Of which teacher-explanation represents)	Demonstration (revision material)	Student practice	Setting homework	Total
		%	%	%	%	%	%	%
Barrow (SSG F)	1	1.3	62.8	(11.1)	0	35.9	0	100
	2	1.0	26.4	(6.6)	0	72.6	0	100
Nore (SSG Fr)	1	2.2	88.8	(26.1)	0.8	6.7	1.5	100
	2	1.7	50.8	(23.7)	1.7	45.8	0	100
Suir (SSG Fr D)	1	2.0	0	(10.0)	41.0	54.0	3.0	100
	2	1.8	0	(9.9)	33.3	64.0	0.9	100
Liffey (SSB Fr D)	1	0.8	38.0	(15.5)	4.6	54.3	2.3	100
	2	0	29.7	(3.0)	5.0	58.4	6.9	100
Lee (SSB F)	1	0.8	0	(0)	0	87.3	11.9	100
	2	0	0	(0)	0	73.4	26.6	100
Lagan (SC Fr)	1	0.6	78.8	(6.8)	0	18.5	2.1	100
	2	0	47.1	(3.7)	0	52.2	0.7	100
Errigal (CS Fr)	1	0	62.2	(5.4)	0	33.3	4.5	100
	2	0	17.8	(0)	0	82.2	0	100
Mourne (VCC Fr D)	1	0	0	(0)	0	97.6	2.4	100
	2	2.2	17.0	(3.7)	0	76.4	4.4	100
Blackstairs (VCC Fr D)	1	4.4	41.7	(16.2)	5.2	47.2	1.5	100
	2	1.6	46.8	(13.7)	3.2	46.8	1.6	100
Nephin (VCC Fr)	1	0	0	(11.5)	58.2	40.2	1.6	100
	2	0	2.4	(0)	0	94.0	3.6	100

Key: SSG F: Secondary girls', fee-paying; SSG Fr: Secondary girls', free scheme; SSG Fr D: Secondary girls', free scheme designated disadvantaged; SSB F: Secondary boys', fee-paying; SSB Fr D: Secondary boys', free scheme designated disadvantaged; SC Fr: Secondary coed, free scheme; CS Fr: Community school, free scheme; VCC Fr D: Vocational/Community college, free scheme designated disadvantaged; VCC Fr: Vocational/Community college, free scheme (where free scheme represents non fee-paying status).

majority of cases from the textbook) and was completed by the students either during the course of the lesson (student work), or at home (homework). Practice of demonstrated methods was conducted individually by the students in their exercise books. In a number of lessons, some interaction between students was evident; this was on an informal basis and was usually confined to students sitting next to each other and conducted quietly in hushed tones. In the lessons where there was evidence of students conferring with each other, the teacher did not give instructions that the students were to work in this way. Instead, there appeared to be a general understanding that this was an acceptable way of working; peer discussion and co-operation was allowed rather than encouraged. The correction of student work and homework was also included in the student practice phase of the lesson script.

The observed lessons also included the statement of *lesson aims* and a segment concerned with the setting of homework, although these were a minor part of the lesson.

What is evident from Table 4.1 is the concentration of class time on the two interrelated activities of teacher demonstration (including revision) and student practice of demonstrated skills. With the exception of the two classes observed in Lee (SSB F), where just over one quarter of one class, and almost one eighth of another was spent setting homework, well over 90 per cent of class time in all other eighteen classes was spent on demonstration and student practice. The balance of the time devoted between these two activities varied depending on the subject matter and the decision of the teacher in a given context. While there were more classes in which student practice was the prevailing work norm,[1] there was also a significant number of classes in which demonstration by the teacher of particular skills was the norm, or in which there was a relatively even balance between the two sets of activities.

Demonstration

Demonstration of mathematical procedures by the teacher was the dominant pedagogical practice of teachers. Although the written demonstration of the method outweighed the verbal explanation for all of the lessons observed, there was considerable variation in terms of content, duration, pace, amount of teacher questioning, and style of questioning used. To a large degree, the demonstration varied according to the ranking of the class grouping in terms of mathematical achievement, particularly with regard to content and pace.

Two illustrative examples of a demonstration are now presented. The first lesson involves a top stream group from a single sex girls' school while the second lesson involves a bottom track group from a coeducational school. Despite great differences in terms of the mathematical attainments of the students, the pedagogical approach is remarkably similar.

A top stream group in Barrow (SSG F)

The first extract is from the first lesson observed in a fee paying, single sex girls' secondary school (Barrow (SSG F)). It involved a demonstration by a very experienced female teacher to a top-stream group. The students were overwhelmingly from a middle class background and achieved a high mean score (29.8 out of a possible 40) on the TIMSS-based mathematics test.

In the course of this particular lesson the teacher covered the factorisation of quadratic expressions with mixed signs, where the coefficient of x^2 is equal to 1 (phase 1) and then where the coefficient of x^2 is greater than 1 (phase 2). Both phases comprised a combination of demonstration and student practice, involving seven and five examples respectively. In her explanation, the teacher used mathematical language and reminded students that they had employed an identical method in a previous lesson. Although aimed at a high stream class, the lesson comprised mostly drill and practice of a particular method, with little explanation of the concepts involved.

After stating the lesson aims, the teacher demonstrated one method of factoring quadratic expressions with mixed signs, namely the trial and error method. Starting with the simplest example of an expression with the coefficient of x equal to 1, the teacher worked through an example on a line by line basis. The demonstration was interspersed with questioning of the whole class and individual students, as can be seen by the following excerpt.

Demonstration: Illustrative Vignette 1

Time code (minutes:seconds)	Activity	Lesson text
8:12	Lesson aim	*Teacher:* All right girls, just before half term we were learning to factorise. We were working with quadratic equations – quadratic statements first of all – where the coefficient of x^2 was 1 and where we had all plus signs in the expression – so today we are going to work with quadratic expressions with mixed signs.

8:43	Demonstration begins: Example 1: Solving quadratic equation with mixed signs Tricks	*Teacher goes to the board*: *Teacher:* So for a very simple example, *and writes*: $x^2 - 5x + 6$ *[Text and Tests 1, p.218 question 4]* *Teacher:* We have certain little tricks for figuring out how we will get this pair of factors that will multiply together to give us this here as our answer (*pointing to $x^2 - 5x + 6$*). The last day we just made 2 little brackets to start with – that was the <u>trial and error</u> method **( ) ( )** *Teacher:* And because this is such a simple example we will try and adopt that approach today.
9:20	Whole class question about method already covered, asking for show of hands	*Teacher:* Can you try and remember what we did with the 2 brackets, to start with – what do we put at the beginning of each bracket? *Hands go up and teacher asks one of these students*
9:25	Catherine answers correctly.	*Catherine:* x
9:25	Teacher explains why this is correct procedure.	*Teacher writes*: **(x) (x)** *Teacher:* The reason we are going to have x at the beginning is that x multiplied by x is going to give me x^2. So the next number that we concentrate on is the +6, the last number – the fact that the sign is plus means that the number we are looking for – in other words the two numbers multiplied together will carry the same sign. Now we have got to say to ourselves – is it going to be 2 pluses or 2 minuses. Now comes the little key. Whatever sign appears in front of the middle number, *[pointing to –5x]* that is the sign that both of the numbers will carry.
9:30	Teacher asks whole class question.	*Teacher:* So what numbers are we going to have here?
9:32	Most of the students answer question, giving correct answer.	*Class:* Minus. *Teacher:* Yes *and writes:* **(x –) (x –)** *Teacher:* And the very last thing that we must think about is – these 2 numbers are restricted in 2 ways – number 1, they must multiply out to give you plus 6 and number 2, they must add together – combine together – to give you minus 5.

10:26	Whole class question asking for show of hands.	*Teacher:* Now who can think of 2 such numbers – whenwe put them together – when they combine together (I hesitate to use the word 'add' because people get a bit mixed up) – can you think of 2 numbers whose product is plus 6 and whose sum is minus 5? *Show of hands by students* *Teacher:* OK, Gemma can you think of two?
10:42	Gemma answers incorrectly.	*Gemma:* Plus one and plus five.
10:50	Teacher responds to Gemma but then moves on to another student.	*Teacher:* I don't think that would work, would it? A plus 1 multiplied by a plus 5 would give me what, when I multiply what would I get? *Gemma:* a plus *Teacher:* Well yeah, it doesn't matter – a minus 5 multiplied by a minus 1 would give me a plus 5 – yeah OK, but I am looking for a plus 6 am I not?
11:10	Whole class question	*Teacher:* Can you think of anything better? Clare?
11:15	Clare volunteers answer.	*Clare:* 2 and 3
11:17	Teacher accepts answer and then demonstrates why this is correct	*Teacher:* OK, 2 and 3. So let's multiply them out together to see what we get **2** **3** and what sort of sign – let's test them out and see.
11:20	Teacher asks whole class question but gets no response. Teacher then answers question and continues with explanation.	*Teacher:* OK, if the numbers are going to be 2 and 3 they must be what sorts of numbers? *No response from class.* *Teacher:* Negative numbers, mustn't they, minus numbers? When I multiply them let me check **–2** **–3** *Teacher:* Does that give me plus 6? *Class and teacher:* Yes, *in unison.* *Teacher:* And when I put them down and combine them together $(-2) + (-3) =$ *Teacher:* Imagine I am walking on the number line.
11:38	Teacher asks Ashling a question.	*Teacher:* What about a minus 2 and a minus 3 – Ashling, when I put them together what do I get?
11:40	Ashling answers question correctly.	*Ashling:* Minus 5.

11:42	Teacher acknowledges Ashling's correct answer with praise, continues with rhetorical whole class question about method.	*Teacher:* Yeah, good girl Ashling! When we are doing these sums one after another we won't go through all of this detail will we? *Class:* No! *Teacher:* We won't put them in our copybook like this but just to start off with we must be careful **(x − 3) (x − 2)** *Teacher:* Now of course if we are really diligent, how can we check to make sure that we are right particularly the day of the exam – we won't just leave the answer and say 'hope for the best' would we – what would we do?
12:08	Teacher asks Niamh how to check if answer is correct.	*Teacher:* What might we do – Niamh?
12:10	Niamh answers question correctly	*Niamh:* multiply the two of them out. *Teacher:* That's right! So let's multiply them quickly – not actually – but doing it (*pointing to her head*) – let's multiply them mentally.
12:30	Teacher directs class to check that this is correct answer by multiplying mentally. Teacher then calls out steps and most of the students join in with her. Teacher then asks whole class if they are beginning to understand.	*Teacher:* x by x is grand – it gives us x^2, doesn't it? Minus 3 by minus 2 is okay – it gives us plus 6. Now the combination is what people get stuck on – now the x by the minus 2 is minus 2x and plus x by the minus 3 is? *Class and teacher in unison:* Minus 5x. *Teacher:* Now are you beginning to understand? *Class in unison:* Yes!

Having completed this example, the teacher worked through four more questions (see below) using this methodology, this time using more whole class questioning and less explanation.

Example Number	Description	Problem	Time (mins.)
2	All negative signs	$x^2 - x - 6$	2.75
3	Mixed signs	$x^2 - 10x + 21$	3.00
4	All negative signs	$x^2 - 2x - 63$	2.50
5	Mixed signs	$x^2 - 17x + 30$	2.25

Overall, the demonstration lasted 14.25 minutes, amounting to approximately one third of total class time. The vignette clearly illustrates the didactic approach to teaching mathematics that was evident in all of the lessons in our study. The pedagogical approach is clearly that of drill and practice in a controlled and organised learning environment. In the course of the demonstration the teacher led the students through five examples alternating between problems with mixed and all negative signs.

For the first four examples, the teacher led the demonstration; here student involvement amounted to answering questions on the particular steps of the procedure. For the fifth example, the teacher requested a volunteer to do the problem by asking the class: 'Who would be able to do this one?' and then selected one student from all those who raised their hands. While she called out the steps of the procedure the teacher prompted her, praising her when she answered correctly: 'Good girl'; 'yes, exactly'; 'yeah, now isn't she right?') and gently reprimanding her when she made a mistake: 'Now think carefully', 'shh – now take your time and think – don't take what you think would be the obvious pair'. On completion, she praised her, saying: 'I think you are very good altogether now'. In all, this last example took approximately half a minute to complete.

In terms of mathematical content, the teacher covered more material than was the case in any of the other lessons. In terms of pace, the lesson moved quickly through the demonstration and onto the student practice aspect of the lesson. The teacher had the complete attention of the class and there were no instances of disruption throughout the lesson.

The fast pace of the demonstration conveys the teacher's confidence in the ability of all the students to understand the material; teaching is directed towards the whole class with no attention being directed to individual students who appeared to have difficulty following the procedure.

A bottom stream class in Mourne (VCC Fr D)

The second extract (see Appendix 4, Illustrative Vignette) involves a designated disadvantaged, non-fee paying (so-called free scheme), coeducational community college (Mourne VCC Fr D, first lesson). It involves a demonstration by a very experienced female teacher to a bottom track group. Two thirds of the students are from a working-class back-ground and achieved a low mean score (13.3 out of 40) on the TIMSS-based mathematics test.

In this extract, the teacher is demonstrating how to factorise quadratic expressions with plus signs. The teacher has been working on grouping expressions with minus signs for a number of lessons. This lesson began with the correction of homework (see Illustrative Vignette 2 in the next section on Student Practice). The teacher indicated that she 'wants to show them today how to get the next lot of factors'. She then re-stated what factors are: 'factors are two things that multiply for your answer'. Following this, the teacher described the next step as follows:

> So you remember when we were learning factors we first of all showed you how to get it by multiplying out – so I want … everybody to multiply **x** plus **7** by **x** plus **8** – and then we are going to try to factorise something by going back.

The teacher then walked around checking whether the students remembered the method. When they did not look like they knew what to do she gave a hint by writing on the board:

$$x(x + 8) + 7(x + 8)$$

Giving the students another couple of minutes to complete the multiplication, she demonstrated the correct approach by writing on the board:

$$x^2 + 8x + 7x + 56$$
$$= x^2 + 15x + 56$$

The teacher instructed the students that she wanted them to practice multiplying out another expression:

> We want to see how you will end up with something like this [*pointing to* $x^2 + 15x + 56$] – in other words, how do you go backwards – if you start with that – how you end up back there – so I want you to multiply **(x+5) (x + 4)**.

In this lesson the teacher demonstrated how to factorise trinomial expressions with all plus signs. Following the introduction described above, the teacher presented a particular method for factorising trinomials with all plus signs as follows:

Factorise: $x^2 + 15x + 56$
Explanation: We want to end up with $(x + 7) (x + 8)$. The middle term is the one we split up (15x).
Rule: The factors we come up with must multiply together to give 56 (third term) and add together to give 15x (middle term).
Step 1: Factorise the x^2 *(x + ?) (x + ?)*

Step 2: Factorise the 56 in terms of the rule. Because the middle term is 15x we require the factors that ADD UP to +15, i.e., 7 and 8.

$(x + 7) (x + 8)$
Step 3: Check if this agrees with rule – 7 times 8 = 56 and $(+7x) + (+8x) = +15x$

As the excerpt indicates, the teacher did not attempt to make a connection with other mathematical topics. Her introduction involved writing the trinomial expression on the chalkboard, saying: 'Now we want to find the factors for this.' The key to understanding the method was understanding and memorising a particular rule.

The demonstration involved three identical examples and the teacher used a combination of whole class and individual questioning to work through the explanation. Overall the demonstration lasted 5.75 minutes or seventeen per cent of lesson time. Similar to the previous example, this lesson comprised drill and practice of a particular method, rather than the explanation of the concepts involved. Use was made of mathematical terminology to explain the difference between quadratic expressions with four terms, and quadratic trinomials with three terms. The teacher's tone was positive, she provided prompts when students were unsure of what to do next and she praised students when they get the 'correct' answer: 'Good girl Majella'; good lad'; 'very good'.

Student Practice

Practice of the demonstrated procedures by the students was the second prevailing pedagogical practice in the lessons observed. It included the doing and correcting of problems assigned to the class by the teacher – either during class time (student work*)* or at home (homework*).* The two extracts that follow are from the same lessons referred to in the previous section on demonstration.

The first extract is from Barrow (SSG F). The students are learning how to factorise quadratic expressions using the trial and error method. Following the demonstration, the teacher moved the lesson on to the student practice phase of the lesson, saying: 'Now would you like to do one for me and see who can get it done first'. Students were assigned two problems, both with all negative signs. Following the correction of these problems the teacher moved on to solving quadratic equations where the coefficient of x was greater than 1.

Student Practice (Student Work: Doing): Illustrative Vignette 1

Time code (minutes:seconds)	Activity	Lesson text
22:12	Student work: Example 6: All negative signs	*Teacher:* Will you do number 26 for me now – I'll put it on the board so that I can do it – and you tell me what the answer is, *and writes:* $x^2 - 11x - 42$ *Students are given approximately half a minute to do the question in their exercise books and then the teacher indicates by nodding to a particular student that she wants her to call out the answer.*
22:44	Student work: correction whole class. Teacher asks Sheila question.	*Teacher:* Yes – Sheila?
22:46	Sheila responds.	*Sheila:* Will I do it now? *Teacher:* Yes – tell me what it is and then we can decide. *Sheila:* Ummh, x + 3 and x – 14. *Teacher writes:* $(x - 14)(x + 3)$ *Teacher:* Yes Sheila, she's a very quick little girl isn't she – I've noticed you before Sheila – you are a very fast little girl when I give you work like this in class. Now everybody else is she right – x minus 14 and x plus 3 – well? – Minus 14 by the plus 3 gives us the minus 42 and certainly x by x is x^2 – Now how do we check the middle term to make sure we are right – x by plus 3 is 3x and x by minus 14 is minus 14x? And yes when we add them we get, *and writes*: $-14x$ $+ 3x$ $-11x$ *Teacher:* So we know we are right – there is no way you should not know that you have done your sum correctly. OK – I will give you one more of these and then I think we could go on to something harder – one more of these – number 25 – because you are too good for this – it's too easy for you.

24:00	Student work: Example 7: All negative signs	*Teacher cleans the blackboard and writes problem 2 on the board*: $x^2 - 33x - 70$
		This time the teacher waits about 15 seconds before asking a student to call out the answer.
24:15	Teacher asks Ellen question.	*Teacher:* Okay – Ellen?
24:16	Student work correction: whole class Ellen answers question.	*Ellen:* Ummh – 2 and 35. *Teacher:* No, no say it properly for me – oh dear, oh dear – factors of a quadratic expression? *Ellen:* minus 35 and plus 2. *Teacher:* I'm looking for factors – you are giving me 2 numbers! *At this point Ellen pulls a face as if she feels like she has really slipped up!*

By assigning practice examples, the teacher is able to ascertain whether students have listened to and understood what was said during the explanation/demonstration phase. In the above excerpt, the emphasis was on speed rather than understanding; in this case the 'quickest' girl was rewarded with a lot of praise. It would appear that the teacher takes it for granted that all of the students were able to understand and keep up with the pace of the lesson. In lessons in other schools, the time given to student practice in class was usually much longer and teachers took the opportunity to walk around and monitor the progress of individual students and assist those having difficulty.

We now turn to the second illustrative vignette from Mourne (VCC Fr D). The lesson begins with the correction of homework from the previous lesson; the homework involved grouping quadratic expressions with minus signs. The previous lesson was devoted to student practice of identical quadratic expressions. Before correcting the homework presented in the excerpt, the teacher checks each student's homework and gives a star to those who attempted all of the assigned problems. While checking the homework in this way, the teacher ascertained that one of the questions caused a problem and she proceeds to correct this question.

Student Practice (Homework: whole class correction): Illustrative Vignette 2

Time code (minutes:seconds)	Activity	Lesson text
	Homework assigned in previous lesson (Lesson 8)	**Q. 14: $2a^2 + 2b - 4ab - a$** **Q. 15: $3x^2 + 4y - 6xy - 2x$** **Q. 16: $2xa - 4ay + 2by - bx$** **Q. 17: $6mp - 2mq + 3mp - mq$** **Q. 18: $mp + 2mp - 6mq - 3mq$**
2:29	Homework correction: whole class Q14 Teacher: asks whole class question.	*Teacher:* OK, so we are going to correct these now – 14 seems to have been the problem …Okay question 14 was … *Teacher calls out and writes the question on the board. Joe is whistling but teacher ignores it.* **$2a^2 + 2b - 4ab - a$** *Teacher:* So, again did you have to rearrange this?
2:45	Class answers question. Teacher asks another whole class question. Class answer whole class question.	*Class, some say:* No *Teacher:* Some people didn't re-arrange it – did it work if you didn't re-arrange it? *Class, some say:* Yes
3:00	Teacher asks Joe question.	*Teacher:* Who got it to work without re-arranging it – did you re-arrange it *(looking at Joe)* *Joe answers:* No *Teacher:* Can you tell me how to do it so?
3:02	Joe answers question.	*Joe:* No *Teacher repeats 'no' after him with a tone of resignation.*
3:05	Teacher asks Stephen question.	*Teacher:* Did anyone else get it to work without re-arranging it? Stephen did you say you did?
3:08	Stephen answers question.	*Stephen:* No
3:09	Teacher asks Margaret a question.	*Teacher:* Margaret did you re-arrange it? *There is quite a lot of noise outside the classroom which makes it fairly difficult to hear what is being said.*

3:15	Margaret answers Teacher question.	*Margaret:* (inaudible – due to noise) *Teacher:* Tell us what you did and we will have a look at it. *Margaret:* 2a into a plus b and minus a into plus 2b plus one … *Teacher writes this on the board.* **2a(a+b) – a(2b+1)**
3:28	Teacher asks whole class question.	*Teacher walks away from the board and looks at what she has written –* *Teacher:* Will this work?
4:05	Class answer whole class question.	*Class:* No *Teacher:* Why won't it work? *Some answer from class:* two different numbers … *Teacher:* Two different factors – so we will have to go back again and try to get the same factors in both of them – okay so we have to re-arrange it
4:15	Teacher asks Anne question. Anne answers teacher question.	*Teacher:* Anne could you suggest how we can re-arrange it? *Anne:* 2a squared minus a plus 2b minus 4ab *Teacher writes response on board* $$2a^2 - a + 2b - 4ab$$ *Teacher:* Now let us take a look at that
4:35	Teacher asks Stephen a question.	*Teacher:* Now Stephen Murphy – what is common in the first 2 of those?
4:40	Stephen answers teacher's question.	*Stephen:* a … *Teacher:* So a times what? *Stephen:* a times 2a plus one *Teacher:* Perfect! *She writes:* **a(2a + 1)** *Teacher:* What's common in the second one? *Stephen:* b … *Teacher:* So 2 times? *Stephen:* 2 minus 4a **a(2a – 1) + b(2 – 4a)**
5:06	Teacher asks whole class question.	*Teacher:* Are we in trouble again?

5:08	Class answer question	*Class:* Yeah *Teacher:* Why? *Class:* Mumbled response *Teacher:* We should try a 2 here and see what happens *– pointing to the place beside the b as follows: 2b ( )* – so if we have a 2a here what do we have inside – 1 minus 2a – **a(2a – 1) + 2b(1 – 2a).**
5:22	Teacher asks whole class question.	*Teacher:* Are we right now?
5:23	Class answer teacher whole class question.	*Class, some answer:* Yeah *and others* No.
5:26	Teacher asks whole class question.	*Teacher:* Why are we not right?
5:27	Class answer whole class question.	*Class:* The 2 are not the same *(meaning the 2 factors)* *Teacher:* Because one of them is 2a minus 1 and the other is 1 minus 2a – what's wrong with that? – how can we make that right?
5:45	Teacher asks 3 whole class questions – class respond to all.	*Class:* Change them around *Teacher:* So if that becomes minus then this becomes? *Class:* Plus *Teacher writes on the board:* a (2a – 1) + 2b (1 – 2a) becomes: **a (2a – 1) – 2b (2a – 1)** *Teacher:* Are we right now? *Class:* Yeah *Teacher:* Because why – because we have a 2a in both and a minus 1 in both – so now it is right – so the factors are: **(a – 2b) (2a – 1)** *Teacher:* So you had to play around a bit to get it right.
	Teacher asks whole class question to check who got it right.	*Teacher:* So who got it right?

In total, 25.75 minutes or seventy-six per cent of lesson time was spent on homework correction. Following the section of the lesson contained in the above extract, the teacher corrects all the remaining questions. Analysis of the discourse, which will be discussed later in this chapter, illustrates some of the core practices. The language used suggests an approach to mathematics as problematic: 'Q14 seems to have been the problem'; 'Why won't it work?; 'Are we in trouble again', with a definite 'right' approach: 'Are we right now?'; 'Why are we not right?'; 'So you had to play around a bit to get it right'; 'So who got it right?'. In addition, appraisal was conducted in the public domain; here 'right' answers were praised with 'perfect'.

Lesson Aims

By stating what material will be covered in the lesson and what relationship this lesson has with topics already covered, the teacher is providing an important learning context for the students. The findings in Figure 4.1 show, however, that the time spent by the teacher on this particular pedagogical practice was marginal. In eight of the twenty mathematics lessons, there was no lead in to the lessons at all, while in the other twelve lessons this pedagogical practice represented a minor part of teaching.

Figure 4.1: Percentage of lesson time spent on stating lesson aims (Base: 20 lessons)

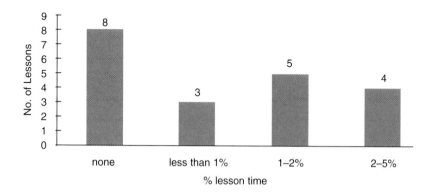

The following vignette is taken from the lesson in which the highest proportion of time was spent on the statement of lesson aims (4.4 per cent) (in Blackstairs (VCC Fr D), first lesson). The excerpt occurs at the beginning of the lesson. The new topic being covered is co-ordinate geometry, specifically finding the midpoint of a line. In this extract we see the teacher providing a context for the lesson. He sets the scene for students, using a mixture of clarification, recall, demonstration and questioning. He also locates the work of the day in the context of the text book.

This extract involves a very experienced male teacher in a designated disadvantaged vocational community college, with a mixed ability group, of whom just over half are female. The school is located in a rural area. One third of the students in the class observed are from a middle class background and overall the students achieved a high mean score of 27.2 out of a possible 40 on the TIMSS-based mathematics test.

Illustrative Vignette: Lesson Aims – Lead In

Time code (minutes:seconds)	Activity	Lesson text
3:10	Lesson aims: Revision mapping co-ordinates	*Teacher:* … just before we start, before we start our class we'll just run back very briefly for about 2 minutes on the co-ordinates.
3:37	Revision: Questioning whole class Reference to U shaped graphs – Chapter 24: Graphs of quadratic functions	*Teacher:* Remember the U shape graphs we were drawing. We did that didn't we?
3:38	Class answer whole class question.	*Class:* Yeah.
3:40	Revision: Teacher – centred Reference to straight line graphs – Chapter 19: Graphing Lines – Simultaneous Equations	*Teacher:* We did the straight line graphs. *Class:* Yeah.
3.47	Teacher demonstrates plotting co-ordinates.	*Teacher:* And before I use the ruler there I'll do it out roughly. Before I begin, before I start the class just to recap on the points – where you had your X and Y axis – and you had your 1, 2, 3 and –1, –2, –3, back here. We'll say. And you had 1, 2, 3 up to 4 and the same distance apart down along here just so that you'll be able to know where the points are.

4:12	Revision: Questioning whole class	*Teacher:* What point for example is one there, one there – that point *(teacher marks in the co-ordinate (1, 3) on graph)?* *Class:* (1, 3) *Teacher:* (1,3), right. Just so that we'll know. And if you were to move down to this one down here – that point would be? *(Teacher marks in the co-ordinate (2, –3) on graph).* *Class:* (2 –3) *Teacher:* (2 –3), correct! And if you were to move over to this quadrant over here, move up to here – hands up for that?
4:48	Revision: Questioning individuals Teacher asks Vinnie question.	*Vinnie:* (–1, 4)
4:52	Teacher asks Amy question	*Teacher:* (–1, 4) correct! Right, and we'll take one more and then we'll be ready to start. Move down to there! Hands up for that? Yeah? *(pointing to Amy)* *Amy:* (–4, –1). *Teacher:* (–4, –1). Correct!
5:11	Lesson aims	*Teacher:* So that is the basis of what we are going to be starting. The basis of this chapter – near the end of the book – we are going to be finding the distance between two of those points *(teacher points to two of the co-ordinates on the diagram)*. We're going to be finding the slope of say that one *(teacher pointing to the line joining two of the co-ordinates)*. We're going to find the midpoint of something from there to there *(teacher again points to same line)*. And we're going to be finding, now that I've two sides drawn we're drawing a third side *(teacher joining up another two of the co-ordinates, now forming a triangle on the diagram)*. And maybe finding the area of that triangle *(teacher points to same triangle)*. What else will we be doing? We have distance, we have midpoint, we have slope, we have the area of a triangle, we might even find, if you're able for it in second year, the equation, find the equation of that line. Find the equation of this line *(teacher points to one of the lines on the diagram)*. And that's about it!

Conclusion

The findings show that all of the twenty lessons observed involved, what is referred to in the literature as, a traditional approach. The traditional approach reflects a view of mathematics as 'a static, structured system of facts, procedures and concepts' (Henningsen and Stein, 1997, p. 524). It is assumed that mathematics is a fixed, clearly defined subject matter. A procedural rather than a conceptual and/or problem solving approach to the subject prevails.

> Specific objectives, which students are to master, have been stated; the teacher's role has been to demonstrate how a manipulation is to be carried out or to explain how a concept is defined; and students have been expected to memorise facts and to practice procedures until they have been mastered. (Romberg and Kaput, 1999: 4)

As is the case in traditional mathematics classrooms, the teachers in our study used a combination of lecture and drill and practice format. Typically, the teacher lectured to the class as a whole and asked questions. Students watched, listened, took notes or copied examples into their exercise books when instructed and answered questions when called upon. Rarely did they ask questions about the material or make comments. This contrasts with a problem-centred approach to school mathematics. This approach is described as 'dynamic and exploratory' (Romberg, 1994) and 'requires one to focus on the active, generative processes engaged in by doers and users of mathematics' (Henningsen and Stein, 1997; Schoenfeld, 1992). In this context, students are encouraged to draw on their previous mathematical knowledge and experience to construct meanings. They do this by actively engaging with other students as well as the teacher.

The use of traditional approaches to teaching is not confined to mathematics however. Our observations in English classes indicate that while there are important epistemological differences between mathematics and English that impact on how these subjects are taught in schools, there are also important similarities in the pedagogical approaches applied in both. In the English classes we observed in this study, demonstration and student practice constituted the core work just as it did in mathematics. English classes were also very similar to mathematics classes in that questioning was strongly teacher-led (see Chapter 8 below for a more detailed discussion). Moreover, a study of classrooms across a wide range of subjects suggests that while a traditional approach to teaching is frequently more pronounced in mathematics than in other subjects, it is by no means confined to this subject. Irish second level classrooms generally operate along strong didactical lines within which subject matter is presented as a relatively fixed and unproblematic body of knowledge (Lynch and Lodge, 2002).

The traditional approach to teaching mathematics that we observed therefore is part of a wider set of cultural and pedagogical practices in teaching. To represent it as a matter of individual teacher choice and responsibility would be to simplify a complex problem in teaching and learning. Mass public education has a long history in western European societies; it is a history that demonstrates a strong allegiance to drill and practice for all subject teaching, not just for the teaching of mathematics (Bowles and Gintis, 1976; Coolahan, 1981; Foucault, 1977).

While teachers are relatively autonomous in their own classrooms, they are also subject to a range of internal as well as external controls. School principals and senior management regulate their access to resources and structure their time and location through timetabling (Meyer and Rowan, 1988). In general, they work in isolation from their colleagues (van Veen et al., 2001) with an expectation that they will maintain a high level of vigilance over their students (Travers and Cooper, 1996). A growing culture of bench marking, quality assurance and the pressures of state examinations, not only create a stressful climate, but also curtail teachers' willingness to use exploratory or innovative teaching methods (Broadfoot, 1979; Murphy and Torrance, 1988; Hargreaves et al., 1996). Furthermore, the multiple roles that teachers and schools are now expected to fulfil have become increasingly complex (van Veen et al, 2001). Teachers experience their own role as both powerful and powerless and this, in turn, influences their capacity and motivation to be innovative or experimental (Davies, 1996).

To understand the prevalence of traditional approaches to the teaching of mathematics, therefore, we need to be mindful of the wider educational and socio-political contexts within which teaching takes place. Even the design and architecture of school buildings and classrooms need to be examined if one is to fully understand the dynamics of teaching and learning. The architecture of the classrooms we observed strongly facilitated a traditional, hierarchical approach to teaching. In all classes students were seated in individual desks that were arranged in rows facing the teacher at the front. While the teacher could circulate around the class when the students were engaged in individual work, and some did, in other classes there was little space to move between desks. The nature of classroom furniture and the size of the classrooms often militated against flexibility in pedagogical approach even when the teachers may have desired it.

Appendix to Chapter 4

Illustrative Vignette – Demonstration (From Mourne (VCC Fr D)

Time Code (minutes:seconds)	Activity	**Textbook:** Condon and Regan *Junior Certificate Mathematics I* , Folens **Chapter:** 17 page 198 **Topic:** Factorising Quadratic Trinomials – page 202
22:12	Demonstration <u>Example 1:</u> $X^2 + 15x + 56$ Teacher asks whole class question	*Teacher: goes back to the board and writes:* **$x^2 + 15x + 56$** *Teacher:* Now we want to see how to get the factors for this – what it is, is that we start here (*pointing to $x^2 + 15x + 56$)* and then we want to end up with this as your answer – (*pointing to $(x + 7) (x + 8)$* – and we are going to take the steps exactly backwards – so what happens if you go from this line (*pointing to $x^2 + 15x + 56$)* this time – now that's exactly the same ((*pointing to x^2)* and that's exactly the same ((*pointing to 56)* and then the 15x gets split up into what? – into 8x plus 7x – Now can anybody think of a reason why it is 8 and 7? – why? – I mean you could split 15x into 14x and 1x and 13x and 2x or 12x and 3x – why is it 8 and 7?
23:24	Stephen answers Teacher asks whole class question	*Stephen:* Because it is more even. *Teacher:* What's more even? *Stephen:* 8 and 7 *Teacher considers this for a moment*
23:32	Teacher asks same whole class question	*Teacher:* Is there any other reason why 8 and 7?
23:37	Rachel volunteers answer	*Rachel:* Because when you multiply 8 times 7 you get 56. *Teacher:* Good girl Rachel – (*and repeats Rachel's answer)* when you multiply 8 times 7 you get 56.
23:48	Teacher asks whole class question	*Teacher:* so what's the number that guides you then?
23:51	Class answer whole class question	*Class and Teacher together:* its 56.
23:53	Teacher explanation	*Teacher:* So you split up the 15 – and the way you split it up is guided by the 56 – and how do you work out what way to do it? – You find 2 numbers to multiply for 56 – so two numbers that multiply for 56 and add for 15? – and we call that they 'multiply for' <u>the product</u> – so we say their product is 56 – and when

		you 'add the two of them together' you call that <u>their sum</u> – so we say their sum is 15 – so you look for 2 numbers that will multiply to give you 56 and add together to give you 15 – and we know the answer to that already – so it is 8x plus 7x plus 56 – so we have changed this line and we have rewritten it by splitting up that middle one – now we are going to do it exactly the same way as you have done all the ones up to now –
24:45	Teacher asks whole class question	*Teacher:* So what would you think you would do next?
24:50	Class answer whole class question	*Class:* Take the x out. *Teacher:* you look at the first two and you take the x out – right! – so that's x times x plus 8, *and writes:* **x(x + 8)**
24:54	Teacher asks whole class question	*Teacher:* And what do you do then?
24:56	Class answer whole class question	*Class:* … *(inaudible) something about* 'the next two terms'. *Teacher:* Get the second two …
25:04	Teacher asks Paul question	*Teacher:* … and take out what Paul?
25:05	Paul answers question	*Paul:* the 7 *Teacher:* Take the 7 out – so it is 7 times x plus 8 – and how do you finish it? *Paul:* x plus 7 times x plus 8, *and teacher writes:* **(x + 7) (x + 8)** *Teacher:* so the factors for x^2 plus 15x plus 56 are x plus 7 times x plus 8 – right let's try one more.
25:22	Teacher asks Conor question <u>Example 2:</u> X^2 + 8x + 12	*Teacher:* suppose we want to get factors for x^2 plus 8x plus 12, *and writes:* **x^2 + 8x + 12** *Teacher:* Now we are going to have to do it like that, so we are going to have to leave the x^2 alone and we are going to leave the 12 alone and we are going to split up the 8x – how are we going to split it Conor?
25:45	Conor answers Teacher question	*Conor:* 2x plus 6x *Teacher:* Good lad and why is that? *Conor:* Because two sixes are twelve. *Teacher:* Because we want two numbers that are going to multiply together for 12 and are going to add for 8 and those two numbers are 6 and 2 – so its x^2 plus 6x plus 2x plus 12, *and writes:* **x^2 + 6x +2x +12**

26:04	Teacher asks Paula question	*Teacher:* Now Paula, what will we do with these first two?
26:10	Paula answers Teacher questions	*Paula: (with teacher prompting her along):* x times x plus 6, *and teacher writes:* **x(x + 6)**
26:18	Teacher asks Margaret question	*Teacher:* and Margaret what will we take out of the next two?
26:18	Margaret answers Teacher question	*Margaret:* two *Teacher:* and we get 2 times: *Margaret:* x plus 6, *and teacher writes:* **2(x + 6)**
26:28	Teacher asks Paul question	*Teacher:* so what are the factors then Paul?
26:30	Paul answers Teacher question	*Paul:* x plus 2 *Teacher:* times? *Martin:* x plus 6, *and teacher writes:* **(x + 2) (x + 6)**
26:35	Teacher asks Joe question <u>Example 3:</u> $X^2 + 7x + 12$	*Teacher:* very good – so we'll try one more – suppose we want to get factors for x^2 plus 7x plus 12, *and writes* $x^2 + 7x + 12$ *Teacher:* we are going to leave the x^2 alone, we are going to leave the 12 alone and we are going to split up the 7x – Joe how will we do it?
26:53	Joe answers Teacher question	*Joe:* 3 and 4 *Teacher:* pardon? *Joe: louder,* 3 and 4 *Teacher:* yeah, we are going to split it into 3x plus 4x plus 12, *and writes* $x^2 + 3x + 4x + 12$ *Teacher:* we wanted two numbers whose product is 12 and whose sum is 7 – so we wanted 2 numbers that will multiply for 12 and add for 7
27:09	Teacher asks Lisa question	*Teacher:* so okay Lisa what will we do now?
27:10	Lisa answers Teacher question	*Note: at this point there is quite a bit of noise outside the classroom.* *Lisa:* x *Teacher:* x times? *Lisa:* x plus 3 *Teacher:* Good, plus? *Lisa:* 3, no 4

		Teacher: 4 times? *Lisa:* x plus 3
27:28	Teacher asks Teresa question	*Teacher:* Teresa how do we finish it off?
27:30	Teresa answers Teacher question	*Teresa:* x plus 4 and x plus 3 *Teacher:* Very good and writes: **(x + 4) (x + 3)**
27:30	Teacher asks whole class question	*Teacher:* Does everyone know what do?
27:32	Class answer whole class question	*Class:* yeah!
27:35	Teacher asks whole class question	*Teacher:* Are you ready to try one yourselves?
27:36	Class answer whole class question	Class: yeah!

Table A4.1: Case-study schools – content of mathematics lessons

School and Lesson		Topic	Mathematics subject — Specific	Level
Barrow (SSG F)	1	Algebra	Quadratic Expression with mixed signs	Continuation
	2	Algebra	Factors by grouping and difference between two squares	Revision L1; Continuation
Nore (SSG Fr)	1	Statistics	Bar charts	New
	2	Statistics	Bar charts and Pie charts	Continuation L1
Suir (SSG Fr D)	1	Statistics	Mean and mode	Revision
	2	Statistics	Mean and mode	Revision
Liffey (SSB Fr D)	1	Simple Interest	Finding principal, interest, time and rate	New
	2	Simple Interest	Finding principal, interest, time and rate	Continuation L1
Lee (SSB F)	1	Algebra	Quadratic equations: problems	Continuation
	2	Algebra	Quadratic equations: problems	Continuation L1
Lagan (SC Fr)	1	Geometry	Length of a circle	New
	2	Geometry	Length of a circle and running tracks	Continuation L1
Errigal (CS Fr)	1	Algebra	Equations with fractions	Continuation
	2	Algebra	Equations with fractions	Continuation L1
Mourne (VCC Fr D)	1	Algebra	Factors: grouping expressions with minus signs	Continuation
	2	Algebra	Factors: grouping expressions with minus signs	Continuation L1
Blackstairs (VCC Fr D)	1	Co-ordinate geometry	Plotting co-ordinates and midpoint of a line	New
	2	Co-ordinate geometry	Length of a line; distance between two co-ordinates	Continuation L1
Nephin (VCC Fr)	1	Money	Electricity bills	Revision
	2	Algebra	Introduction and removing brackets	Continuation

Notes

[1] The classes in which student practice was clearly the prevailing pedagogical style were Barrow 2, Suir 2, Lee 1 and 2, Errigal 2, Mourne 1 and 2, Nephin 2. Teacher demonstration was the prevailing style in Barrow 1, Nore 1, Lagan 1 and Errigal 1.The remaining classes have a more even balance between the two pedagogical practices.

5

Classroom Interaction:
An in-depth analysis

Introduction

Chapter 4 examined the dominant pedagogical practices in the classrooms observed. This chapter explores the dynamics of interaction within those different practices, namely the patterns of engagement between teachers and students and the nature of questioning and instructing. All public interactions are analysed along two dimensions, in terms of who initiated them and their specific character. As the unit of analysis was the class and its processes, rather than the experience of individual students, the analysis focuses primarily on the public aspect of the lessons. In the context of teacher-student initiated interactions, those directed to the whole class as well as to individual students were analysed. Public interactions directed by individual students to the teacher were also included in the analysis.

Not included in the analysis were private exchanges between the teacher and the students, or among the students themselves. While work-related interactions conducted privately between the teacher and the students occurred in seventeen out of the twenty lessons, they did not command much class time. Sometimes they involved merely a glance over a student's shoulder to check work, while in other cases it involved giving guidance on a specific task. Such interactions were generally initiated by the teacher and were of short duration. They occurred mostly during the student practice phases of the lesson, such as during the student work in class phase, or when homework was being corrected or partly undertaken in class.

One of the reasons for excluding these private exchanges from the analysis was the logistical impossibility of hearing and recording such interactions systematically on video. Most of the exchanges occurred when the teacher went to check or help an individual student, or (very infrequently) when students conferred with one another in quiet tones. Given the over-riding prevalence of public, teacher directed work in classes, and the lack of co-operative work between students, the exclusion of private exchanges also seems justified in research terms.

Patterns of public interaction

Overall, teacher initiated interactions comprised over ninety-six per cent of all interactions that took place over the twenty mathematics lessons. By contrast, student initiated interactions accounted for just less than four per cent of all interactions (Figure 5.1).

Figure 5.1: All public interactions: teacher–student initiated and student–teacher initiated interaction (n = 2980)

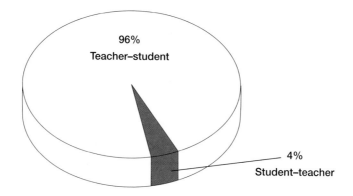

These teacher-student public interactions throughout the twenty mathematics lessons were fairly evenly distributed between those directed to the whole class and those addressed to individual students (Figure 5.2).

Figure 5.2: Distribution of teacher–student interactions (n = 2980)

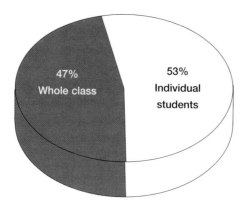

In ten of the twenty mathematics lessons, between a quarter and a half of all teacher-student public interactions were directed to the whole class, while it exceeded 50 per cent in nine lessons (Figure 5.3). The use of whole class teaching contributes to a controlled environment that typifies the traditional view of mathematics.

Figure 5.3: Distribution of teacher–student public interactions by lesson (n = 20)

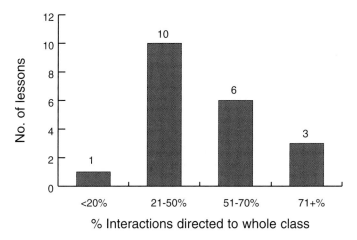

Figure 5.4: Categories of teacher–student interactions (n = 2980)

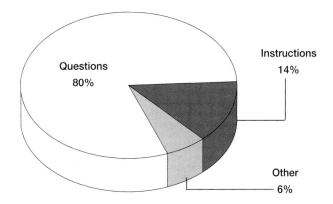

Teacher-student questioning

The nature of the interactions in which teacher and students are involved in the classroom is of central importance. Analysis of the twenty lessons revealed that questioning is the dominant mode of interaction between teacher and student. Teacher-student questions accounted for almost 80 per cent of the total teacher-student public interactions. The remaining interactions comprised either instructions to students or organisational or social exchanges (Figure 5.4). Teachers tended to use questioning to ensure that students were equipped with facts and procedures. The teacher's role was to demonstrate and explain while the role of the student was to memorise and practice.

The Nature of Teacher Questioning : Drill and Recitation

In their analysis of active teaching, Good and Brophy (2000) identify a range of questioning procedures in classrooms. Among these are drills or fast-paced review questioning which is designed to test or reinforce knowledge of specific facts. In such questioning the emphasis is on obtaining the right answer, and questioning tends to move at a brisk pace. Another form of questioning is recitation activity questioning. This includes questioning that occurs between presentation segments of lessons, questioning during periods in which teachers are going over the material, board work, and questioning occurring in the process of preparing students for assignments. Recitation activity questioning is not all of a kind however: it can vary in pace and cognitive level.

A third major form of questioning is discussion questioning which is designed to stimulate students to respond diversely at higher cognitive levels. Such questioning tends to move at a slower pace and the emphasis is on developing insights and implications. There may be acceptable answers to questions and no single right answer (Good and Brophy, 2000).

Examination of the teacher-student questions in the twenty mathematics lessons shows that, in keeping with the traditional mathematics style, questioning falls into either drill/fast-paced review questioning or recitation-type questioning. Further examination reveals that these two types of questioning tend to occur in different phases of the lesson. Specifically, drill questioning is largely confined to student practice phases such as homework or revision phases. Recitation-type questioning occurred mainly during the explanation and demonstration phases of the lessons. The absence of discussion questioning across all lessons is evidence of the strong traditional approach to the teaching of mathematics in the classes observed.

Drill Questioning

When drill procedures are utilised, questioning moves at a brisk pace with an emphasis on obtaining the 'right' answer. In a homework correction phase, for example, the teacher may ask the students to call out the final answer to each problem. In such a situation the teacher may correct a large number of homework problems in a short period of time.

The following extract is an example of drill-type questioning. It involves a very experienced male teacher in a designated-disadvantaged vocational community school located in a rural area (Blackstairs (VCC Fr D)). This was the second lesson with a mixed group, 51 per cent of whom were girls. The school is located in a rural area and one third of the class is from a middle-class background. The class achieved a high mean score of 27.2 out of a possible 40 on the TIMSS-related mathematics test.

Co-ordinate geometry is the topic of the lesson. The teacher is correcting ten homework problems assigned to the students the previous day. In each problem the students were asked to find the midpoint of a line. Throughout this phase, students were called on to give the correct answer to each problem. As each answer was given the teacher checked to see how many students got the correct answer and then moved on to the next homework problem.

Illustrative Vignette: Drill Questioning

Time code Activity (minutes:seconds)		Homework Questions
		(Texts and Tests I Exercise 27C p. 376 Question 2) Use the midpoint formula to find the midpoint of the line segment joining each of the following pairs of points: **1.** (2,1) and (4,3); **2.** (1,1) and (7,7); **3.** (1,2) and (3,6); **4.** (–2, 1) and (4,3); **5.** (1, –3) and (3,5); **6.** (–2,–3) and (4,–1) **7.** (0,4) and (–2,2); **8** (–2,0) and (4,0); **9.** (2,-3) and (–2, 5); **10.** (3,–2) and (0,–2).
3:35	Homework correction begins Teacher asks general questions about the homework, looking for specific difficulties.	*Teacher:* How many questions did we have? *Class:* Ten. *Teacher:* Ten questions for homework. (*Inaudible*) the answers will be at random. Get the midpoint of the following. Any difficulties in any of them? Did some of them come out as fractions? As halves? *Class:* The last one. *Teacher:* OK, the last one. OK, any difficult ones? We might do one or two of them on the board. Where will we start? We'll start at the back with Denise?

4:02	Teacher questions Denise on first homework problem.	*Teacher:* Read out the question for me please. Denise? *Denise:* Ah – 2, open brackets, 2 coma 1, close bracket, 4 comma 3, close brackets. *Teacher:* And the midpoint? *Denise:* Open brackets 3,2. *Teacher:* (3,2) (3,2). When you give me the answers in future will you forget about the brackets. We know you have them in, at least we hope you have them in, you don't have to put the commas as well. Read out the points and the answers.
4:29	Teacher moves on to next homework problem naming a different student.	*Teacher:* Alright, next? Shane? *Shane:* 4,4 *Teacher:* Is that the answer now? *Shane:* Yes
4:35	Teacher questions whole class.	*Teacher:* Alright we'll just take the answers then. Hands up all who got that 4,4 very good everybody got (4,4).
4:41	Teacher moves on to next homework problem asking Angela.	*Teacher:* Next one, the answer just? *Angela:* (2,4).
4:44	Teacher asks whole class question.	*Teacher:* Hands up for that one (2,4). We're doing well so far.

All of the homework problems were corrected in this way. Eleven of the thirty-two students were involved in this homework correction phase of the lesson, which lasted just over two minutes.

The second extract is taken from a designated-disadvantaged single sex boys' secondary school in an urban area (Liffey (SSB Fr D), second lesson). It involves a very experienced male teacher and a top-stream group, almost three quarters of whom are working class. The class achieved an above average score of 24.4 out of a possible 40 in the TIMSS-related mathematics test.

The excerpt is from the homework correction phase of the lesson. The teacher has broken down the problem into a number of steps, calling on either individual students or the whole class at different times to provide the answer to each part of the problem. Overall, the teacher spent just over five minutes correcting one of the two assigned problems. Even though this is a much more detailed correction of homework than the previous example, it again illustrates the use of drill questioning with an emphasis on obtaining the right answer and moving quickly through the problem.

Illustrative Vignette: Drill Questioning

Time code (minutes:seconds)	Activity	Content
1:08	Homework correction: whole class Homework Assigned: Q.5 and 6 *Exercises 12.2 on page 87: Q5: A man invests £850 at 6% and £1200 at $8^1/_4$%. What is the total interest gained on these investments after 2 years? Q6: Calculate the simple interest on £265 for $2^1/_3$ years at $3^3/_4$% per annum. Teacher corrects Q6 only with whole class	*Teacher:* OK. Enough is enough! Right the big problem created with <u>question number 6</u> in so far as the answer in the book is completely different or looks quite different to the answer that you would normally get, right. In <u>question **6** **calculate the**</u> **simple interest on 265 for 2 and 1/3 years at 3 and 3/4.** Now for anybody who didn't do it *(teacher pauses).* Now for anybody that didn't get the answer, the people who wrote out the question that's good enough for an attempt mark in an exam but we are aiming higher for higher than just an attempt marks, OK. So when we're doing these questions as we said <u>the principal by the time by the rate over 100</u>, this is question 6 – the one that's causing the problems.
	Teacher questions Brian.	*Teacher:* The principal in that particular question is ?
2:01	Brian replies.	*Brian:* 265
2:03	Teacher continues.	*Teacher:* 265, right so the interest is equal to 265 multiplied by the rate or the time, put the time second *(Teacher is writing this on the blackboard)*
2:12	Brian replies.	*Brian:* $2^1/_3$
2:14	Teacher continues.	*Teacher:* $2^1/_3$ times the rate?
2:17	Couple from the class shout up.	*Class:* 3 and $^3/_4$
2:21	Teacher continues, asks whole class question.	*Teacher:* All over 100, now this is one of the ones who warranted an asterisk, the reason being that there were big numbers that do not cancel out that nicely and you're left with a big multiplication question. Right. Now yesterday when we were dealing with these what did I tell you to do with them?

$$\frac{265 \times 2^1/_3 \times 3^3/_4}{100}$$

2:35	A lot of students from the class answer up.	*Class:* Turn them into top heavy fractions.
2:37	Teacher continues.	*Teacher:* Top heavy fractions, right Leo! So that as a top heavy fraction is?
2:41	Couple from class mutter.	*Class:* $^7/_3$
2:43	Teacher replies.	*Teacher:* Good lad! Leo!
2:45	Leo replies.	*Leo:* I didn't say nothing.
2:47	Teacher continues.	*Teacher:* Did you not? *(sarcastically)* 265 multiplied by 7 over 3 *(muttering going on in the classroom)*. Right Billy?
2:51	Billy enquires.	*Billy:* Yeah?
2:53	Teacher asks.	*Teacher:* $3^3/_4$?
2:54	Billy answers.	*Billy:* $^{15}/_4$
2:56	Teacher continues (writing on the blackboard).	*Teacher:* $^{15}/_4$ and you have 100 on the bottom again. Now if you look at those numbers very little cancel out, the reason being. Well you can go 3 into 15, 5 times, this 265 over 100 you can do a little bit with that, by doing something with it – changing the 100 which is a very easy number to divide by. So what we've got here is 265 by 7 by 5 over 100. So if you want to cancel out you can. That into that goes? $$= \frac{265}{100} * \frac{7}{3} * \frac{15}{4}$$ Cancel down (1) $\frac{15}{3}$ = 5 (15 = 5 and 3=1) (2)$\frac{5}{5}$=1 and $\frac{100}{5}$ = 20 (5=1 and 100 = 20) (3) $\frac{20}{5}$ = 4 and $\frac{265}{5}$ = 53
3:31	Class replies.	*Class:* 20
3:33	Teacher continues.	*Teacher:* Go again and 25 by, sorry, 5 into this goes 53, so you've got 53 on the top by 7 divided by 16. Right, so if you're not into multiplication which some of you are not, take it down as far as you can. Now that gives you 53 by 7 OK? Seven 3s are 20?
4:01	Class answers.	*Class:* 1
4:03	Teacher continues.	*Teacher:* Seven 5s are 35 and 2?

4:06	Class answers.	*Class:* 37
4:07	Teacher continues. Mark has his hand up but teacher is writing on the board and does not see him. He gives up after putting hand up for 2nd time.	*Teacher:* So you've got 371, I think 5 by 7, that's right, yeah. So you've 371 and you want to divide that by 16. $= \dfrac{53}{4} * \dfrac{7}{1} * \dfrac{1}{4} = \dfrac{371}{16}$ *Teacher:* So clearly straightforward division after that so 16 in this part? Kevin?
4:24	Kevin offers answer.	*Kevin:* Twice
4:26	Teacher continues.	*Teacher:* Twice so that gives you 32, take off the 5, 16 into 51, Kevin?
4:34	Kevin replies.	*Kevin:* Twice.
4:35	Teacher encourages.	*Teacher:* Go again.
4:36	Kevin replies.	*Kevin:* Three times.
4:37	Teacher continues.	*Teacher:* Three 16s are?
4:40	Liam shouts up.	*Liam:* 48.
4:41	Teacher continues.	*Teacher:* 48 from 51 leaves you with?
4:42	Liam answers.	*Liam:* 3.
4:44	Teacher continues.	*Teacher:* 3, bring down the?
4:45	Liam answers.	*Liam:* 0.
4:48	Teacher continues.	*Teacher:* Right, so you've 16 into 30 goes?
4:50	Class answers.	*Class:* Once.
4:52	Teacher continues.	*Teacher:* Once, that gives you 16, take off, you're left with 14, 16 into 140?
4:56	Class replies.	*Class* 9
4:57	Teacher continues.	*Teacher:* 9 times, nine 6s are 54, nine 1s are 9 and 5 are 14 so it's too high, but not very high because in questions such as this you're going to be left with a decimal part of a penny. And if you're left with a decimal part of a penny you'll be bringing it to the nearest penny anyway. So it's almost 19 so you can leave it 19 anyway. OK? So that the question is one of the ones where the instruction is at the beginning of the exercise was <u>to the nearest penny where necessary</u>.

Long division:

$$
\begin{array}{r}
23.19 \\
16\overline{)371} \\
32 \\
\hline
51 \\
48 \\
\hline
30 \\
16 \\
\hline
140
\end{array}
$$

Teacher: Now after that, that's the hardest one that you will get, very, very rarely that you will have a situation whereby that would come up in any exam, very rarely you would you come across that example even if you were talking about ordinary maths. Ok, any question on that?

Recitation Type Questioning

In the twenty mathematics lessons, recitation type questioning occurred mainly in the explanation or demonstration phases of the lesson. In the presentation of a new topic, the problem was broken down into a number of steps and the students were questioned in relation to each step. Unlike drill questioning, the teacher took a number of different answers from the students at each step before continuing the demonstration. This recitation type questioning also tended to move at a slower pace than drill questioning. However, this type of questioning is again very much in keeping with the drill and practice methodologies being employed, emphasising the importance of procedural knowledge in the traditional mathematics classroom.

An example of this type of questioning is seen in the first lesson observed in Blackstairs ((VCC Fr D); see Appendix 5 for extract from the class transcript). The lesson involves a demonstration by a male teacher to a non-streamed mixed group.

The topic being covered in this lesson is co-ordinate geometry: plotting co-ordinates and the midpoint of a line. In this excerpt the teacher is demonstrating how to find the midpoint of a line, which is a new topic for this class.

The teacher has drawn X and Y axes on the board and labelled them, and has instructed the students to do the same in their copies. He has taken two points (3,2) (–1, –2), and joined them up and has asked the class to find the midpoint. The teacher stated: 'If you have an accurate diagram drawn you probably will have a good indication as to what the mid-point is going to be anyway.' The teacher then asked the class to estimate (from their diagrams) where the midpoint is. The class answered (1,0). At this point the teacher stressed that diagrams are used as a guide and explained that there is a formula for the midpoint of a line:

> Diagrams are only used as a guide. There are little formulae, unfortunately, that we have to know. We have to learn the formula. The proper way to do it is to use the formula.

In this extract the teacher demonstrates the formula and where it comes from. The demonstration is interspersed with whole class and individual questioning.

The extract (Appendix 5) illustrates the use of recitation questioning. The teacher involved the class in the demonstration of the application of the formula and encouraged the class to suggest answers: 'Hands up, right, hands up? What's on the clock?[1] Hands up? Come on, come on, more of you than that! Come on – what is on the clock? Later in the lesson the teacher continued this encouragement, stressing that it does not matter if wrong answers are given:

> I'm going to take a few answers. We're going to have wrong answers I know we are but so what? What about it? You can guess it, if you're not too sure. You're guessing it.

Despite the teacher's assertion that it was acceptable to give wrong answers, it was only when the 'right' answer was given by a student that the teacher investigated the question further: 'Where did you get the 15, Alex?' Little attention is given to the method of arriving at the incorrect answer and the reasoning behind that procedure.

The importance placed on procedural knowledge was also evident later in the lesson when the teacher invited a number of students up to the board to work through examples using the formula. During these practice examples he told the class that there is 'no need to draw the diagrams every time' but he stressed the importance of knowing and learning the formula: 'The formula must be written down every time'.

Level of Questioning

Teacher-student questioning has been differentiated in the literature into low level or high level cognitive activities. Low level activities require the student to apply a routine procedure to find an answer (Fennema, 1987). Often the student must recall specific facts or use a memorised algorithm. In this way the student is being taught a mechanical procedure for arriving at a solution. In high level cognitive learning, the mental demands are greater, requiring the student to understand, interpret or apply mathematical knowledge. To solve a high level problem the student must deduce how to solve it (ibid).

In both drill and recitation type questioning, the vast majority of teacher-student questions were low level knowledge or comprehension questions. Analysis of all teacher-student questions throughout the twenty mathematics lessons show that almost 82 per cent were lower order questions. Higher order questions comprised just over 5 per cent of all teacher-student questions. The remaining teacher-student questions were made up of behaviour questions, real life applications[2], checking student understanding and organisational questions (Figure 5.5).

Figure 5.5: Types of teacher-student questions (n: 1451)

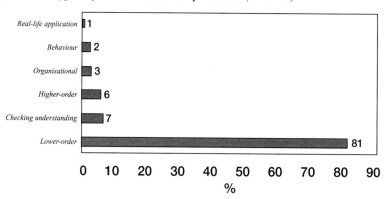

Below are some examples of lower order teacher-student questions from two lessons, again illustrating the emphasis on procedural learning.

Examples of teacher-student low-level questioning

Liffey (SSB Fr D), second lesson: The lesson, taught by a male teacher, involves the continuation of a new topic covered on the previous day. The topic is simple interest. This extract occurs at the beginning of the lesson in the homework correction phase. The problem being corrected involves calculating simple interest. The teacher has broken down the problem into different stages. This part of the procedure involves long division.

Teacher:	So you've 371 and you want to divide that by 16. So clearly straight forward division after that so 16 in this part?
Kevin:	Twice.
Teacher:	Twice so that gives you 32, take off the 5, 16 into 51, Kevin?
Kevin:	Twice.
Teacher:	Go again.
Kevin:	Three times.

Errigal (CS Fr), first lesson: The topic being covered in this lesson is algebra: equations with fractions. The topic is being continued from the previous day. The teacher is correcting one homework question:

$$\frac{6}{3x + 2} - \frac{5}{3x - 2}.$$

She has broken down the problem into different steps. This part of the procedure involves addition:

Teacher: And over here then – minus 12 and minus 10 – Elaine, what will that give me altogether?

Elaine: Minus 22.

Higher order questions mainly included those prefixed with how or why in relation to mathematics method or procedure. Examples of high level questions asked by teachers follow. It should be noted that these are among the highest level of questions that we found in the course of our analysis of teacher questioning.

Examples of teacher-student high-level questioning

Barrow (SSG F), first lesson: The topic being covered in this lesson is quadratic expressions with mixed signs. In this excerpt the teacher is demonstrating how to factorise quadratic expressions when the terms are negative. Through teacher questioning, the class has arrived at the final solution (x+2) (x-3).

Teacher: … does it really matter whether I write $(x + 2)$ first followed by $(x – 3)$ or the other way around?

Class: No.

Teacher: …not at all! Why does it not matter?

Class/Teacher: Because the product is going to be the same either way.

Lagan (SC Fr), first lesson: The topic being covered in this lesson is length of a circle. It is a new topic for this class. The teacher has worked through a number of examples. In this extract she has moved on to a more difficult example and is asking the class for suggestions as to how to approach the question.

Teacher: Have we any idea how we'd do this?

Student: Divide by 2

Teacher: Divide what by 2, eh, Mark?

Student: The answer, so 44 divided by 2.

Teacher: You divide the 44 by 2 to give you 22. So we know that the length of this circle is 44, yeah, so you're saying to me to divide by 2. Why are you saying that it sounds like a good idea? Why are you saying that?

Student: It's the opposite of the way you get the length.

Teacher: Yeah, you're doing well, right you're saying divided by two.

Good and Brophy (2000) point out that although higher order questions are intended to elicit higher order responses, many students often respond at a lower cognitive level than the question demands. In many cases in our study, student answers to such questions are of a low cognitive level and the teacher either provides the correct answer, or asks further low level questions until the required answer has been reached. The students' responses to higher level questioning by teachers are indicative of the normal level of questioning in a typical lesson. The fact that students hesitate or mumble answers to higher order questions might suggest that they are more used to, and therefore more comfortable with, low level questioning requiring short or one word answers.

This is illustrated in the following extract. This example concerns a free scheme secondary coeducational school located in a small town (Lagan (SC Fr), second lesson). It involves a demonstration by an experienced female teacher to a top stream group. Almost 52 per cent of the class are girls. Two thirds of the students are from a middle-class background. The class achieved a high mean score of 28.5 out of a possible 40 in the TIMSS-related mathematics test.

Illustrative Vignette: Higher order question

Time code (hours:minutes:seconds)	Activity	Lesson Text
1:18:56	Demonstration Example 3: Q4(iv) Find the perimeter of each of the following shapes:	*Teacher:* OK, we're going to go on today with the ones where you're given a shape that involves a part of a circle, and you want to work out what the circumference or what the perimeter of those kind of shapes are, and we did one the last day where they gave us half of a circle and a quarter of a circle, so what we want to look at now is say one with three quarters of a circle, like this, with a radius of 7. How would you work this one out?
		(Teacher draws three quarters of a circle on the board.)

1:19:27	Teacher asks Frank a question.	*Teacher:* Well Frank, what do you think, what would you do with this one, if you're looking for the perimeter, that's what we're looking for, so what will we do?
1:19:37	Frank answers question.	*Frank:* eh? *Teacher:* What fraction of a circle is it? *Frank:* Three quarters *Teacher:* Yeah good, it's three quarters of a circle. How do you know it's three quarters? *Frank:* Because *(hesitates)...* *Teacher interrupts:* Is there any hint there that it is actually three quarters exactly?
1:19:53	Teacher asks Lorna same question.	Lorna?
1:19:54	Lorna answers question.	*Lorna:* It's the little line. *Teacher:* The little line means? *Whole class answer:* That it's a right angle. *Teacher:* That it's a right angle, so it's 90 degrees OK. So 90 is one quarter, so there's three quarters there. So we're going to have to do three quarters of a circle.

The teacher is demonstrating how to find the perimeter of parts of a circle. Here, the teacher asks a higher level question about the fraction of the circle: 'How do you know it's three-quarters'. The first student asked hesitates; the teacher reverts to a more procedural approach moving to another student who gives the required 'correct' answer. Thus while the teacher begins the topic with a higher order question, she returns to a more procedural approach as it becomes clear that the students are not really engaged with this type of question. Here we see how the students are responding at a lower cognitive level than the initial question allows.

Teacher instructions

Teacher instructions accounted for 14 per cent of all public interactions throughout the twenty mathematics lessons. The main types of instructions issued were mathematics related. Such instructions involved the teacher telling the class what to do next, or instructing the class to follow certain procedures or to copy worked examples from the board into their copies. Non-learning instructions included organisational or behavioural instructions.

The nature and scope of the instructions given indicate the high level of

teacher control in the mathematics classrooms. Instructions from teachers were definitive so that students had little opportunity to make an input into the organisation of their own learning environment. On the whole, students obeyed the instructions, without question.

The nature of mathematics related instructions also point to assumptions of certainty and truth in the epistemological approach to mathematics. Instructions were given for operationalising procedures for resolving mathematics problems, with an emphasis on the correct way of doing things. These procedures were accepted by the students without question. Some examples of teacher instructions follow.

Illustrative Vignette: Mathematics related teacher instructions

Liffey (SSB Fr D), second lesson: In this lesson the teacher is continuing the topic of simple interest from the previous day. Today's lesson is concerned with finding the principal, time and rate. The teacher has just run through the formulae for finding each of these. In this extract she is about to do some practice examples but before this she gives the following instructions with regard to remembering the formulae.

'So you've three new formulae all derived from the one formula, and all those are given as an exception in the book. OK, now after a while when you've gone through these a few times, if you write them down – as you're going along you won't have any difficulty in learning them and remembering them, which is more important, as the further you go on you will not have these formulae given to you OK. .... Now the most important aspect of any of these questions you are dealing with from here on in is to identify whether you are dealing with the principal or the time or the rate OK, whichever you are dealing with. And remember the fourth part of the equation is the interest. So be very careful with how you do the questions.'

Suir (SSG Fr D), second lesson (bottom stream): The topic being covered in this lesson is statistics: bar charts. It is a revision class. The teacher has set the class work from a revision sheet. She is walking around the room and checking the students' work. Before proceeding to the next topic of pie charts the teacher issues these instructions in relation to bar charts.

'You all should nearly know how to do all the bar charts. They're the ones that you'd need the bars the same thickness all the way through, … You need to be very consistent … need to be consistent with your marks up along this side … If you start with 2s, you must go up consistently in 2s, if you start with 5s, you must go up in 5s. OK and along this side, make sure that you label your axes so think every time you're going to draw a chart for someone – someone outside the class wants to be able to read it. So you need to be able to show them on your diagram.'

Blackstairs (VCC Fr D), second lesson (mixed group): The topic being covered in this part of the lesson is co-ordinate geometry. The teacher has demonstrated the

formula for finding the distance between two points. Before beginning to work on some practice examples the teacher issues the following instructions with regard to the formula.

And that's the <u>formula</u> for the <u>distance between two points</u>. If $a(x_1, y_1)$ and $b(x_2, y_2)$ are two points, then $| ab |$ is: $\sqrt{(x_2 - x_1)^2 + (y_2 - y_1)^2}$. So any two points you get, all you do is, you don't even need a diagram for them. Use that formula here … here … If you had a point like this, very roughly now $(3, 5)$ and oh whatever $(4, 6)$. What's the distance between those two points? You just draw your $X_1 \, Y_1 \, X_2 \, Y_2$. Whatever you call X_1 you must call its partner Y_1. In other words – X_2 – sorry! That's a mistake there. Let me call X_2 it should be Y_2. There's nothing stopping you from calling that one X_2 as long as you call its partner Y_2. The order doesn't matter. If it's X_1 it must be Y_1. So you just go on the distance between those, the square root of $X_2 - X_1$. Write the formula down every time. You square that, plus $Y_2 - Y_1$

Instructions were also issued by teachers to regulate student attention levels in class.

Illustrative Vignette: Behaviour related instructions

Nore (SSG Fr), frst lesson (mixed group): The topic being covered in this lesson is statistics: bar charts. It is a new topic for this class. The teacher is working through some examples from the textbook. At this point he has instructed the class to do a simple calculation. All of the students except one girl commence the calculation in their copybooks.

Teacher:	So have a go, quick add them all, quick.
	Not in your head Grainne, on paper. This is recorded for posterity only if you get it wrong it'll be back to haunt visit you in 50 years' time.

Liffey (SSB Fr D), second lesson (top stream): The topic in this lesson is simple interest. The teacher is working through an example on finding the rate. In this extract the teacher asks Tony a question. He has already reprimanded this student a few times for misbehaviour.

Teacher:	Tony! Right rate is equal to, from the formula down there, yeah… Come on it's in the book. 100 multiplied by? Have you got the right page even Tony? *(Teacher sounds annoyed at this stage.)*
Tony:	Yes!
Teacher:	Try page 88 there Tony. Yes thank you very much, it's good to see you paying attention again, yeah. Rate? Tony? *(There is laughing and giggling in the classroom.)* Today some time.

Student-teacher interactions

As noted above, student-initiated interactions accounted for just 4 per cent of all classroom interactions. The vast majority of these – just less than three quarters – comprised questions. The remainder consisted of other interactions (Figure 5.6).

Figure 5.6: Total student–teacher interactions (n = 106)

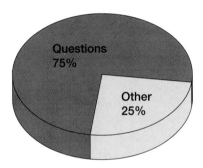

As in the case of teacher-student questioning, the majority of student questions were mathematics related and were of a low cognitive level. Below are some examples of student-teacher questions.

Student-teacher questions

Lee (SSB F), second lesson: The topic being covered in this lesson is quadratic equations. It is now about halfway through the lesson, the homework correction phase. The teacher has broken down the problem into different steps. This part of the procedure concerns multiplying 2 brackets **(10+2x) (8+2x).**

Student:	Did you multiply that out by saying the first thing in the first bracket by all in the second bracket?
Teacher:	That's how you multiply two brackets, yes. First thing in the first bracket, by all in the second bracket?
Student:	then use 0…?
Teacher:	*(interrupting)* Same as you normally do. Multiply out and factorise your answer then.

Lee (SSB F), second lesson: This excerpt occurs towards the end of a lesson on quadratic equations. The teacher is setting homework. She has called out a homework problem for the next day. The problem mentions consecutive numbers. At this point she asked the students to give examples of consecutive numbers. Having done this she seems satisfied that they understand this term. Moments later a student asks the following question:

Student: For the second number, what is a consecutive number?

Teacher: A consecutive number is just numbers straight after each other. If the question said 3 consecutive numbers, that would be 1,2,3,4,5,6. But it says consecutive, even numbers so it is the next even number each time. 2,4,6,8. Right?

Nephin (VCC Fr), second lesson: The topic being covered in this class is algebra: removing brackets. It is the continuation of a topic from a previous lesson. While the teacher is checking homework the students have been instructed to work ahead on questions from their textbook which concern removing brackets and multiplying.

Student: Does a minus by a minus give a plus?

Teacher: If you're multiplying a minus by a minus give it plus, yes.

Student-initiated other public interactions included public comments directed by students to the teacher during the mathematics lesson. These involved comments such as pointing out a teacher's mistake, informing the teacher of an organisational problem or a problem they have encountered with the mathematics, or making a smart/humorous remark. Examples of some student-teacher comments follow.

Student-teacher comments

Lagan (SC Fr), first lesson: The topic being covered in this lesson is length of a circle. The teacher is working through examples from the textbook. She has made an error, working out the problem based on the length of the diameter instead of the radius.

Emlyn: Eh, miss.

Teacher: Yeah

Emlyn: That's the diameter

Teacher: That's the diameter, well pointed out to us. Good man, Emlyn! Alright, so if it's the diameter that's 10 what should we have done there?

Class: 5

Teacher: We should have used the radius as 5 – that's where it shows to read the question.

Well done Emlyn! OK – I didn't notice that! So it says (*reads question from Texts and Tests 1*) using 3.14 as the approximate of pi, calculate the length of the following circles giving the length of the diameter in each case. Is that OK? So, what should I have done here? Instead of using 10 we should have used?

Class: 5

Nephin (VCC Fr), first lesson: This is a revision class covering bills and taxable income. In this excerpt the teacher is setting up an example to explain how to calculate taxable income and is interrupted by a student.

Michael: We did this before.

Teacher: Hmm?

Michael: We did this in first year.

Teacher: I beg your pardon Michael?

Michael: Nothing sir.

Teacher: You're muttering there again, don't be shy *(class laughs)*. It's not like you to be quiet.

Nephin (VCC Fr), second lesson: In this extract which occurs at the end of a revision lesson, the teacher has just finished working through an example of how to calculate bills.

Michael: Sir, I got that one wrong.

Teacher: Did you? The multiplication part?

Michael: No, the taking away part.

              (Teacher goes over to Michael and looks at his copybook.)

Student-teacher questioning

An important consideration when examining student questioning is to determine the number of students actually involved. Figure 5.7 shows that in six lessons there was no incidence of student-teacher questioning. In a further eleven lessons, student-teacher questioning involved 20 per cent or fewer of the students in the class. In the final three lessons, between a quarter and a half of students in the class initiated questions of the teacher. There were no classes in which half or more of the students asked questions therefore, and in only three of the twenty did 21-50 per cent ask questions.

Figure 5.7: Student-teacher public questions (n = 79)

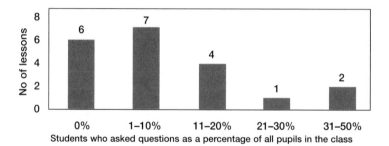

What was clear from the video analysis was that students were not encouraged to ask questions, and few did. Moreover, it was boys who were most likely to initiate questions with teachers, be it in coeducational classes or when single sex classes were compared. (Gender differences in student questioning and classroom participation will be discussed in more detail in Chapter 6).

Overall therefore, student-teacher initiated interactions were confined to a small number of predominantly male students. In four of the three single sex girls' classes, only one student asked a quesiton (Barrow and Nore), while there were only six students who asked questions in the eight coeducational classes observed (Lagan, Errigal, Mourne, and Blackstairs).

Table 5.1: Breakdown of student-teacher questions by lesson

School	Lesson	No. of students in class	No. of student-teacher questions	% of students in class who asked question
Barrow (SSG F)	1	28	0	0
	2	28	0	0
Nore (SSG Fr)	1	24	1	4
	2	23	0	0
Suir (SSG Fr D)	1	12	6	42
	2	10	3	20
Liffey (SSB Fr D)	1	23	3	9
	2	22	6	18
Lee (SSB F)	1	26	7	8
	2	26	13	19
Lagan (SC Fr)	1	30	1	3
	2	31	1	3
Errigal (CS Fr)	1	30	1	3
	2	30	0	0
Mourne (VCC Fr D)	1	19	2	11
	2	14	0	0
Blackstairs(VCC Fr D)	1	33	1	3
	2	32	0	0
Nephin (VCC Fr)	1	10	20	30
	2	10	14	50

Key: SSG F: Secondary girls', fee-paying; SSG Fr: Secondary girls', free scheme; SSG FrD: Secondary girls', free scheme designated disadvantaged; SSB FrD: Secondary boys', free scheme designated disadvantaged; SSB F: Secondary boys', fee paying; SC Fr: Secondary coed, free scheme; CS Fr: Community School, free scheme; VCC FrD: Vocational/Community College, free scheme designated disadvantaged; VCC Fr: Vocational/Community College, free scheme (where free-scheme represents non fee-paying status).

Student responses to teacher-student mathematics questions

Figure 5.8 shows that students mainly gave the 'correct' or 'right' answer in response to mathematics related questions from the teacher. These responses accounted for almost two thirds (65 per cent) of all student answers. 'Incorrect' responses accounted for just 11 per cent of student answers. A slightly higher proportion of responses (13 per cent) comprised progress reports: these included follow-on responses to teacher questions regarding 'correct' or 'incorrect' answers. Other categories included 'no answer/hesitation/mutter' and 'no chance to answer' (before teacher/other student intervened).

The teacher's reaction to 'correct' responses is illustrated in Figure 5.9 showing that teachers mainly acknowledged or accepted these answers without praising the student. 'Asking an additional question' of the student who provided the 'correct' answer was the next most common type of teacher feedback, accounting for almost one third (32 per cent) of all teacher feedback. Other types of feedback included the teacher checking with the rest of class to see who got a particular answer (3 per cent).

Figure 5.8: Student responses to teacher mathematics questions (Base: 1386)

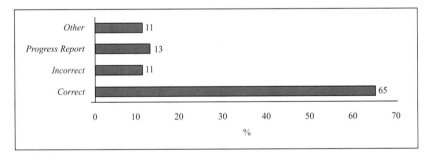

Figure 5.9: Teacher feedback to 'correct' student response (Base: 895)

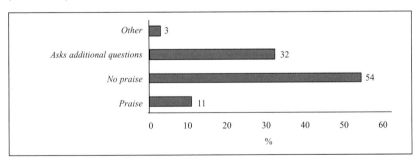

Epistemological assumptions and related pedagogies

Mathematics was presented to students generally as a subject a) that had a fixed body of knowledge; b) that was abstract in character; c) that required demonstration of procedures rather than explanation; and d) that comprised discrete elements.

It was presented as a body of expertise that is transmitted directly from teacher to student, in the classic banking mode defined by Freire (1972).[3] Moreover, it was also characterised by what Bernstein (1977) has referred to as systems of strong framing and classification:[4] not only was mathematics defined as a discrete subject, and taught without relationship to other disciplines, it was also separated within itself (strong classification). In addition, students had little control over the pedagogical relationship, over what they learned or how they learned it. Teachers also exercised little control over content (strong framing).

Lessons were strictly organised in terms of particular topics: each theme was treated as a discrete entity be it quadratic equations with mixed (positive and negative) signs (Barrow (SSG F), first lesson); simple interest (Liffey (SSB Fr D), both lessons); or the length of a circle (Lagan (SC Fr), first lesson). Problems were identified within these topic areas, and in no case was there evidence of more than one method being identified and prescribed for solving the problem.

There was also little evidence of students being given a substantive explanation of the mathematics being taught: written demonstration of a single procedure for solving a problem was the norm; there were few examples of verbal explanations. Learning appeared to be defined primarily as a matter of memorising procedures and facts. Teachers generally demonstrated a procedure and then instructed students to practice the method. The objective was to ensure that students perfected their procedural skills, although such an objective was never overtly stated. There were very few examples in the lessons of teachers providing the students with a reason or explanation as to why they were studying a particular field of mathematics.

Much of the literature has highlighted the importance of developing understanding in mathematics (Fennema and Romberg, 1999). In order to understand the mathematics, and therefore to remember what has been learned, the student needs to be capable of making connections between ideas, facts and procedures. Analysis of lesson organisation in our twenty classes showed that a very small proportion of overall lesson time was given to making connections or explaining relationships in this way. The emphasis instead was on speed, in terms of covering a maximum amount of material in a lesson and being able to complete problems quickly. Such an approach reduces opportunities for discussion, an activity that may lead to greater understanding

An abstracted view of mathematics is what underpinned the teaching of the subject in all classes. Mathematics was presented as something separate from the outside world. There were few real life applications of mathematical concepts or principles. In only two of the twenty lessons observed was there any reference to the application of mathematics. Students were generally not given the opportunity to see how mathematics had applications in every day life.

Given teacher focus on procedural skills, it was not surprising to find that mathematics was taught in a didactic manner in all twenty lessons. This involved a combination of lecture and drill and practice of prescribed methods. Typically, the teacher lectured to the class as a whole and asked questions. Students watched, took notes or copied examples into their exercise books when instructed, and answered questions when called upon. There was little evidence of student-initiated interaction.

Discourse

There were three prevailing themes in the teachers' discourse in classrooms. First, it was evident that teaching for examinations (or more correctly, 'the exam', meaning the Junior or Leaving Certificate) was an overriding preoccupation in the teaching of mathematics. Second, mathematics itself was defined in binary, hierarchical terms as being either 'hard/difficult' or 'easy'. Third, student answers to mathematics questions were defined in a binary polarised code as being either 'right' or 'wrong'.

'The Exam'

In 6 out of the 10 schools, the teacher mentioned the exam at least once over the course of the two observed lessons. Examples of references to the exam include the following:

> *Teacher:* So the first thing then, if you are in an **exam** how do you recognise this type of sum? (Errigal CS Fr, first lesson)

> *Teacher:* Now of course if we are really diligent, how can we check to make sure that we are right particularly the day of the **exam** – we won't just leave the answer and say 'hope for the best' would we – what would we do? (Barrow SSG F, first lesson)

> *Teacher:* Alright – Richard?
> *Richard:* Miss, I got it all right to the end and then I forgot to do that.
> *Teacher:* To go back and get the second one? Right, well you'd loose a mark for that in the **exam**. (Lee SSB F, first lesson)

These excerpts imply that achievement in the exam (in this case, the Junior Certificate) is the main objective for learning mathematics. The goal is to 'learn mathematics' in a way that will facilitate achievement in the examinations. In this context, teachers are required to teach 'to the exam', a view which was expressed by the ten teachers in the interviews (see Chapter 9 for a more detailed discussion of this issue). In keeping with this finding, there is little reference in the lessons to any other rationale for studying mathematics, for example for fun, for its intellectual challenge, for broadening the mind, or for use in everyday life.

'Right' or 'wrong'

There was a strong emphasis on getting the 'right' answer in all mathematics classes. The focus was not on the rationale for resolving a problem in a given manner, or on different methods for resolving it; getting the 'correct' answer was the primary objective. All of the lesson transcripts contain numerous references to 'right/correct' and 'wrong' answers. The following excerpts illustrate the context:

> *Teacher:* What are we trying to find here Emma?
> *Emma:* Emm, what x is equal to.
> *Teacher:* What x is equal to. So you need to sort out a bit don't you?
> *Emma:* Put a line down the middle of the x or the equals.
> *Teacher:* The equals, OK. (*Teacher draws a line down from the middle of the equals sign*):
>
> $$4x - 2 + 9 - 3x = 12$$
>
> *Teacher:* Right or wrong? (*Teacher points to 4x.*)
> *Emma:* Right. (*Teacher places a tick over 4x.*)
> *Teacher:* Right or wrong? (*Teacher points to –2.*)
> *Emma:* Wrong.(*Teacher places an x over –2.*)
> *Teacher:* Right or wrong? (*Teacher points to +9.*)
> *Emma:* Wrong. (*Teacher places an x over +9.*)
> *Teacher:* (*Teacher points to –3x.*)
> *Emma:* Right. (*Teacher places a tick over –3x.*)
> *Teacher:* (*Teacher points to 12.*)
> *Emma:* Right. (*Teacher places a tick over 12*):
>
> $$✓ \quad ✗ \quad ✗ \quad ✓ \quad ✓$$
> $$4x - 2 + 9 - 3x = 12$$
>
> *Teacher:* Now what do we do with the ones that are right then?
> *Emma:* Emm, put them down. (Errigal CS Fr, second lesson)

> *Teacher:* Yes, she is absolutely right, and we won't go into all the nitty gritty as to why that is right because we DO KNOW now, don't we?
> *Class:* Yeah! (Barrow SSG F, first lesson)

The language employed by teachers indicated a strong adherence to certainty about mathematical procedures and solutions. There appeared to be little room for the discussion or exploration of alternatives to the prescribed methods. Moreover, being 'wrong' or making mistakes did not appear to be part of the learning process: students were encouraged to get the 'right' answer. Being 'wrong' was something that students feared. Such fear made them unwilling to experiment or even to participate publicly in working out answers to questions (see Chapter 10 below for a further discussion of this point)

'Hard' or 'Easy'

The language used by teachers to describe their subject suggested that they defined mathematics in polarised, hierarchical terms as 'difficult' or 'hard', 'easy' or 'simple'. Classifying a mathematics problem as 'hard' implied immediately that the student was likely to have difficulty resolving it, or that she or he might not be able to resolve it. This automatically created a barrier between the student and the subject. Equally, references to a problem being 'easy' was likely to be alienating for students having difficulties understanding or keeping up with others in the class. It was likely to reinforce a student's sense of incompetence if she or he were unable to do the 'easy' tasks.

Yet use of this type of language was common in the case-study lessons.

Teacher: Now shall I start now with a slightly harder question. Now let's see how we perform on the slightly harder ones ... OK, that's harder because there is a minus in it you see – so we must pay attention to the detail – this is the problem. (Barrow SSG F, first lesson)

Teacher: Our statistics today is going to be nice and easy ... So this is our bar chart – the first type we've come across and we have bars – now notice the bars are all equal widths but different heights – right easy enough! (Nore SSG Fr, first lesson)

Teacher: Now we have 9 per cent so we multiply that by £3.40 and multiply the answer by 4. It's very simple – simple mathematics – it's not difficult stuff. (Liffey SSB Fr D, first lesson)

Teacher: It says, a carpet 8 metres by 10. You see it on the board! Pay attention to the board while we're doing it to see where you're making your mistake. This one is quite difficult so you may not be able to do it. (Lee SSB F, first lesson)

Conclusion

The analysis of the video material on classrooms revealed three important findings in relation to the teaching of mathematics. First, it is evident that mathematics is taught within a clearly defined essentialist epistemological framework. It was a classic example of what Bernstein (1977) has identified as a subject with strong classification and strong framing. Mathematics was generally presented as a fixed body of knowledge, separate from other subjects. Little time or attention was devoted to the problem-solving nature of mathematics, to the application of mathematics in the world, or to alternative methods of solving mathematical problems, other than those prescribed by the text or the teacher. Learning for the examination was the central task.

The pedagogical style that prevailed in the teaching of mathematics both reflected and reinforced the epistemological principles underpinning the subject matter being presented. Classes were strongly teacher directed, with teachers generally using a didactic approach to the presentation of material. Teacher initiated interactions with students comprised 96 per cent of all public interactions in the twenty mathematics classes observed. Teachers were far more likely to use lower order than higher order questioning, and to use drill and repetition rather than discussion-type questions, to teach mathematical concepts. The work programme of the class therefore was strongly teacher determined, with a resultant lack of student participation in the organisation of their own learning.

Finally, the discourse of mathematics classrooms was remarkably uniform. There were regular references to 'the exam'. The subject matter was defined in binary codes as either 'difficult' or 'easy', 'hard' or 'simple'. Answers were classified also along polarised lines as either 'right' or 'wrong'. The subject of mathematics was one therefore in which there was a clear judgement of the student's work, a judgement that was often made in public. This implicitly, and at times explicitly, judgemental atmosphere created anxieties and tensions for students in relation to the subject of mathematics itself.

As noted in Chapter 4, however, the epistemological and pedagogical frames utilised in the teaching of mathematics is but a variation on a wider theme. While mathematics is arguably more essentialist in content, and is taught in a more didactical style than other subjects, a system of strong framing and classification characterises most subject teaching in Irish second level schools. School subjects, with some minor exceptions, have clearly defined boundaries and content; they are not presented in an integrated manner. In addition, the syllabus is presented largely as a set of certainties or skills 'to be grasped' by students for 'the exam'. While there are variations in epistemological assumptions and pedagogical practices, and in the discourses employed across subjects (as can be seen below in our analysis of English classes in Chapter 8), there are also several remarkable similarities between them (Lynch and Lodge, 2002).

Appendix to Chapter 5

Illustrative vignette – recitation questioning (from Blackstairs (VCC Fr D))

Time Code (minutes:seconds)	Activity	Content
10:58	Explanation/ demonstration: teacher-centred	*Teacher:* What is the formula for this? OK – so I'm going to rub off what I have over here and we'll try and explain and find out where this formula comes from. We'll start off over here. Don't write this down now. At a particular point, at a venue.
11:26	Explanation/ demonstration: questioning whole class	*Teacher:* Anyone here from Inis? No, hands up, two! OK we're driving from Inis to over here to C, which is? *Class:* Cluan *Teacher:* Cluan, right! And we'll start off here. Press the milometer button here at 00. Start there at nought. How far is it from Inis to Cluan? About? *Class:* 4 or 5:

I   **C**

●————————————————————●

(00 miles)   (05 miles)

Teacher: Is it 3 or 4 or 5, say 5 miles from here? OK – so it's 5 to there. So you're passing through Cluan and you see 5 miles on it now you go south towards a big town south down here – BL – what's BL?
Laughs from class
Class: Umm, Bunloch.

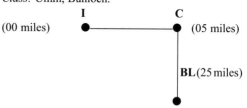

Teacher: Right now when you arrive in Bunloch you see on the milometer that it is 25, all right. On this route here just about half way, a very important place there its called?
Class: Students answer (inaudible)
Teacher: What's it called?

Class: Students laugh.
Teacher: Why is that important?
Class: Because you live there.
Teacher: Because I live there!

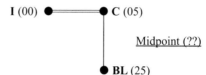

12:50	Explanation/ demonstration: questioning individuals. Teacher asks John.	*Teacher:* So as you pass this particular here point – special place there *(laughs from class, teacher pointing to midpoint between C and BL)* – you look at the milometer just there, what's on the clock? Shhh – think about it. Hands up, right, hands up? What's on the clock? Hands up? Come on, come on, more of you then that! Come on – what is on the clock? You have Inis (00), Cluan (05) and Bunloch you have (25). What's on it there, right in the centre of it – when you're stopping for a cup of tea? *(Laughter)* Right, hands up, come on, there are a few, come on, hands up. Yes, you have your hand up, so you think you know it?
13:54	John answers teacher's question.	*John:* 10 miles
13:56	Explanation/ demonstration: questioning whole class	*Teacher:* 10 miles. Hands up all who agree with him, thinks it's 10? One, two, three – three people for 10! *Teacher writes this on the board.* **10 (3)**
14:08	Explanation/ demonstration: questioning individuals Teacher asks Michael question.	*Teacher:* Any other answers? *Michael:* 17 and a half.
14:11	Explanation/ demonstration: questioning whole class	*Teacher:* 17 and a half. Anybody else think it's 17 and a half? *Class laughs.* *Teacher:* Nobody, nobody, not much support there.
14.19	Explanation/ demonstration: questioning individuals Teacher asks Gary question.	*Teacher:* Hands up again, yes Gary? *Gary:* 15 *Teacher:* 15 – Hands up all who say it's 15. A lot of support there Gary! Where did you get the 15 Gary? *Gary:* Because it's five over to there. *Teacher:* Over to Cluan – right!

		Gary: And 25 total *Teacher:* Right! *Gary:* So take away – take away the 5 from the 20 and you're left with 20 – *class laugh at mistake* – and half way – I mean take 5 from 25 and you're left with 20 – and half way between that is 10 and 5 is 15.
14:50	Explanation/ demonstration: questioning whole class	*Teacher:* Right, yeah it's a roundabout method *(laughter from students)*. Yeah – any other way cutting down to just half of this, half of say 25 if you add, what 25 and?
15:01	Explanation/ demonstration: questioning individuals Vicky volunteers answer to teacher's question and teacher then asks this same question of Vicky.	*Vicky volunteers answer:* 30 *Teacher:* Add what Vicky? *Vicky:* Add 25 and 5 *Teacher:* Add 25 and 5 and what do you get? *Class answers:* 30 *Teacher:* 30. And half it is 15, right, grand – 15 is correct! Right we got it! So you added, what will we call it, X_1 (00) for the minute and that's X_2 (25). So we added X_1 and X_2 and then halved it right.
15:25	Explanation/ demonstration: questioning whole class Teacher asks whole class question.	*Teacher:* Supposing you were driving a Japanese car *(laughter)* it's not in miles now sure its not. What's it in? *Class:* Kilometres *Teacher:* Kilometres so, well start it off at 00. How many kilometres in 5 miles? *Class:* 8 *Teacher:* How many? 8 is correct.
15:46	Explanation/ demonstration: Questioning Individuals	Teacher: We're going through Cluan – any Japanese cars out there – anyone selling Japanese cars in Inis? *(laughter)* 8 kilometres so that's the kilometres so there 8 to Bunloch, who can tell me, hands up, how many kilometres would be on the clock when you're passing Bunloch?
16:04	Sean answers teacher's question without being asked.	*Sean:* 40
16:05	Teacher responds.	*Teacher:* Shh I didn't ask you. *Students laugh*
16:07	Teacher asks Andrew a question.	*Teacher:* 5 – there's 25 here. Hands up – that's 25 – 5 times more than that *(teacher pointing to 8km)*. Come on! You should know it. Andrew – you're the first hand up?

16:17	Andrew answers question.	*Andrew:* 40
16:20		*Teacher:* 40, good man, 40. Now you're passing through this place here again, this place in the centre. Who can tell me this time, I want to see more hands up this time, how many kilometres is it when you look at your clock there. Come on 8, 12,13 hands yes, this time what is it?
16:45	Maria volunteers answer.	*Maria:* 24
16:47		*Teacher:* 24 yes. How did you get it?
16.48		*Maria:* Add 40 and 8 and then half it:

I (00)●————————● C (05)
[00 km]   [8 km]

● Midpoint (15)
   [24 km]

●

BL (25) [40 km]

| 16:50 | Explanation/ demonstration: teacher centred. | *Teacher:* That's right – so it's 24 – OK. So you added – that was X_1 and X_2 right – so who gave me that one at the beginning that told me to add 25 and 5 is 30 and the half of that is 15? So you added your X_1 and X_2 and divided by two here. What would you call that one – Y_1 (08) and that's Y_2 (40) – you add up the 2 of them and divide it by 2 and that is you're mid point-formula. Add your two Xs and divide by two. Add your two ys and divide by two so <u>MP</u> right underneath – where you have the midpoint here. You don't need this but if you wanted it to help you, take it down at the side. Your midpoint (MP) is equal to, what did we say again? X_1 plus X_2 and we divided by two, comma, and we had Y_1 plus Y_2 and we divided that by two. And if we go back to our two points that I asked you in the beginning – for example, a is minus one minus two $(-1,-2)$, b what did we say, plus three plus two $(3, 2)$: $(-1, -1)$ $(3, 2)$ |

Over head of those, we just write down $X_1 Y_1 X_2 Y_2$
and write down the mid-point is equal to formula X_1
plus X_2 over 2, Y_1 plus Y_2 over 2:
$(X_1 Y_1) (X_2 Y_2)$
$(-1, -1) (3, 2)$
$$MP = \left(\frac{x_1 + x_2}{2} \right), \left(\frac{y_1 + y_2}{2} \right)$$

Notes

[1] The clock refers to the milometer on a car and is used as an illustrative example by the teacher. See Appendix 5 for a more detailed explanation.

[2] An example of real life application questions from our study involves a situation where the teacher asks the students for information, their shoe size for example, in order to demonstrate mean and mode. Checking understanding includes the teacher checking student progress during student practice, as well as asking the class if they understand the method or procedure.

[3] Freire (1972) claimed that mainstream education was suffering from narration sickness. Students went to school to receive bundles of knowledge from the teachers that they then banked in their memories and reproduced, generally uncritically, on examination days. The 'dividend' the students received on the time and effort they invested in banking the knowledge was the educational certificate or credential awarded.

[4] Bernstein (1977) suggests that strong classification exists when the content of each subject is strongly insulated from that of others and when there is a low level of subject integration. Classification therefore refers to the *boundaries* between subjects rather than the content of the subject matter itself. Framing refers 'to the form of the context in which knowledge is transmitted and received. Frame refers to the specific pedagogical relationship of teacher and taught' (ibid, p. 88). It refers to the degree of control the teacher and student possess over the selection, organisation, pacing and timing of the knowledge transmitted. Strong framing exists when neither the student nor the teacher have much control over what is taught and how it is taught.

6

Gender Differences
in Classrooms

Introduction

In Chapter 5 we analysed the learning and teaching climate of the twenty mathematics lessons, in terms of the epistemological approach and pedagogical practices. The dominant approach to teaching mathematics was found to be *traditional*. Most lessons were highly structured, teacher-led, featuring low levels of student-teacher-initiated interaction. Of the public interaction that occurred in the lessons, almost all was work-related.

While the general findings revealed a high degree of uniformity in approach and pedagogy, an analysis of the *relations* between the principal actors, namely teachers and students, revealed important differences. Chapters 6 and 7 are devoted to an analysis of these differences. Chapter 6 examines gender differences in terms of the teacher-student relations; this includes teacher-student initiated, as well as student-teacher-initiated interaction.[1] Differences related to classroom grouping practices and social class will be discussed in Chapter 7.

This chapter begins with an analysis of gender differences in interaction patterns within co-educational classes. It then examines the factors associated with different patterns of gender interaction and attempts to explain why these emerge. Following this, differences in interaction patterns within single sex girls' and boys' schools are analysed. The final section presents the conclusions

Coeducational classes

Teacher-student initiated interaction

As the main form of public interaction in classrooms was teacher – rather than student-initiated, the gender dynamics of these interactions will now be examined. The focus of the analysis will be on the following:

1. the extent to which teachers interacted with girls and boys overall, and in terms of questions asked in particular;

2. gender differences in the context and nature of teacher-student questions;

3. distribution of teacher-student questions by gender;

4. gender differences in the nature of student responses to teacher-student mathematics questions;

5. gender differences in the nature of teacher feedback to correct and incorrect student responses.

Tables 6.1 and 6.2 provide details of the mean level of public interactions involving girls and boys in each of the ten coeducational lessons as well as the overall average for each gender.[2] The data in Table 6.1 shows that although overall differences were not statistically significant, boys received more interactions than girls in eight of the ten coeducational lessons. In half (four) of these however, there was a statistically significant difference in the mean amount of interaction between the two genders: boys got significantly more teacher attention in both lessons in Blackstairs (VCC Fr D) and Nephin (VCC Fr). In the two lessons where girls received more interactions than boys, the difference was statistically significant in one case (Lesson 2, Lagan SC Fr) while it was minor in the other (Lesson 2, Errigal CS Fr).

As shown in Chapter 5, teacher-student interaction was made up of almost entirely questions (accounting for 96 per cent of all interactions) with the remainder of the engagements involving instructions, organisational or social exchanges. Of the total number of questions, almost all (96 per cent) were work-related; the remaining questions were evenly divided between behaviour (correction and care) and organisational issues.

An analysis of gender differences in the teacher-initiated questions was conducted to test whether teachers were directing more of their questions towards boys compared with girls. Not surprisingly, the findings (Table 6.2 and Tables A6.1) were almost identical to those reported for all teacher-initiated interactions, confirming that boys received significantly more teacher-initiated questions than girls. In the main, therefore, we can conclude that boys were more involved in the main business of the lessons than girls in the coeducational classes observed.

Nature of teacher-student questions
Having established that boys receive more questions than girls, the next issue concerns the nature of the questions asked and whether this varied by gender. The vast majority (81 per cent) of the teacher-initiated questions

Table 6.1: *Gender differences in teacher-student interactions in coeducational classes*

School name, code and lesson no.		Teacher-female student interactions (n)	Teacher-female student interactions per females in class	Teacher-male student interactions (n)	Teacher-male student interactions per males in class	Male/female interaction ratio	Chi-square
Lagan (SC Fr)	1	21	1.50	27	1.68	1.12:1	0.16
	2	98	6.12	53	3.53	0.58:1	10.67*
Errigal (CS Fr)	1	74	3.89	55	5.00	1.29:1	1.97
	2	145	7.63	81	7.36	0.96:1	0.06
Mourne (VCC Fr D)	1	22	2.44	28	2.80	1.15:1	0.22
	2	23	3.83	31	3.87	1.01:1	0.00
Blackstairs (VCC Fr D)	1	11	0.64	25	1.66	2.59:1	7.36*
	2	12	0.70	29	1.93	2.76:1	9.37*
Nephin (VCC Fr)	1	17	5.66	91	13.0	2.30:1	10.45*
	2	2	0.66	40	5.71	8.65:1	12.73*
Total		425	3.48	460	3.93	1.12:1	3.23

*: Significant at $p<0.05$ level

Key: SSG F: Secondary girls', fee-paying; SSG Fr: Secondary girls', free scheme; SSG Fr D: Secondary girls', free scheme designated disadvantaged; SSB Fr D: Secondary boys', free scheme designated disadvantaged; SSB F: Secondary boys', fee paying; SC Fr: Secondary coed, free scheme; CS Fr: Community school, free scheme; VCC Fr D: Vocational/Community college, free scheme designated disadvantaged; VCC Fr: Vocational/Community college, free scheme (where free scheme represents non fee-paying status).

comprised lower order cognitive questions. Following this, the next largest categories were questions to ascertain student understanding of the mathematics being taught (7 per cent) and higher order questions (6 per cent).

Table 6.2: Gender differences in teacher-student questions in coeducational lessons

School name, code and lesson no.		Male/female interaction ratio	Chi-square
Lagan (SC Fr)	1	1.12:1	0.16
	2	0.56:1	10.95*
Errigal (CS Fr)	1	1.21:1	1.14
	2	0.96:1	0.06
Mourne (VCC Fr D)	1	1.16:1	0.25
	2	1.01:1	0.00
Blackstairs (VCC Fr D)	1	5.22:1	10.78*
	2	3.01:1	10.54*
Nephin (VCC Fr)	1	2.50:1	11.68*
	2	16.87:1	14.40*
Total		1.12:1	3.03

*: Significant at p<0.05 level
Key: SC Fr: Secondary coed, free scheme; CS Fr: Community school, free scheme; VCC Fr D: Vocational/Community college, free scheme designated disadvantaged; VCC Fr: Vocational/Community college, free scheme (where free scheme represents non fee-paying status).

Within the coeducational lessons, a significant difference was found only in relation to higher cognitive order questions (Figure 6.1, Tables A6.2). Boys received more of these questions compared with girls. On average, the boys received 0.3 higher-order questions per lesson (fifty-one interactions observed), and girls 0.1 interactions per lesson (sixteen interactions observed). The value of chi-squared was 8.42, well exceeding the critical value.

The patterns in single sex classes follow that in coeducational classes, although there were fewer lower order *and* fewer higher order questions overall in the single sex sector; there were however, more organisational, process checking and behaviour-related questions (Tables A6.2). While both girls are boys were generally asked lower order questions, almost 10 per cent of the questions asked of boys in single sex classes were of a higher order nature while only 1.6 per cent of those asked of girls were higher order. More process-checking and organisational questions were asked of girls than was the case for boys (Tables A6.3).

Figure 6.1: Gender differences in higher and lower order questioning in coeducational classes

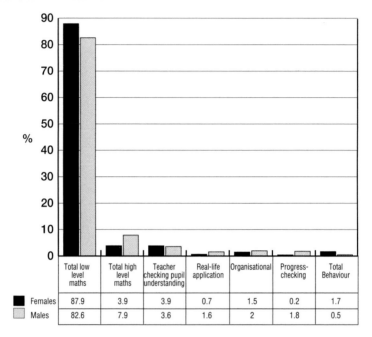

	Total low level maths	Total high level maths	Teacher checking pupil understanding	Real-life application	Organisational	Progress-checking	Total Behaviour
Females	87.9	3.9	3.9	0.7	1.5	0.2	1.7
Males	82.6	7.9	3.6	1.6	2	1.8	0.5

When coeducational classes are compared with single sex classes, it is clear that there are few higher order questions in both (6 per cent and 4.8 per cent respectively). However, there were slightly more higher order questions asked of girls in coeducational classes than in single sex classes, while the opposite was true for boys: 3.9 per cent of girls and 7.9 per cent of boys were asked higher order questions in coeducational classes; the comparable figures in the single sex classes were 1.6 per cent of girls and 9.7 per cent of boys.

Distribution of interaction
Having established that the teachers interacted to a greater degree with boys than girls in the coeducational lessons, in this section we will turn our attention to the distribution of teacher questions between gender groups.

Within the coeducational sector, an overall average of 29 per cent of students were not asked any questions while 43 per cent were asked in excess of three questions. More girls were 'not asked any questions' than boys, albeit to a marginal degree (31 per cent and 27 per cent respectively). In addition, boys (27 per cent) were more likely than girls (21 per cent) to be asked five or more questions (Table 6.3).

Table 6.3: Gender differences in the distribution of teacher-student questions in both coeducational and single sex schools

School and Lesson	Distribution of questions by gender											
	% Girls				% Boys				% All Students			
	Not asked	Asked at least one question …			*Not asked*	Asked at least one question …			*Not asked*	Asked at least one question …		
		1-2 Qs	3-4 Qs	5+ Qs		1-2 Qs	3-4 Qs	5+ Qs		1-2 Qs	3-4 Qs	5+ Qs
Single sex girls (6 classes) Average	9	41	31	19	–	–	–	–				
Single sex boys (4 classes) Average	–	–	–	–	57	15	6	22				
Coeducational (10 classes) Average	31	28	20	21	27	29	17	27	29	28	19	24

While aggregate figures for the coeducational classes suggest that teacher questioning is male-biased, but not greatly so, the average rate conceals very large disparities between individual classes. In both classes in Blackstairs (VCC Fr D) most of the girls (71 per cent and 83 per cent) were not asked any questions while 64 per cent of girls in Lesson 1 in Lagan (SC Fr) and 67 per cent in Lesson 2 in Nephin (VCC Fr) were not asked any questions. The only class where the majority of the boys were not asked a question was Lesson 1 in Lagan where 62 per cent were not asked a question (Tables A6.4).

Some of the most striking differences between students were within rather than between genders, however most especially *between boys* in single sex classes. In the two boys' schools, most boys (57 per cent) were not asked any questions in the four mathematics classes we observed. In single sex girls' classes only 9 per cent were not asked a question. When one examines the proportions being asked in excess of three questions, the difference between single sex girls' and boys' classes remain substantial: 50 per cent of girls were asked three or more questions compared with 28 per cent of boys (Table 6.4).

The overall pattern therefore was of relatively high levels of participation by girls in single sex classes, with 91 per cent being asked at least one question compared with 43 per cent of boys in single sex boys' classes. Within coeducational classes, most girls (69 per cent) and boys (73 per cent) were asked at least one question but the balance favoured boys at all levels of questioning: 27 per cent of boys were asked five or more questions compared with 21 per cent of girls. The comparable figures for single sex schools were 22 per cent of boys and 19 per cent of girls.

Student responses to teachers' mathematics questions

More than two thirds of the student responses to teacher-initiated mathematics questions were 'correct'. 'Incorrect' responses accounted for a small proportion of student answers (11 per cent). A similar proportion of responses (13 per cent), categorised as progress reports, concerned questions to which students gave a partially correct or incorrect answer to a particular mathematics problem. Other categories included 'no response' or 'no chance to respond' before another student intervened; in all, these categories accounted for 8 per cent of responses.

In the coeducational lessons, gender differences emerged, and to a statistically significant degree, in relation to two of the main categories, namely 'incorrect' and 'progress report' responses (Table 6.4). Boys were found to respond 'incorrectly' and to give a 'report of progress' to the teacher more frequently than were girls.

Table 6.4: Gender differences in student responses to teachers' mathematics questions (base: coeducational classes)

	Gender differences in student responses		
	Number of interactions		
	Females (n=123)	Males (n=115)	Total (n=238)
	%	%	%
Correct	73	62	68
Incorrect	8	14	11*
No Answer/hesitation/ mutter	4	6	5
Progress report	11	15	13*
No chance to answer before teacher/other student intervenes	3	2	2
Other	1	1	1
TOTAL (n)	394	430	824
%	100	100	100

*P<0.05

It is interesting also to compare the overall breakdown of responses by gender in the girls' and boys' schools. The patterns were quite similar to coeducational classes, with girls being more likely to give 'correct' responses than boys and being less likely to give 'progress reports'. There were differences, however, in relation to levels of interruption inhibiting a response: these were much greater in boys' classes than in single sex girls' (or coeducational) classes. Boys in single sex classes were slightly less likely however, to give an 'incorrect response' than were girls in single sex classes (Tables A6.5).

Teacher feedback to student responses

Looking specifically at teacher feedback to 'correct' responses from students in the coeducational sector, the only gender differences that emerged related to praise. Here, girls were shown to receive a disproportionate share of praise compared with their male peers, although the number of 'praise' incidences overall is very small (Tables A6.6). This pattern obtains also in relation to single sex schools (Tables A6.7).

Teacher feedback to 'incorrect' student responses is presented in Tables A6.8. In both the coeducational lessons and single sex lessons, the most usual teacher feedback involved prompting the student in some way, by asking a further question, repeating the same question or prompting towards the correct answer. This type of feedback was given to 58 per cent and 85 per cent of incorrect answers in the coeducational and single sex sectors respectively. Girls were more likely to receive this type of feedback compared with boys, and to a greater degree in the coeducational schools. These findings must be interpreted with caution however, as the numbers involved are quite small.

Looking at teacher feedback overall, we can conclude that although the incidence of students being praised for achievements is small, neither are they criticised when they make mistakes. Notwithstanding this however, students are reluctant to risk giving an 'incorrect answer' and most only respond when they are sure they have the correct answer.

Student-initiated interaction

As already indicated in Figure 5.1 in Chapter 5, the incidence of student-initiated interaction in the observed classes was very low. Of the total 2,980 interactions, just 106 (4 per cent) were in this category. Work-related questions comprised the great majority (75 per cent) of these interactions, while a mixture of other comments and social interaction accounted for the remaining 25 per cent.

Table 6.5: Gender differences in student-teacher interactions: coeducational classes

		% of students who initiated interaction with teacher		
School name and lesson		% Girls	% Boys	% All students in class
Lagan (SC Fr)	1	7	13	10
	2	6	7	6
Errigal (CS Fr)	1	5	0	3
	2	0	0	0
Mourne (VCC Fr D)	1	22	30	26
	2	0	13	7
Blackstairs (VCC Fr D)	1	12	0	6
	2	0	0	0
Nephin (VCC Fr)	1	33	57	40
	2	33	86	70

Table 6.5 presents the proportion of the students in each of the coeducational lessons who initiated public interaction with the teacher. Student-initiated interactions occurred in eight of the ten classes.

In the majority of these lessons (six of the eight) most of these interactions were initiated by the boys rather than the girls. The aggregate figures for boys in coeducational classes conceal important differences between classes, however. Most student-initiated interaction occurred in one small bottom-stream, coeducational class Nephin (VCC Fr) and almost half (47 per cent) of student-initiated interaction occurred in the two lessons in this class. Here, the boys dominated this interaction and to a significant degree (see Table 6.2 above). Yet in Errigal (CS Fr) and Blackstairs (VCC Fr D) no boys initiated interaction with the teacher and few girls. In Lagan (SC Fr) while the boys initiated more interactions with the teacher than girls, the level of such interaction was low in both cases.

Factors associated with gendered interaction

In keeping with Irish and international research findings, our study reports important differences between female and male students in both the quantity and quality of their interactions with teachers in coeducational classrooms. We now consider whether these patterns vary by the gender balance of the class, gender of the teacher and size of the class grouping.

Gender composition of the class, gender of the teacher and class size

The gender composition of Irish second-level schools is distinctive in two ways: single sex schools comprise a relatively high proportion of all schools and girls attend these schools in substantially greater numbers than boys. Consequent upon this, the coeducational sector has a greater proportion of boys than girls (Department of Education and Science, 2000b).

Due to the gender imbalance in the coeducational sector as a whole, it was considered important to examine whether the gender composition of the classes had any influence on the pattern of interaction. To obtain a measure of the gender composition of the classes, we first calculated the male:female ratio for each class. As a summary measure, we next grouped classes into one of five categories. The aim was to group classes into particular ranges of the male:female ratio so that the composition of individual classes could be understood along a continuum. Following Drudy and Uí Chathain (1999), we used a five-fold classification to represent the gender composition of the classes ranging from those in which boys were very much in the majority to ones in which girls were very much in the majority (Tables A6.9).

Table 6.6 presents the distribution of the gender composition of the ten coeducational classes according to this classification. There was an even gender balance in five of the ten coeducational classes. In three further classes, boys were in the majority, while in the remaining two, girls were in the majority.

Table 6.6: Gender composition of the ten coeducational classes

School and Lesson		Girls (n)	Boys (n)	Male/female composition of class ratio	Summary of gender composition
Lagan (SC Fr)	1	14	16	1.14:1	Evenly balanced
	2	16	15	0.93:1	Evenly balanced
Errigal (CS Fr)	1	19	11	0.57:1	Girls in the majority
	2	19	11	0.57:1	Girls in the majority
Mourne	1	9	10	1.11:1	Evenly balanced
(VCC Fr D)	2	6	8	1.33:1	Boys in the majority
Blackstairs	1	17	16	0.94:1	Evenly balanced
(VCC Fr D)	2	16	16	0.94:1	Evenly balanced
Nephin (VCC FR)	1	3	7	2.3:1	Boys in the majority
	2	3	7	2.3:1	Boys in the majority

Although five of the ten coeducational classes had an even gender balance, boys strongly dominated two of these (both classes in Blackstairs) while girls dominated one. The other two classes had balanced gender interaction patterns although teachers were slightly more inclined to interact with boys in both. Boys also dominated the interaction in the three classes where they were in the majority (second lesson in Mourne and both lessons in Nephin). In the two classes where girls were in the majority, boys slightly dominated the interaction in one while girls slightly dominated the other (Table 6.7).

Although Drudy and Uí Chatháin (1999) found that the greater the gender balance of the class, the more even the balance of interactions, our data only provides limited support for this thesis. While gender-balanced classes had somewhat more gender-balanced patterns of interaction, this did not apply in all cases.

Given the small number of teachers involved in the study, it is difficult to generalise about the impact of teacher gender on classroom interaction. There were three female and two male teachers in the coeducational classes. Of the six classes taught by female teachers, four were gender balanced in terms of classroom interaction while girls dominated in one and boys in the other.[3] Boys dominated in all four classes taught by the two male teachers. Size of class did not seem to be an important variable in influencing the gender patterns of interaction. While there is some tentative evidence that female teachers may be more gender balanced in

Table 6.7: Relationship between gender composition, teacher gender, class size and interaction patterns in coeducational classes

School and lesson	Lesson	Summary: Gender composition of class	Male/female teacher-student interaction ratio	Summary: Interaction category	Gender of the teacher	Class size*
Lagan (SC Fr)	1	Evenly balanced	1.12:1	Balanced	Female	Large
	2	Evenly balanced	0.56:1	Girls dominant		Large
Errigal (CS Fr)	1	Girls in the majority	1.21:1	Boys dominant	Female	Large
	2	Girls in the majority	0.96:1	Balanced		Large
Mourne (VCC Fr D)	1	Evenly balanced	1.16:1	Balanced	Female	Small/medium
	2	Boys in the majority	1.01:1	Balanced		Small/medium
Blackstairs (VCC Fr D)	1	Evenly balanced	5.22:1	Boys dominant	Male	Large
	2	Evenly balanced	3.01:1	Boys dominant		Large
Nephin (VCC FR)	1	Boys in the majority	2.50:1	Boys dominant	Male	Small
	2	Boys in the majority	16.87:1	Boys very dominant		Small

* Size of class categories: small (12 or less); small/medium (13-19); medium/large (20-25); large (26+)

their approach, this seems to have more to do with the teacher attitude than gender *per se*.

Gender balanced classes and teacher attitudes

Both lessons in Mourne (VCC Fr D) and one of the two lessons in Lagan (SC Fr) and in Errigal (CS Fr) were gender-balanced in their inter-action patterns, with the balance in favour of boys in the other lesson in Errigal being relatively small. Two of the three teachers involved demonstrated quite a strong gender-awareness in their discussion of teaching practice.

The first excerpt illustrates how balanced interaction can occur when class composition is either evenly balanced or has boys in the majority. This concerns Ms Malone who was teaching what was defined in the school as a 'bottom stream' in Mourne (VCC Fr D), a designated disadvantaged coeducational school. Although this class was a challenging one to teach (and the boys were in the majority in the second of the two lessons observed), Ms Malone maintained a gender balance overall in her work with the students. This is not accidental as she had a gender proofing policy of alternating between girls and boys when asking questions:

> I deliberately try to do both evenly. I have an absolute policy that it's a boy, a girl, a boy, a girl, because otherwise it would slip into … If you're not conscious of what you're doing, you will automatically or you will be more likely to ask a boy more often to shut them up! But I deliberately ask a boy, a girl, all the time.

It is noteworthy that the teacher managed to achieve this balance in a classroom context where at least three of the boys, and especially one of these three, were unattentive and disruptive. This points to the importance of gender awareness in achieving a gender balanced pedagogy:

> *Ms Malone:* Demands for attention? The boys! Definitely! Yeah! They don't get it though! I hope! (*then with a laugh*) But they try!
> *Interviewer:* Why do you think that is the case?
> *Ms Malone:* I suppose the kind of extroverted personalities are all boys in that class and Wayne tries to get as much attention as he can. And Stephen tries to get as much attention as he can. Now let me think what happens with the girls? Melanie tries a bit. But she really actually tries to get help as much as anything. Agnes tries to get it by becoming invisible – I'd say she could be quite lively but she thinks she can become invisible because I'm going to comment again that she wasn't there the day before. But in general – I'd definitely say the boys look for more attention than the girls. But then not all of them do. A lot of boys are quiet.

The second excerpt illustrates how balanced interaction can occur in a class where the numbers of girls and boys are equal. While Ms Leydon in Lagan (SC Fr) was also gender balanced in her approach, she did not operate a conscious gender policy in her class. However, she was gender aware and this was evident in both her analysis of the lack of a gender policy in her school (a school that was originally single sex girls' but is now coeducational) and in her observations about boys demanding more 'correction' time:

> *Ms Leydon:* When the school changed we didn't focus on that at all. We took in boys from first year. It was gradual. We've had many people in over the years on various issues to talk to us but not anybody to specifically talk about gender... The girls generally would be quieter and they are more diligent. The lads – there would be a few who are certainly chatty – not particularly <u>bad</u> but certainly a bit chatty. They swing in the chair and they like to look relaxed whereas the girls would even appear more diligent in the way they sit and look.

In response to a question about the class we observed she said:

> *Ms Leydon:* In that class I would say there's very little difference in who takes up most of my time because a few of the girls are probably better for asking questions and I don't consider that taking up my time. I think it's very valuable. But certainly in a different group the lads would take up more of my time in terms of correction.
> *Interviewer:* You mean in terms of discipline?
> *Ms Leydon:* Oh yes – and they can! It's not relevant in relation to this group but in another group the lads will take up more time even saying answers and looking for why you are doing it in a certain way. The girls are more – they just want the answer to a particular question. They're not out to cause a difficulty.

Finally, the third school where we observed gender balanced interaction was one in which girls formed the majority of the class. This involved a middle stream class in Errigal, a community school taught by a female teacher. Ms Ennis maintained that there was no difference between the girls and the boys in demands for attention. Extending her comments beyond the particular class to her general experience of gender differences she explained:

> *Ms Ennis:* I find that the boys would not take up any extra time. The girls would be more inclined to perhaps come in at the beginning in a fluster. They might say 'Oh Miss, I couldn't do that [homework] last night'. When you start to correct you find that what they couldn't do was get the answer in the back of the book and they will get into a bit of a tizzy over nothing. The boys are cooler about it. I find that would be the typical situation. The boys maybe like you to be nice to them but they don't take over.

When asked if there were any students in the class who do not ask for help, Ms Ennis primarily identified girls.

Ms Ennis: I'd say Mary would not always ask. I'd say Monica wouldn't always ask when she would need help. I am running up and down through the class to think. Angela – I wouldn't think she would ask either. I had her last year in the weaker group and she was more inclined to ask there. She has been moved up on the basis of other subjects and I find this year she doesn't ask.
Interviewer: Do you think she feels intimidated in this group?
Ms Ennis: Yes, definitely. I'm trying to think now. I think there is another girl Vanessa and I think maybe she could need help and she doesn't ask. She is a terribly, terribly quiet girl. But never asks – you know, there's another – Siobhan, very, very quiet. She gets her work right so maybe she doesn't have a question, but she wouldn't be all that vocal. Let's see – again Paula wouldn't ask. It's not that she's not able, she doesn't ask and you'd wonder why. Then Peter, I think he's terribly – I wouldn't say his verbal skills would be great.

Despite Ms Ennis' awareness that the girls were reluctant to ask for help, the following excerpt demonstrates that she feels it is necessary to engage with some of the boys.

Ms Ennis: Seamus is a bit scattered and the lad down in the bottom corner, Noel I don't know whether it came across or not but I would generally keep an eye on him as well. Not that he would fall asleep but he is the sort of guy that you don't know what he is at. Does okay in tests – like he's a bright enough chap ….
Interviewer: Are you saying that he does not concentrate?
Ms Ennis: Yeah. Sometimes I would be conscious of him not concentrating. I'd watch him all the time and he would be aware that I watch him. He's a quiet chap but often I would ask him a question and he would not know what I had said to him. That's why I watch him and why I said to him: 'Are you with us Noel?' He will tend to do that. But I would never give out to him and I don't move children.
Interviewer: You mean you don't tell them where to sit?
Ms. Ennis: No, I don't tell them where to sit. If they sit wherever and they are comfortable with that I leave them. That Seamus yesterday, he would be a sensitive enough type of child. He is very quiet and so if he is willing to say something I'm very happy to grasp it with him. There is another boy, Sean, terribly, terribly quiet. And he might not always ask. But with the others I think they are happy enough to ask – I would like to think they are anyway.

In Errigal, the girls are shown to conform to the norm of 'quiet girls', with the exception of one student.

Ms Ennis: There is one girl who always demands attention – she didn't do it yesterday or the day before – but she would be a kid and if there was a pause at all she feels she should ask something: Ciara. Now whether her parents at home have said: 'Ask the teacher' and that's fine but I sometimes feel that she asks for the sake

of asking. But I would never put her down for it. But sometimes I would
humorously answer her and she would laugh it off. I would never put her down and
I would never say: 'You are asking too many questions'. I wouldn't do that to her.
Sometimes I would say: 'Hang on, I will come down to you' and I will speak to her
on her own. I often find that that might be the end of it for that class but she does
like the attention, because I always see that when she asks she looks around. She's
a nice kid but she does like a bit more attention.

On the other hand, 'quiet boys' are shown to be more of a concern for
the teacher, thereby requiring extra attention.

What our data tentatively suggests is that, while having a gender-
balanced or female-dominated class may facilitate gender-balanced
interactions in class, it does not guarantee it. The level of teacher
awareness about the importance of gender balance also appears to have
some impact. The only school in which both lessons were balanced in
terms of teacher attention was the one in which the teacher had a clear
gender proofing policy.

Male dominated classes and teacher attitudes

The learning atmosphere in half of the coeducational classes was
characterised by a male dominated pattern of interaction. This involved
three schools, Blackstairs (VCC Fr D), Nephin (VCC Fr) (both lessons),
and one lesson in Errigal (CS Fr) but to a much lesser degree. In terms of
gender composition in the individual classes, Blackstairs was balanced,
Nephin had more boys than girls, while Errigal had more girls than boys.
Both Blackstairs and Nephin had male teachers, while the teacher in
Errigal was female.

Of these three schools, the classes in Nephin (VCC Fr) were the most
male dominated in composition (2.3: 1.0) and in patterns of interaction and
so will be drawn on for illustrative purposes here. In this particular school,
the 'male dominated interaction' pattern applied to both teacher- and
student-initiated interaction. This class accounted for most of the student-
initiated interaction recorded in this study.

The teacher in this school expressed a preference to teach in a
coeducational rather than a single sex setting. His previous teaching
experience was in an all girls' school with a strong academic ethos but he
preferred the coeducational school:

Mr Nally: What I prefer here is the gender mix. I tell these kids where I used to teach
and they think I am talking about planet Mars. You know – all girls in one place –
especially the girls cannot stand the thought of it, not having fellas around. The
fellas would be quite okay with all fellas – they do kind of stick to themselves –

even boyfriends and girlfriends wouldn't sit in the same row. I think it [coed school] is much more normal and natural. If you could get the mix in some of the teaching staff you'd be alright. After going to all that trouble to have a coed school and we have an all female staff – not all female but almost.

When we asked the teacher if he spent more time interacting with the boys than the girls, he reported that the boys got the greater share of his attention.

> *Mr Nally:* If you take Tanya out of the equation, the boys [get more attention]. And mostly correcting – with Liam getting things right all the time and John getting things right or trying to get things right.
> *Interviewer:* So you mean they would ask you to correct what they are doing?
> *Mr Nally:* Yeah – there would just be much more interaction with the boys.
> *Interviewer:* Does the same pattern apply in terms of boys and girls asking for help?
> *Mr Nally:* Yeah. John would have no qualms about calling me down to help – 'My da said this is the way to do it and I don't understand it'. John starts all his sentences that way. Or 'My da did this for me last night and I pretended to understand it but I don't – Will you explain it to me please?'

The examples used by this teacher to situate mathematical procedures involved sport and exclusively involved the boys in the class. This is illustrated in the following excerpt; the topic was income tax and the teacher wrote the relevant rules on the board at the beginning of the lesson:

Income – tax free allowance = taxable income

Tax = taxable income x tax rate

Net income = gross income – tax

The teacher uses the names of the Manchester United players for illustrative purposes and to involve the students in the lesson:

Minutes:seconds

4:38	Revision: teacher-centred	*Teacher:* OK, so lets do a few [examples]. We've done Mr. Irwin, so lets do Mr. Keane. *(Knock on the door, Louise walks back into classroom).* *Teacher:* OK Louise, just continue from where you are there. Now, we'll do Mr.Keane, Mr. Johnson, Mr. Butt, Mr. Scholes, Mr. Yorke *(class laughs)*

5:11	Teacher asks class for suggestions	*Teacher:* Anyone suggest the next name for me?
	Different boys respond to teacher's request	*Steven:* Schmeichel *John:* Cole *Steven:* Peter Schmeichel *Teacher:* I can't spell Schmeichel. *Class:* Cole, Cole *Teacher:* Cole would be much easier yeah. *John:* Can't spell Schmeichel!! (laughs)
5:22	Revision: Questioning individuals Teacher asks Liam question	*Teacher:* Now OK. Take these down please. I'm going to get you to do the Gross Income first. Well, what should you take for the incomes? OK, we'll put Keane. How much does Keane get? Liam?
5:29	Liam answers question and teacher responds	*Liam:* Uh… *Teacher:* Annual? *Class:* (shout) 50 … 25,000 *Teacher:* Annual, and just… *Liam:* £50,000 *Teacher:* 50, thanks Liam, that's what he gets a month, but anyway (*laughing*)… Yeah, Mr. Johnson? *Liam:* Am, 96,000 *Teacher:* You're paying him more than Keane? *Liam:* yeah.
5:44	John mocks teacher on football knowledge	*John:* Who's he sir? (class laughs). *Teacher:* Ah, here … Obviously you're not Manchester United fans. *John:* I am yeah. It's <u>Johnsen</u> (*emphasising the correct pronounciation*) *Teacher:* Oh excuse me! Ronnie Johnsen, yes. I beg your pardon! I stand corrected! (*Class laugh at teacher's comment.*)
5:55		*Teacher:* Right, OK put Mr. Butt on £100,000. *Shane:* Ah, he's left footed (laughs). *Teacher:* Put Mr. Scholes back on £90,000.
6:03	Teacher asks Shane question	*Teacher:* Put Mr. Yorke on …?
6:05	Shane responds	*Shane:* 110.
6:08	Teacher continues	*Teacher:* Yeah, we'll pay him £100,000. He's, he's doing well these days and we'll put Mr. Cole on £150,000. Right, take that list down quick. Now, we're going to give the same tax allowance to them all.

The teacher reported that girls respond better in mathematics class 'when you give them a bit of personal attention'; this contrasts with the situation for boys, whom 'you can dictate to and they'll take it'. He justified his differential treatment of girls and boys on the grounds that a substantial number of the girls in the school do not want to be asked a question in class:

> **Mr Nally:** The girls are much more reticent about being asked a question. They hate it. In fact some will say: 'Don't ask me – I asked you not to ask me'. They just won't. They'll refuse. They won't co-operate. In fact you never ask them. You won't embarrass them a second time. Whereas the boys – even if they're totally wrong and they have no idea of what the right answer is, they'll give you an answer because they love talking. They are much more to the fore.

The qualitative data suggest that three factors contributed to a male-dominated atmosphere in this class. First, boys were disproportionately represented in the class relative to girls. Second, a disproportionate amount of attention was expected and given to the boys by the teacher. Third, there was a greater propensity by the boys themselves to initiate interaction with the teacher than was the case for the girls in the class. Given that the examples given in this class were more male-specific, and that the teacher did not regard the lack of a gender balance in interaction as a problem, it is not surprising perhaps that girls were quite invisible in the main business of the class.

Single sex classes

We now turn our attention to an examination of gender differences in the single sex sector. Lynch's (1989) national study of the hidden curriculum of second level schools found that boys' and girls' schools socialised their students in different ways. Strict control of dress and behaviour was a more likely feature of girls' than of boys' schools. In addition, the development of self-discipline and/or self-control were cited as school aims in the girls' schools only. Overall, and by contrast with boys' schools, it was found that girls were socialised into attitudes of academic achievement combined with docility, compliance and caring for others. A more recent study suggests that while there are changes in ethos over time, girls' schools still display strong evidence of surveillance and a persistent focus on academic achievement (Hannan et al., 1996; Lynch and Lodge, 2002). Boys' schools retain their focus on sport with strong peer regulation of social behaviour (Lynch and Lodge, 2002). While it is difficult to ascertain learning outcomes from the codes in the hidden curriculum, it is a reasonable assumption that these differences in social climate play an important role in how teachers and students interact in the classroom. Certainly, in this study there were observable differences in the social climate of boys' and girls' classes.

Learning environment in single sex classrooms

The visible and active involvement of a minority of boys was a key feature of boys' classes. What was most striking here was how the active involvement of a minority of boys could have such a significant impact on the learning environment in these lessons. The greater willingness of some of the boys in single sex schools to ask questions and/or to initiate other types of interaction with the teacher contributed to a more active/lively learning environment. This stands in contrast with the much more controlled and quiet learning environment in the girls' schools.

Compared with the girls' schools, however, the findings also point to a more unequal involvement of students in terms of the interaction initiated by the teacher. A possible explanation is that it may be more difficult for teachers to consciously include all, or most, students in the boys' classes, as the assertiveness of some boys demands more of the teacher in terms of control and regulation.

Boys' schools

On a general level, what was particularly striking from our observation of the lessons and viewing of the videotapes was how different the *atmosphere* was in the boys' compared with the girls' schools. The atmosphere can best be described as one of active participation in the boys' schools and largely non-assertive participation in the girls' schools. Active participation refers to the greater propensity of (a minority) of the boys to make themselves visible in the classroom in the following ways.

- *Movement*: the boys frequently moved about in their seats, stretching and yawning out loud.
- *Dress:* many of the boys wore their ties loosely arranged and were often seen to have their shirt- tails hanging out. Non-wearing of school uniform by a minority of the boys was observed only in relation to Liffey (SSB Fr D).
- *Behaviour:* 'Boisterous' and 'disruptive': in one of the two schools (Lee SSB F) students behaved in what can best be described as a boisterous manner. That is, they were seen to avail of every opportunity to talk and laugh and to make (usually inaudible) smart comments. In the other

school (Liffey SSB Fr D), just one student exhibited disruptive behaviour during the lessons. He interrupted the teacher with off the point questions and distracted other students by talking to them, attempting to make them laugh, poking them in the back or saying their name out loud in an effort to get their attention. This behaviour was particularly marked during the student practice phase of the lesson.

- *Initiation of classroom interaction:* although the overall level of student-initiated interaction was low, 8-19 per cent of boys initiated an interaction with the teacher in each of the four classes (Table A6.11). The boys who asked questions however, were quite open about not understanding a mathematical problem/procedure or having done a problem incorrectly .

The boys' classes were noisier than girls' classes: there was more movement out of desks, more overt stretching and yawning, and a good deal of quiet muttering that was generally inaudible to the teacher and the researchers. While most (91 per cent) girls in single sex classes were questioned by the teacher (about work) during class, most boys (57 per cent) were not. The work interactions with the teacher in boys' classes therefore were dominated by a minority of students, something that did not happen in the girls' classes (Tables A6.4).

The two boys' schools in the study were strikingly different, in terms of the average social class background and their academic climate and ethos. As a fee paying school, Lee (SSB F) had a selective intake of upper middle-class students of high academic attainment while students in Liffey (SSB Fr D) were mainly from a working class background. The class that participated in the research in the latter school was not particularly representative of the student body, having a higher level of academic achievement and fewer disciplinary problems, while the class observed in Lee (SSB F) was formally defined as 'mixed ability'.

Despite the aforementioned differences, both the mean mathematical achievement and the range of mathematical attainment was similar in Liffey (SSB Fr D) and Lee (SSB F), based on the TIMSS. Both classes had a wider spread of scores in the TIMSS-related tests than all other classes. While this is to be expected in a mixed class like that in Lee, there is generally an assumption of homogeneity in streamed classes such as that in Liffey.

Liffey (SSB Fr D) was quite unique in terms of the schools in the study, in that it was not the norm for the higher level mathematics course to be offered in the school. Although the teacher hoped that a substantial proportion of the particular class we observed would sit the Higher level paper in the Junior Certificate examination, only four out of the twenty-four students finally did so. In the Junior Certificate year, all three levels were accommodated within the same class. By contrast, it was school policy in Lee (SSB F) for all of its students to follow the Higher level course in mathematics for the Junior Certificate, with the expectation that only a tiny minority would eventually sit the Ordinary level examination. In this way, the general academic expectations for students were very different in these two schools although the TIMSS-related results would not suggest this should be the case.

There were fewer teacher-student interactions in Liffey (SSB Fr D) than in the other nine schools in the study (Table A6.4). In addition, more than two thirds of the students in Liffey (SSB Fr D) were not asked any questions during either of the two lessons. And the boys in these classes who were asked questions tended to be asked only once during the lesson (Tables A6.4). An examination of the particular students who were nominated to answer questions did not reveal any patterns by attainment (as measured by the TIMSS-based mathematical test).

Looking in more detail at the classroom context in Liffey (SSB Fr D), it would appear that the teacher used questioning partly as a mechanism to control one somewhat troublesome student. The student, Tony, was selected to answer 47 per cent of all questions in the first lesson and 28 per cent of questions in the second lesson. The following excerpt (from the first lesson) provides an illustration of how questioning was used in this way by the teacher. In addition, it provides an illustration of the willingness of certain boys to ask questions during the lesson. During the demonstration of a particular mathematical procedure to the whole class, Tony interrupted and asked the teacher a somewhat off the point question. While the teacher answered Tony's question, it was obviously interpreted by the teacher as an attempt to interrupt or divert the lesson.

(Minutes:seconds)

5:49	Tony (*boy sitting at the back of the class*) is fidgeting and trying to distract the boy sitting beside him. The teacher sees this and reprimands him.	*Teacher:* Tony! You're going to work hard, Yeah?
5:52	Explanation/ demonstration: Questioning individuals	*Teacher:* So if you're looking for the interest you will find it by getting the amount. You add the interest to your principal and that's all that's in it. So you have got £340 plus £122.40.

		(Teacher writing on blackboard and Tony has his hand raised) So as you can see from that, you have £462.40. That's the amount. So we have now added an extra term to this one over here the principal, the interest, the time, the rate and the last one Tony if you want to tell me will be?
6:30	Tony answers	*Tony:* (*Tony pauses*) Amount.
6:31	Teacher continues (*with sarcastic tone*)	*Teacher:* Well done! Very good! I love getting my question in before yours! Yeah?
6:36	Tony asks	*Tony:* What's the difference between simple interest and compound interest?
6:40	Explanation/ demonstration: teacher-centred Definition of Simple vs. Compound Interest	*Teacher:* Compound interest is far more intricate, right. Simple interest is basically you put your money in and make no more allowances for it, you leave it there and take your interest at the end of the first year and take it out. So there's a principal change for the start of the second year. You take the interest out, there's no change in the principal, it stays the same. So for instance if you take the very simple idea of just £100, you put all of it in the first year.
7:13	Explanation/ demonstration: Questioning whole class:	*Teacher:* What interest will we get at the end of the first year at 9 per cent?
7:15	Whole class answers	*Class:* £9.
7:18	Teacher continues	*Teacher:* £9, very good! Now if we put in £9. Take out your interest, and you decide you're going to fling it all in Cleary's or wherever, and still you have your £100 at the start of the second year. Now at the end of the second year you still have another £9 to take out – but what's happened to your £100? *Class:* No response. *Teacher:* Still the same! Right! *Although he asked the question Tony is not paying attention and is messing about.* *Teacher:* No problem with that Tony? *Tony:* Tony shakes his head. *Teacher:* Right. Take out your £9. The principal is still the same, your interest rate is still the same so you're actually getting £9 every year for 4 years, the principal hasn't changed. Now compound interest, on the other hand, you will leave your interest in, your principal will change every single year so at the

end when you're coming into working out your amount it's not just your £36 which is your four 9s because your interest is on a bigger sum of money every year. Is that OK, does that answer your question?

| 8:13 | Tony answers | *Tony:* Yeah. |

Having pinpointed Tony as somewhat troublesome, the teacher explained that he was 'no problem' compared with two other boys, one of whom was just suspended and the other who decided to opt out of the research project:

> I would have quite big reservations about them doing any level in maths because they don't seem to function very well in the group, but I make a conscious effort to at least sit with them for at least two or three minutes every day. Of the rest of them, there's absolutely no problem.

The absence of the two most troublesome boys from the lessons we observed would suggest that discipline was generally an issue in this class.

Turning to the other boys' school (Lee SSB F), a substantial proportion of the boys were either not asked questions at all or were asked in excess of three questions (Tables A6.4). In the first lesson, 39 per cent of the class were not asked any questions while 46 per cent were asked in excess of three questions. In the second lesson, the corresponding figures were 54 per cent and 38 per cent.

The teacher maintained that there are 'three or four of them that would misbehave'.

> There would be four, possibly five who would rule the class if I can put it like that. They would be the ones who would be always in trouble, the ones that in a way are the leaders in the class. You get that in every class. You get a couple of the louder or more boisterous ones.

When we examined the profile of students who were nominated to answer questions in the two lessons in Lee (SSB F) again, the results revealed that there was no particular selection by level of mathematical attainment. However, as a result of the mix in the class, there were occasions where some students were shown to demand more of the teacher's attention. This is demonstrated in the following excerpt; it was at the start of the second lesson and the teacher was quickly moving around the room to check that the students had completed their homework. The incident involved one of the lower achieving students in the class who either deliberately did not do all his homework or was unable to do it.

1:15	Homework correction: individually	*Teacher:* Open your books at page 323 – Can you get your homework out for me please.
	Teacher questions Sean about the whereabouts of his homework	*Oisin has his hand up – Teacher goes to his desk and asks what his problem is. After teacher has answered his question she asks to see Sean's homework.*
		Teacher: Sean can I see yours too? Where's question 20 and 25?
		Sean: We didn't have 25.
		Teacher: Did I not tell you to try 25, no?
		Other student (unknown): Yeah you did!
		Teacher (to Sean): Bring me up your journal after class.
		Sean: I couldn't do it.
		Teacher: As long as you attempted it then I don't care. Where's 20? Where did you try them? Right where did you try 20 and 25?
		Sean: I couldn't do those.
		Teacher (with annoyed tone of voice): Where did you try them? I didn't ask you could you do them. Where did you try them?
		Sean: On a rough sheet.
		Teacher: On a rough sheet. Yeah! (*sarcastically*)! I'll have your journal up at the end of class.

Equally, in Lesson 1, a lengthy exchange took place between this student (Sean) and the mathematics teacher, following an inquiry by the teacher as to whether everyone understood the first part of the homework problem they had just corrected. Sean did not understand what was going on and so the teacher took some time to explain it to him again, asking questions as she moved through each step. However, having attempted to explain this part of the solution to Sean without much success, the teacher moved on to solving the next part of the problem and nominated a different student to answer.

Compared with Liffey (SSB Fr D), the atmosphere in Lee (SSB F) was perceived to be more boisterous than disruptive. In Liffey (SSB FrD), the main business of the lesson took place in quiet competition with Tony's disruptive behaviour. By contrast, in Lee (SSB F), while the boys were actively participating (in terms of movement, behaviour and level of participation described above), no one individual was attempting to dominate the atmosphere of the class with disruptive behaviour, although a small number of high and low achieving students did get more attention than others.

Overall then, the most striking finding from the two boys' schools was the tendency of certain boys to dominate the learning environment. This included both disruptive/boisterous behaviour and the initiation of mainly work-related interaction by students. In Liffey (SSB Fr D), the disruptive behaviour of one of the students had the effect of interrupting the learning environment of the class, both in terms of the time the teacher spent controlling him and Tony's attempt to distract the students around him. The willingness of the students to initiate interaction with the teacher was more striking in Lee (SSB F) than in Liffey (SSB Fr D). From our observation, and from the information in the questionnaires, it was evident that the students in Lee were confident and self-assured. This may explain their lack of inhibition to admit failure or ask questions. In this school, the apparent problem that certain students had in keeping up with the class also had an important impact on the learning environment. Questions and requests for further explanation had the effect of interrupting the flow of otherwise fast-paced lessons (see discussion on 'mixed ability' in Chapter 7) and was not interpreted positively by the teacher.

Girls' schools

Girls' classes were characterised by a less assertive form of participation. Girls were more conforming in class, participating more at the request of the teacher than on their own initiative. The more controlled environment in girls' classes found expression in the following ways:

- *Movement*: the girls sat upright in their chairs and remained fairly still for the duration of the lesson.
- *Dress:* in Barrow (SSG F) and Nore (SSG Fr), the uniform code was in the traditional feminine genre, namely skirts and knee socks without the option of trousers. Students were only allowed to wear specified items of jewellery and make-up was not permitted. Although the uniform code was similar in Suir (SSG Fr D), a minority of the girls wore slightly different tops or tracksuit bottoms than those prescribed by the school. Some also wore jewellery and make-up. Their dress was tolerated rather than approved of by the school.
- *Behaviour:* the girls were attentive and did not disrupt the lessons in any way.
- *Initiation of classroom interaction:* while there was a relatively high level of student-teacher initiated interaction in Suir (SSG Fr D), there was none in two of the six girls' classes, while only 4 per cent were involved (one person) in taking initiative in each of the other two. By

and large the girls in the single sex schools only spoke when spoken to and the incidence of student-initiated talk was not a significant part of classroom interaction (See Table A6.11).

• *Lack of evidence of domination by the few:* there was no evidence in girls' classes of the pattern observed in boys' classes, of a small number of students dominating public action.

The ethos of girls' and the boys' classes also differed in terms of the type of language and examples used by the teachers.

What was most striking about the lessons in the girls' schools, was the controlled nature of the learning environment, although the control seemed to be internal to the girls themselves, rather than externally imposed. What contributed to this atmosphere was the absence of disruptive or boisterous behaviour by the girls and their general reticence to initiate interaction with the teacher. However, an examination of teacher-initiated questioning in the three girls' schools in our study showed that it tended to be inclusive of all the students in the class. A possible explanation for the more equitable distribution of teacher questions may relate to the absence of disruption, thus making it easier for the teachers to pay attention to the involvement of all or most of the students in the lesson. The absence of disciplinary problems was explicitly mentioned by one teacher.

> I like teaching here. I'm comfortable with it because I can teach and I don't have to concentrate on discipline (Barrow SSG F).

In the three girls' schools, there was no reference to disciplinary problems. However, not all students were considered to be the same and teachers pointed to different types of students within their respective classes. In Barrow (a top stream) and Nore (a mixed class), girls were expected to be quiet and co-operative. In Barrow, asking for help when it was not needed was regarded as deviant behaviour and defined as 'showing off', while in Nore it was described as 'unmannerly behaviour'. In Suir, the class we observed was described by the teacher as having 'bottom-stream students', as 'the weakest group I ever had'. Group placement rather than student gender seemed to exercise an over-riding influence on the learning climate of that class.

The teacher in Barrow (SSG F) described her students as falling into one of two categories: either 'the show girls' or the 'quiet ones':

> The show girls are there in abundance. But perhaps there is one girl who would require a lot of my attention but it's only by way of being the class clown and adding

to the drama. She's an attention seeker and she over-dramatises her difficulty. She doesn't really have a difficulty but she just thinks it's nice to keep on asking.

According to the teacher in Barrow, alongside the confident show girls are the students who are seen as so quiet that they don't ask for help when they need it:

Teacher: These students can be intimidated by other girls in the class. If they are super-sensitive and perhaps not the most mathematically talented, they can certainly be intimidated by the better girl and they are afraid to open their mouths and ask a question. I feel there is lot of competition, quiet competition. Perhaps they don't want to always show their weakness. It's not a real weakness but maybe just what they perceive to be a weakness.

Interviewer: We noticed in the classes we observed that you frequently asked if there were any questions – you even said 'you must have some questions' – do you usually have to encourage them to that degree or do they ask questions when they need to?

Teacher: No, you really have to drag it out.

Although the teacher claimed that there were show girls in her classes, we did not see any in the lessons we observed. In fact, quiet co-operation with teacher-directed learning was the norm. We will show in later chapters that an unwillingness to seek help in class was commonly found among girls in both single-sex and coeducational classes.

In Nore, the teacher also spoke of having two different types of student in his class: in his opinion there were the 'nice girls' and the 'hard chaws'. With this combination, he explained how he maintained order in the classroom.

The girls, I give them places. I tend to put the hard chaws with a nice girl. Sometimes this is hard on the nice girl but on the other hand you don't want all the toughies in the back row and you hope that they'll learn a bit of manners if nothing else.

In this excerpt there would appear to be a strong suggestion that 'mannerly behaviour' is a standard expectation in this classroom. In addition, the reference to 'learning manners if nothing else' suggests that the 'chaws' are likely to be the less-achieving girls. In the lessons observed there was no evidence of deviant behaviour by this minority of 'hard chaws'. Although the teacher did not explain what he meant by this distinction, the observations and comments made would suggest that the 'hard chaws' were those who deviated from the gendered norm of quiet attentiveness.

As explained in earlier chapters, students in Suir (SSG Fr D) had the lowest TIMSS-related score of the three girls' classes observed. The class in question was described in the school as a bottom stream; there were only twelve girls in the group. Observation of the class suggested that one of the over-riding characteristics of the girls was their lack of confidence in mathematics: students were reluctant to undertake tasks without guidance or assistance from the teacher. The teacher recognised this too: she described the students as either being 'so quiet' or 'afraid of me' that they would 'never ask for help unless they were really, really stuck' or as making 'demands on her time' by interrupting too much.

Suir provides a contrast to the other two girls' schools in that student-initiated interaction was more a feature of the learning environment, albeit to a marginal degree. However, when we examine the questions asked, we found that the majority of the questions were requests for information or direction from the teacher, indicating a lack of confidence among the students. In the excerpt that follows from the first lesson, the teacher had spent the first seven minutes of the class revising how to find the mean in statistics. She had just assigned a revision exercise from a worksheet she distributed and asked the students to get started on this. In the excerpt, a number of the students are shown to ask procedural questions about the work.

(Minutes:seconds)

7:58	Student work: Teacher gives instructions re. worksheet	*Teacher:* OK, if you're … if you've got your copies in with you, put on the top of the copy 'Revision and Statistics'. *(Students at desks, organising books, pens etc., and teacher walking around classroom, talking.)*
		Teacher: And you've to identify which kind of mean is it. Is it the list of numbers or is it the frequency table? *Nuala:* Do we do Question 2, first? *Teacher:* Yeah, I just want you to find question 2, part 1. *Nora:* There are two part one's? *Teacher:* Just do part 1 for me, yeah. We're going to do number 1 for the moment Nora – just that one there. *(Students start working. Teacher looks around to see if everything is OK. Teacher sees Niamh talking to Jackie and speaks to Niamh.)* *Teacher:* Are you OK Niamh? Do you understand what you need to do? *(Teacher goes over to Niamh).* *Niamh: conversation with teacher inaudible.* *(Nuala looks back at the teacher).*

> *Nuala:* Miss, is ...
> *Teacher realises that Nuala does not know what to do.*
> *Teacher: (pointing to Niamh's worksheet)* I just want you to do that one there for me.

Overall then, the most striking finding from our observation of the lessons in the girls' school was the absence of disruptive/boisterous behaviour and the reticence of students to initiate interaction with the teacher.

Interviews with the teachers showed that students were constantly compared with each other, and with an image of what was 'normal' in that particular class. What was 'normal' was influenced by a combination of factors including gender, social class background and the group placement of the students. All three teachers had expectations of co-operation and quietness in the girls' classes. In Barrow (SSG F) the teacher classified the girls as either 'the show girls' (if they sought too much attention) or 'quiet ones'; in Nore (SSG Fr) they were seen as either 'nice girls' who did their work or 'hard chaws' who distracted others; in Suir girls were seen as either 'making demands on my time' or 'so quiet' that they would never ask for help.

Conclusion

One of the primary objectives of this study is to examine gender differences in classroom practices. The focus was primarily on coeducational classes although we also examined differences across single sex schools.

The classroom data showed that boys received more teacher attention than girls in eight of the ten classes, and significantly so in four. Girls received more teacher attention than boys in two of the ten classes, and significantly in one. Girls were, on average, less likely to be asked a question than boys, and were also less likely to be asked a high number of mathematics related questions. As almost all public interaction is work-related, the findings indicate that boys are effectively more involved in the business of the mathematics lesson than girls in coeducational schools.

However, aggregate scores for all classes conceal major variations between individual classes: four of the ten coeducational classes were quite gender balanced, with two others being female dominated (one significantly so) and four being significantly male-dominated (Table 6.2). Second, it was a minority of boys who dominated the coeducational classes. These boys dominated the interaction compared with other boys as well as girls.

When the nature of teacher interactions and questioning of students was examined, no major differences were found between genders. Most classes were dominated by lower order mathematical questions, although boys did receive a higher proportion of higher order questions in coeducational classes. Boys were also more likely than girls to take the initiative and ask questions in mathematics classes, although it was only a small number of boys who were engaged in this way.

When the factors associated with different gender patterns of interaction were examined, the most important factor appeared to be teacher awareness of the need for gender balance. The classes that were most gender-balanced were those in which the teachers were gender aware. Of the five teachers of coeducational classes, it was the three female teachers who displayed most awareness, with one teacher operating a systematic policy of gender balance in her class.

While there was some tendency for gender-balanced classes, in terms of composition, to be gender-balanced in terms of interaction, this was not true for each one. Gender-balanced composition only facilitated gender-balanced interaction, it did not guarantee it.

On the other hand, the analysis of classes that were most male-dominated suggested that having a disproportionately large number of boys in the class, having a teacher who focused on boys and their interests, and having a teacher who had low gender awareness, all contributed to lack of gender balance.

Gender differences within coeducational classes are but one element in the gender picture however. The differences within coeducational classes are no greater (and are sometimes less notable) than the differences in social climate and educational practices *between* single-sex girls' and boys' classes.

The tendency for a small number of boys to dominate classes was not confined to coeducational classes; for example, it also occurred in single sex boys' schools. In all, 57 per cent of boys in single sex classes were not asked any questions while this occurred to only 27 per cent of boys in coeducational classes. The proportion of girls who were not asked any questions by the teacher in coeducational classes however, was much higher (31 per cent) than in single sex girls' classes (9 per cent).

On the other hand, a greater number of higher order questions were asked of girls in coeducational classes than was the case for girls in single sex schools, although the number of higher order questions was very low for girls and boys in all classes. Praise was also limited, although girls in all types of classes received somewhat more of it than boys.

Student-initiated interactions were relatively infrequent in all classes, whether single sex or coeducational. They were more frequent in single sex boys' classes however than in others, although much of this interaction is accounted for by a small number of boys.

The findings confirming the dominance of boys in coeducational classes is in accord with the general findings in other studies internationally (Drudy and Uí Catháin, 1998; Howe, 1997; Lee, 1993; Sadker and Sadker, 1985; Warrington et al., 2000). However, the findings also suggest that aggregated gender scores for classroom interaction conceal important differences between classes (Lodge, 1998; Lynch and Lodge, 2002). Moreover, male dominance in classes is accounted for often by a minority of boys (and this happens to a greater degree in single sex boys' classes than in coeducational classes). Such boys control the learning environment not only for girls but also for other quieter boys in the class (ibid).

The boys who dominated exercised hegemonic learning styles (by shouting out answers, calling for attention, moving and shuffling at their desks, or interrupting other students and the teacher). They dominated the verbal, and sometimes the physical, space of the groups to which they belonged. They had interactional styles that were competitive in attention-seeking terms, and exhibited traits of dominance commonly associated with hegemonic forms of masculinity (Mac An Ghaill, 1994; Connell, 1995).[4] Teachers seemed to co-operate with dominating students when their dominance involved work interactions; they were forced to engage with it when it involved disruptive behaviour.

Although Howe (1997) has drawn attention to the fact that there is a lack of evidence linking male dominance in class with superior examination performance, nonetheless our findings do raise questions about the overall long term effects for girls and certain quieter boys, of being subordinate in their classroom experiences. While the lack of control may not influence performance, it is most certainly a form of socialisation. Certain young women and subordinate males are practising being relatively silent in the presence of other young men in coeducational classrooms. A minority of boys also seem to strongly dominate single sex boys' classes. It is hard to accept that such practised subordination is unproblematic. In addition, the learning implications of such public disengagement are also far from clear. There is an arguable case that public disengagement may well reinforce negative attitudes to traditionally 'non-female' subjects among girls (such as mathematics) even if it does not directly influence examination performance (Jovanovic and King, 1998).

The data do indicate however, that not all coeducational classes are male-dominated. Those classes in which teachers were strongly gender aware were the most egalitarian in terms of interaction. Such gender balanced learning environments have been found to promote improved attitudes to learning among girls in non-traditional subject areas (ibid).

The data also highlights important differences across single sex schools with girls' classes having the most inclusive environment and boys' classes the least inclusive. This suggests that the reinforcement of gender stereotypes is not the prerogative of coeducational schools (Ball and Gewirtz, 1996; Ball, 1997; Hannan et al., 1983; Lynch, 1989; Lynch and Lodge, 2002).

Moreover, gender is but one 'code' within schools and classrooms (Arnot, 2002): it interacts with, and is influenced by other differences. Binary oppositional categorisations based on gender alone are not adequate for analysing classrooms (Gordon, 1996, p. 36). Social class, track position, race, ethnicity, sexuality etc., all mediate the impact of gender. The impact of social class and of grouping practices on classroom climates, and how these interface with gender, are presented in Chapter 7.

Appendix to Chapter 6

Table A6.1: Gender differences in teacher-student questions in coeducational lessons

School Name and Code and Lesson No.	Teacher-female student inter-actions (n)	Teacher-female student inter-actions per females in class	Teacher-male student inter-actions (n)	Teacher-male student inter-actions per males in class	Male/ female inter-action ratio	Chi-square
Lagan 1	21	1.50	27	1.68	1.12:1	0.16
(SC Fr) 2	93	5.81	49	3.26	0.56:1	10.95*
Errigal 1	74	3.90	52	4.72	1.21:1	1.14
(CS Fr) 2	145	7.63	81	7.36	0.96:1	0.06
Mourne 1	21	2.33	27	2.70	1.16:1	0.25
(VCC Fr D) 2	23	3.83	31	3.87	1.01:1	0.00
Blackstairs 1	4	0.23	18	1.20	5.22:1	10.78*
(VCC Fr D) 2	11	0.64	29	1.93	3.01:1	10.54*
Nephin 1	15	5.00	88	12.57	2.50:1	11.68*
(VCC Fr) 2	1	0.33	39	5.57	16.87:1	14.40*
Total	408	3.34	441	3.76	1.12:1	3.03

*: Significant at p<0.05 level

Key: SC Fr: Secondary coed, free scheme; CS Fr: Community School, free scheme; VCC FrD: Vocational/Community college, free scheme designated disadvantaged; VCC Fr: Vocational/Community college, free scheme (where free scheme represents non fee-paying status).

Table A6.2: Nature of teacher-student questions to individual students (base: 10 coeducational mathematics lessons)

Context of interaction	Number (and percentage) of questions in each category		
	Number of interactions		
	Females (n=123) %	Males (n=115) %	Total (n=238) %
Total low level maths	87.9	82.6	85.1
– Answer/solution	92.4	89.9	91.1
– General difficulty	–	0.3	0.1
– Specific difficulty	7.3	9.8	8.7
– Agreement with student answer	0.3	–	0.1
Total high level maths	3.9	7.9	6.0*
– Explain method	75.0	80.0	78.4
– Explain concept	25.0	20.0	21.6
Teacher checking student understanding	3.9	3.6	3.8
Real life application	0.7	1.6	1.2
Organisational	1.5	2.0	1.8
Progress checking	0.2	1.8	1.1
Total behaviour	1.7	0.5	1.1
– Care/concern	42.8	50.0	44.4
– Regulation	57.2	50.0	55.6
Total interaction (n)	407	442	849*
%	100.0	100.0	100.0

* Significant at p<0.05 level

Note: The main categories are shown in the table in bold.

Table A6.3: Nature of teacher-student questions to individual students (base: 10 single sex mathematics lessons)

Context of interaction	Number (and percentage) of questions in each category		
	Number of interactions		
	Females (n=125) %	Males (n=97) %	Total (n=222) %
Total low level maths	78.8	75.0	77.2
– Answer/solution	99.7	86.4	94.6
– General difficulty	–	2.3	0.9
– Specific difficulty	0.3	11.3	4.5
– Agreement with student answer	–	–	–
Total high level maths	1.6	9.7	4.8
– Explain method	66.7	100.0	93.1
– Explain concept	33.3	–	6.9
Teacher checking student understanding	3.6	5.5	4.3
Real life application	3.0	–	1.8
Organisational	5.7	0.4	3.7
Progress checking	5.7	4.7	5.3
Total behaviour	1.6	4.7	2.9
– Sanctioning	16.7	72.7	53.0
– Care/concern	66.6	–	23.5
– Regulation	16.7	27.3	23.5
Total interactions (n)	366	236	602
%	100	100	100

Note: The main categories are shown in the table in bold.

Table A6.4: *Gender differences in the distribution of teacher-student questions in both coeducational and single sex schools: breakdown across all schools*

School and Lesson		% Girls				% Boys				% All Students			
		Not asked	Asked at least one question …			Not asked	Asked at least one question …			Not asked	Asked at least one question …		
			1-2 Qs	3-4 Qs	5+ Qs		1-2 Qs	3-4 Qs	5+ Qs		1-2 Qs	3-4 Qs	5+ Qs
Single Sex Girls													
Barrow (SSG Fr)	1	21	36	29	14	–	–	–	–	21	36	29	14
	2	7	43	32	18	–	–	–	–	7	43	32	18
Nore (SSG Fr)	1	8	42	42	8	–	–	–	–	8	42	42	8
	2	4	52	17	27	–	–	–	–	4	52	17	27
Suir (SSG FrD)	1	0	17	50	33	–	–	–	–	0	17	50	33
	2	0	50	20	30	–	–	–	–	0	50	20	30
Average		9	41	31	19	–	–	–	–	9	41	31	19
Single Sex Boys													
Liffey (SSB FrD)	1	–	–	–	–	75	17	4	4	78	13	5	4
	2	–	–	–	–	64	23	5	8	64	23	5	8
Lee (SSB F)	1	–	–	–	–	39	15	11	35	39	15	11	35
	2	–	–	–	–	54	8	4	34	54	8	4	34
Average	–					57	15	6	22	57	15	6	22

continued overleaf

Table A6.4 (continued): Gender differences in the distribution of teacher-student questions in both coeducational and single sex schools: breakdown across all schools

School and Lesson		Distribution of questions by gender											
		% Girls				% Boys				% All Students			
		Not asked	Asked at least one question …			Not asked	Asked at least one question …			Not asked	Asked at least one question …		
			1-2 Qs	3-4 Qs	5+ Qs		1-2 Qs	3-4 Qs	5+ Qs		1-2 Qs	3-4 Qs	5+ Qs
Coeducational													
Lagan (SC Fr)	1	64	0	14	22	62	19	6	13	63	10	10	17
	2	0	31	38	31	13	33	20	34	7	32	29	32
Errigal (CS Fr)	1	0	48	26	26	37	18	9	36	13	37	20	30
	2	5	26	16	53	18	18	0	64	10	23	10	57
Mourne (VCC Fr D)	1	0	67	22	11	0	50	40	10	0	58	32	10
	2	0	17	50	33	25	12	25	38	14	14	36	36
Blackstairs (VCC Fr D)	1	83	17	0	0	47	40	6	7	66	28	3	3
	2	71	23	6	0	20	40	40	0	47	31	22	0
Nephin (VCC Fr)	1	0	0	66	34	0	14	15	71	0	10	30	60
	2	67	33	0	0	14	14	29	43	30	20	20	30
Average		31	28	20	21	27	29	17	27	29	28	19	24

Table A6.5: Student responses to teacher-student mathematics questions (base: 10 single sex schools)

	Proportion of students responding in each category		
	Number of interactions		
	Females (n=125) %	Males (n=97) %	Total (n=222) %
Correct	66	52	61
Incorrect	12	9	11
No answer/hesitation/mutter	6	10	7
Progress report	11	16	13
No chance to answer before teacher/other student intervenes	4	12	7
Other	1	1	1
TOTAL (n)	339	223	562
%	100	100	100

Table A6.6: Teacher feedback to 'correct' student responses following teacher-student mathematics questions (base: coeducational lessons)

	Proportion of students receiving particular forms of teacher feedback		
	Number of interactions		
	Females (n=123) %	Males (n=115) %	Total (n=238) %
Praise	11	6	9*
No Praise	49	51	50
Asks additional question	37	39	38
Other	3	4	3
TOTAL (n)	289	268	557
%	100	100	100

*Significant at p<0.05 level

Table A6.7: Teacher feedback to 'correct' student responses following teacher-student mathematics questions (base: single sex lessons)

	Proportion of students receiving particular forms of teacher feedback		
	Number of interactions		
	Females (n=123) %	Males (n=115) %	Total (n=238) %
Praise	17	8	14
No Praise	72	41	61
Asks additional question	9	47	22
Other	2	4	3
TOTAL (n)	223	115	338
%	100	100	100

Table A6.8: Teacher feedback to 'incorrect' mathematics questions in coeducational and single sex lessons

	Teacher responses in each category Base: Coeducational lessons					
	Females (n=123)		Males (n=115)		Total (n=238)	
	n	%	n	%	n	%
Asks further question	8	27.6	10	18.5	18	21.7
Repeats same question	7	24.2	4	7.4	11	13.3
Prompts towards correct answer/solution	10	34.6	9	16.7	19	22.9
Critical	0	0	6	11.1	6	7.2
Teacher answers questions	1	3.4	11	20.4	12	14.5
Teacher addresses student difficulty	1	3.4	4	7.4	5	6.0
Teacher asks for class reaction to answer	1	3.4	9	16.7	10	12.0
Other	1	3.4	1	1.8	2	2.4
TOTAL	29	100	54	100	83	100
	Base: Single sex lessons					
	Females (n=125)		Males (n=97)		Total (n=222)	
	n	%	n	%	n	%
Asks further question	21	53.9	7	43.8	28	50.9
Repeats same question	7	17.9	5	31.3	12	21.8
Prompts towards correct answer/solution	6	15.4	1	6.2	7	12.7
Critical	–	–	–	–	–	–
Teacher answers questions	3	7.7	1	6.2	4	7.4
Teacher addresses student difficulty	2	5.1	–	–	2	3.6
Teacher asks for class reaction to answer	–	–	–	–	–	–
Other	–	–	2	12.5	2	3.6
TOTAL	39	100	16	100	55	100

Table A6.9: Gender composition ratios: summary measure

Gender composition: summary measure	Male/female ratio range
Boys very much in the majority	3.80:1 and above
Boys in the majority	1.19:1 – 3.79:1
Boys and girls evenly balanced	0.85:1 – 1.18:1
Girls in the majority	0.33:1 – 0.85:1
Girls very much in the majority	0.32:1 and below

Table A6.10: Gender interaction ratios: summary measure

Boy/girl interaction ratio: summary measure	Male/female ratio range
Boys very dominant	3.8+:1
Boys dominant	1.19 –3.79:1
Evenly balanced	0.85 – 1.18:1
Girls dominant	0.33 – 0.84:1
Girls very dominant	0.32-: 1

Table A6.11: Gender differences in student-teacher interactions: single sex classes

School name and lesson		% of students who initiated interaction with teacher		
		% Girls	% Boys	% All students in class
Barrow (SSG F)	1	0	na	0
	2	4	na	4
Nore (SSG Fr)	1	4	na	4
	2	0	na	0
Suir (SSG Fr D)	1	42	na	42
	2	30	na	30
Liffey (SSB Fr D)	1	na	9	9
	2	na	18	18
Lee (SSB F)	1	na	8	8
	2	na	19	19

Notes

[1] We will return to the issue of gender in Chapter 10 when examining the views of the teachers. In this way, the gender differences that appear in the teachers' pedagogical practices can be compared with their views about the issue.

[2] The mean number of interactions was found by taking the total number of public teacher-girl interactions in a lesson, and dividing by the number of girls in the class. Similarly for boys: in Lesson 1, Lagan (SC Fr), for example, there were 27 public teacher-boy interactions, and as there were 16 boys in the class the mean value is 1.68 interactions per boy. The ratio given is based on these mean values. For Lesson 1, Lagan 1.68 (mean teacher-boy interactions) divided by 1.50 (mean teacher-girl interactions) gives a ratio of 1.12:1. In this example, girls received fewer interactions than was the case for boys, albeit to a marginal degree. Finally, we conducted an analysis using a chi-square test (with one degree of freedom) to determine whether the emergent gender differences were statistically significant (see final column of Table 6.2). To do this, we compared the proportion of interactions that each gender received in relation to the proportion of students in the class of that gender.

[3] As can be seen from Table 6.7, three of the six classes taught by women teachers were gender-balanced in terms of composition (both classes in Lagan and the first class in Mourne; in two (both classes in Errigal), girls were in a clear majority, while in the third (second class in Mourne) boys slightly in the majority. Of the four classes taught by male teachers, the two in Blackstairs were gender balanced while there were more boys in both classes in Nephin (2:1, male to female).

[4] Connell (1995) suggests that domination of women and subordinate men is one of the defining features of hegemonic masculinity.

7

The Impact of Grouping
and Social Class

Introduction

While a student's gender has an impact on his or her learning experience, it is but one of a series of factors that influence the learning process. A student's classroom experience is also influenced by age, ethnicity, sexuality, social class, colour etc. (Lynch and Lodge, 2002). In this study, we found that the track or group to which a student was allocated in school, and their social class background, impacted strongly on their learning experiences in mathematics classrooms.

Grouping of students[1]

As can be seen from Table 7.1 below, most of the schools involved in the case studies tracked students into higher or lower bands, streams or sets for most subjects.[2] Banding was the most common method of grouping in all years, being used in five schools in second year (Suir (SSG Fr D); Lagan (SC Fr); Errigal (CS Fr); Mourne (VCC Fr D); Nephin (VCC Fr)). Streaming was the most hierarchical form of grouping and it was used in both Liffey (SSB Fr D) and Blackstairs (VCC Fr D) in second year, and in Liffey throughout the Junior Cycle. Setting only operated in one school, Barrrow (SSG F); it operated in second and third year while there were mixed classes in first year. Only two schools (Nore (SSG Fr) and Lee (SSB F)) had mixed classes for all subjects in the Junior cycle. These were also the only schools that had entirely mixed classes for mathematics in second year, the year group focused on for this study.

Social class background

Given our findings regarding differences between advantaged and designated disadvantaged schools in terms of mathematical attainment (see Chapter 2), schools that might help explain such differences were chosen for the case study. In addition, we also wanted to examine the

Table 7.1: Grouping procedures in the Junior Cycle

Schools	1st Year	2nd Year	Junior Cert Year
Barrow (SSG F)	Mixed	Set (streamed) for mathematics and Irish, mixed for all other subjects	Set (streamed) for mathematics and Irish, mixed for all other subjects
Nore (SSG Fr)	Mixed	Mixed	Mixed
Suir (SSG Fr D)	Banded	Banded	Banded but streamed for mathematics
Liffey (SSB Fr D)	Streamed	Streamed	Streamed
Lee (SSB F)	Mixed	Mixed	Mixed
Lagan (SC Fr)	Banded	Banded	Banded
Errigal (CS Fr)	Mixed, Banded for Irish, English, mathematics, French, German	Banded	Banded
Mourne (VCC Fr D)	Mixed, Banded for Irish, English, mathematics	Banded	Banded
Blackstairs (VCC Fr D)	Mixed	Streamed	Streamed
Nephin (VCC Fr)	Mixed, banded for core subjects	Banded	Banded

Key – Table 7.1 and 7.2: SSG F: Secondary girls', fee-paying; SSG Fr: Secondary girls', free scheme; (SSG Fr D): Secondary girls', free scheme designated disadvantaged; SSB Fr D: Secondary boys', free scheme designated disadvantaged; SSB F: Secondary boys', fee paying; SC Fr: Secondary coed, free scheme; CS Fr: Community school, free scheme; VCC Fr D: Vocational/Community college, free scheme designated disadvantaged; VCC Fr: Vocational/Community college, free scheme (where free scheme represents non fee-paying status).

teaching and learning climate in schools that were in the middle range in terms of mathematical attainment. Three types of schools, therefore, were chosen for in depth analysis. These included four designated disadvantaged schools, where one was a girls' school, one a boys' school, and two were coeducational vocational schools. Two advantaged schools (one girls' and one boys'), determined by their fee-paying status, were chosen. Four schools that were in the middle range in terms of mathematical attainment were also chosen. Two of these were secondary schools, one single sex girls' and one coeducational; one was a community school and the other a vocational school, both were coeducational.

The social class profile of the students in the study reflected the targeted and selected nature of the case study schools. While the student profile is clearly not representative of the school population generally, it is indicative of the social class profile of students *within* particular school types. Like previous studies (Hannan et al., 1996; Lynch and Lodge, 2002) we found that students in vocational schools were more likely to be working class compared with those in secondary schools. Not surprisingly, students in fee paying schools are more upper middle class than those in other school types, with those in designated disadvantaged schools having the most working class profile of all schools (Table 7.2).

Table 7. 2: Social class profile of students in mathematics classes

School	Total middle class	Total working class	Total % (n)	Class organisation Streamed/banded or mixed
Barrow (SSG F)	96.0	4.0	100 (25)	Streamed-top
Nore (SSG Fr)	66.7	33.3	100 (21)	Mixed
Suir (SSG Fr D)	20.0	80.0	100 (10)	Banded-bottom
Liffey (SSB Fr D)	23.8	76.2	100 (21)	Streamed-top
Lee (SSB F)	100	0	100 (25)	Mixed
Average SS	79.4	20.6	100 (102)	
Lagan (SC Fr)	62.1	37.9	100 (29)	Banded-top
Errigal (CS Fr)	13.6	86.4*	100 (22)	Banded-middle
Mourne (VCC Fr D)	23.5	76.5	100 (17)	Banded-bottom
Blackstairs (VCC Fr D)	34.4	65.6	100 (32)	Streamed-top
Nephin (VCC Fr)	37.5	62.5	100 (8)	Banded-bottom
Average Coed	37.0	63.0	100 (108)	
Overall average	52.4	47.6	100 (210)	

*In Errigal, most of the working class students were from skilled backgrounds. In the designated disadvantaged (DD) schools there were higher proportions from unskilled and semi-skilled backgrounds within the working class category (see Chapter 3 for more details).

There were also differences between single sex and coeducational schools: almost 80 per cent of the students in the single sex-sector were from a middle class background, compared with 37 per cent of those attending coeducational schools. While this was indicative of the differences between the more middle class secondary sector and the more working class vocational/community sector generally, it was also an outcome of the targeted nature of our case study schools. We had a disproportionately high number of students in single sex schools that were middle class in intake while the opposite was true of the coeducational schools.

Differences in the social class profile of schools is mirrored in the profile of tracks within schools. All the upper middle class students, and the great majority of students from middle and lower middle class backgrounds were either in top track or 'mixed ability' classes. While students from working class backgrounds are represented in top tracks, they are more strongly represented in middle and lower tracks than middle class students.

Table 7.3: Relationship between social class and track position

Social Class	Class Organisation				
	Top stream/ band %	Middle stream/ band %	Bottom stream/ band %	Mixed %	Total % (n)
Upper middle class	54			46	100 (39)
Middle class	56	3	7	34	100 (41)
Lower middle class	47	7	23	23	100 (30)
Total Middle class	54	14	28	85	
Upper working class (skilled/manual)	44	22	24	10	100 (70)
Working class (semi-skilled/ unskilled)	60	13	27		100 (30)
Total working class	46	86	72	15	
Total %	51	10	17	22	100
(n)	(107)	(22)	(35)	(46)	(210)

While the selective nature of case study schools does not allow for any generalisation about the relationship between social class background and track placement, it does lend support to claims that stream or track placement is inherently class biased. There is a large corpus of evidence from a number of different education systems showing that students from lower socio-economic groups are more likely to be located in lower tracks in school (Ball, 1981; Douglas, 1964; Jackson, 1964; Taylor, 1993; Rees et al., 1996; Boaler, 1997a, 1997b). Research on Irish second-level schools shows that working class students are not only more likely to attend schools that stratify classes by levels of attainment (Hannan and Boyle, 1987; Lynch, 1989), but are also disproportionately represented in low tracks when schools operate streaming or banding (Lynch and Lodge, 2002).

Teacher-student interactions: differences across streams

To understand the implications of different forms of tracking for the teaching of mathematics, we examined the pedagogical practices of the teachers across groups. In keeping with other studies (Hacker et al., 1991), we found little difference in the overall frequency of teacher interaction with students across different groups. However, in agreement with much of the literature, we did identify differences in relation to the *type* and *quality* of instruction across the streams and bands.

Of the twenty lessons, eight were top streams or bands (Barrow (SSG F), Liffey (SSB Fr D), Lagan (SC Fr) and Blackstairs (VCC Fr D)), six were bottom streams (Suir (SSG Fr D), Mourne (VCC Fr D) and Nephin (VCC Fr)) and one was middle stream (Errigal (CS Fr)). The remaining four classes were defined as 'mixed ability' and will be discussed later in this section. The most striking differences emerged between the top and bottom tracks. To illustrate the qualitative differences in the type and quality of the pedagogical approaches, a bottom-stream group (from Suir (SSG Fr D)) and a group from a top track (from Lagan (SC Fr)) will be compared.

The first school, Suir (SSG Fr D), is a designated disadvantaged single sex girls' school. There were twelve students in this bottom stream group, ten from a working class background. This class is from one of the four schools in the study to have completed the Junior Certificate examination during the course of the research. In the examination, 31 per cent of the class took the Foundation level mathematics paper, while the remainder (69 per cent) took the Ordinary level paper. The class achieved a mean score of 13.2 (out of a possible 40) in the TIMSS-related mathematics test. This was the second lowest average score among the ten schools. The teacher of this particular mathematics class is a woman with almost five years' teaching experience; she has a strong mathematics background.

The lesson under consideration here was the first mathematics lesson observed with this group. The topic covered was 'statistics: mean and mode'. It was a revision lesson.

The second school, Lagan (SC Fr), is a coeducational secondary school. There were thirty students in this top track – fourteen girls and sixteen boys. The majority of the class (almost two-thirds) are from a middle class background. Although this group had not yet completed the Junior Certificate, almost all of the class (96.8 per cent) expected to take the Higher level paper in the forthcoming examination, with a minority (3.2 per cent) stating that they would take the Ordinary level paper. The group achieved a mean score of 28.5 (out of a possible 40) in the TIMSS-related mathematics test which was the second highest among our ten schools. The teacher of this group is a woman who has over twenty years' teaching experience.

The lesson under consideration with this group concerned 'geometry: the length of a circle'. It was a new topic for this class.

Pedagogy for the bottom stream

Suir (SSG Fr D) was a small bottom band class in a large girls' school. This school had quite a wide range of social classes attending, being the main school providing girls' education in the area. The class observed was the lowest stream within the banded system and was named as such by teachers. Although it was clear from the lessons observed, and from interviews with their class teacher, Ms Scanlon, that she worked hard with this group, her aspirations for them were framed by their low stream status. In the interview she described this class as follows: 'I've never had such a weak stream before'.

In general the teacher commented on her different approaches with varied 'ability' groupings:

> I'd push [the higher group] more and more… I know I can get it out of them so I'd push them and get them to think, try and relate topics … If I was doing differentiation for instance, I'd try and get them to think back to the equation of the line and link it in and get the tangent to something… but once you're with [this group] you have to really push to get the information out of them and they can't relate topics at all … I reckon that some of them … have missed out on some of the basic skills. This particular class doesn't retain stuff, they would lose it – we're doing revision at the moment and it is statistics and it's very, very hard. You might tell them a story to try and bring them along but they'd only remember the stories, not the theory at all … It's awful.

Ms Scanlon's expectations of the group were reflected in her pedagogical style and the way she related to the class. She began the revision lesson on statistics with the following statement:

> Right, we're going to go down through the theory of it to see if ye can really remember back that far.

She then asked a number of low level questions in relation to the topic. She moved very slowly through this part of the lesson, checking to see if the class understood the relevant mathematical terms being used. During this process the teacher was patient and encouraging with students who were slow to respond to her questions. She was also quick to praise when provided with the correct answer. We see an example of this in the following excerpt.

Lesson Aims (Minutes:seconds)	**Activity**
0:05 Review Questioning Individuals	*Teacher:* The three Ms we did – 3 M-words.
0:17 Teacher asks Roisin question	*Teacher:* Anybody who can think of one of them? Keep your copies closed for a minute. The first one. Anybody remember it? *(Roisin's hand goes up.)* *Teacher:* Roisin
0:22 Roisin answers question and teacher responds	*Roisin:* Mean. *Teacher:* Good girl yourself, mean. We'll put that up on the board here.
0:27 Teacher asks Leslie a question (no response)	*Teacher:* Anybody remember then, hands up, what the/that means … that actually the word itself means ? Leslie, I think you're going to be able to tell me something, are you ? *(Leslie smiles and shakes head.)* *Leslie:* No *Teacher:* Even guess at it. *Leslie:* What does that mean ? *Teacher:* What that the word itself … what would it mean? *(Leslie shakes head again.)* *Teacher:* You haven't a clue – OK.
0:43 Teacher asks Doreen same question	*Teacher:* Anybody else… think about it – a 'mean'?
0:46 Doreen answers	*Doreen:* Average *Teacher:* Average – who said the average there, real quiet? *(Doreen puts up her hand.)* *Teacher:* Doreen, good girl yourself. Average.

Following this, the teacher proceeded to revise the method for finding the mean (which she constantly referred to as the 'average') distinguishing between lists of numbers and frequency tables. She did this by the use of a real life example. Here she asked the girls to call out their shoe size and used this to demonstrate the use of 'mean'.

As the teacher moved through these phases she took the time to explain each step relating to the topic. She concentrated on basic skills, calling on students to provide answers to some basic algorithms as part of the procedure. When she received the correct answer, she praised the student. In the case of questions that required the students to provide a *method*, there were mumbled answers or silences much of the time. In such cases the teacher gave hints or provided the answer herself. Throughout these phases of the lesson, the teacher continually restated the relevant definitions and procedures.

Thus a slow pace, repetition and an emphasis on the practising of basic, procedural skills characterised the teacher's pedagogical approach. Such an approach also gives an important insight into the expectations that the teacher holds in relation to this bottom stream group. The depth of explanation used, her use of real life examples and her questioning demonstrate her attempt to both engage the class with the topic and to hold their interest.

Twice during the lesson the teacher set work for her students. She distributed worksheets for this phase, instructing them to try one of the questions on their own. In the interview afterwards she commented on her use of worksheets and alternative resources.

Ms Scanlon: I make them up myself – I just pick it out of my head. I just pick something that would be easy enough for them to divide at this stage – like any type of division they find it very hard – so I make it easy and relate it to what they would like – say to shopping. And the one I used today – about barcharts – I made that up as well and just did it up on the computer. I use other handouts as well – like the one with a puzzle – with a crocodile. Like it starts with: 'What's a crocodile's favourite game?' and they would all answer 'Snap'. Sometimes I would cut off that part because they would go along and would work it out – and not do the sums – they would try and finish it before each other.
Interviewer: So then you do use a fair amount of non-textbook methods?
Ms Scanlon: Well with them in particular – you would have to kind of, you know, bring them to the computer room and do something on the computer – get into the internet. We just finished … decimals or angles and they worked on a site and when they were finished it said: 'Congratulations – you got five out of ten, or whatever'. It is something different for them – something to keep them interested. It is great fun for them – you know, anything to get out of class and walk somewhere.

During the two student work phases of the lesson, which lasted just over eight minutes, the teacher walked among the students providing help and checking on their progress. A number of students asked her questions during one of these phases – most of these questions involved the students confirming which question they were to do. Although the teacher had stated clearly at the start of the phase which problem they were to work on, it appeared that five of the twelve students were unsure as to what question they were to do. The teacher repeatedly answered the same question from different students without comment or criticism.

Although there appears to be a higher incidence of student initiated interaction with this class in comparison to some of the other classes in the study, the quality of the interaction between the students and their teacher pointed more to the dependent learning style of the students rather than to initiative-taking by the students. The type of student-teacher questioning that dominated the class suggests that the students needed ongoing direction and guidance in relation to their work.

A dialectical relationship appeared to exist between the pedagogical style of the teacher and the response of students: as the students sought guidance and assistance from the teacher, arising from their lack of knowledge and confidence in mathematics, the teacher responded by reinforcing their dependency. There was no systematic attempt to encourage students to take initiative. The lesson was highly structured by Ms Scanlon. She continually issued instructions and guided the class throughout every phase of the lesson – even down to copying examples into their copybooks. This is illustrated in the following extract.

(Minutes:seconds)

11:44 Revision: teacher centered	*Teacher:* Now that was the first word. So into your copies, just underneath where you've written that, write down the word 'mean'. If you haven't got your copies, use the back of the sheet that I've given out to you.
	(Stephanie holds up her sheet to check.)
	Teacher: That's fine, good girl … And then write: that word actually means to find the average. There are two types; a list of numbers or a frequency table. OK, so, we'll write that … part 1: list of numbers … part 2: frequency table (points to Stephanie's copy) Exactly like that.
	OK 'Frequency'
	(Teacher spells out the word) F-r-e-q-u-e-n-c-y … frequency table. That's it. So when you're asked to find the mean of something, you look at it firstly and you see if it's a list of numbers or if it's a frequency table. Turn over to the sheet again – you've got it in front of you … It's fine if you don't – we'll write it on the back of the sheet.

The teachers' expectations for her bottom stream group were also reflected in the language used and some of the comments made in the course of the lesson. Ms Scanlon seemed to try and avoid the use of mathematical terms as much as possible. She referred to the mean constantly as the 'average' and towards the end of the lesson stated: 'Mean is the fancy word for average'.

At another stage in the lesson the teacher asked a lower order mathematics question. Before the student answered the teacher said to her: 'Now Sheila, don't try to do too many things at the one go'. The teacher wanted her to break down the problem and work it out in steps. This again illustrates the importance the teacher places on basic procedural skills and her expectation that this was all that this group could undertake.

Towards the end of the lesson the teacher assigned homework. Again she took the time to ensure that the class knew exactly what was required of them:

> Have we got our homework taken down? We've got to do question number 2, part 2 ... you're asked to find the mode and the mean, so underline 'mode', circle 'and' and underline 'mean'. So you know that you're being asked for two parts to that question – two parts to be answered.

Once the teacher had set the homework, she allowed the students to begin working on it and told them to call her down to them if they had a question on it. In the interview the teacher commented on homework.

> When you give [them] homework, you might be lucky if three of them do it. With this particular class now, I would let them work on homework in front of me so that they get the work started and I can see exactly – I can see straight away who has a problem and who hasn't. So they come up then and you can go through it with them – but then they wouldn't revise it at home again for you so you're back to square one again with them.

Streaming and social class

Although Ms Scanlon worked very conscientiously with this bottom stream, both the pace and tone of the class, and the level at which mathematics were taught, were dictated by their corporate low stream status. Variability in the interest and competencies of different students in mathematics within this class was not recognised in any visible way. Being called a bottom stream, they were collectively and publicly defined as 'weak'. In line with a range of other studies, we found that their corporate identity as a low stream framed their classroom experience (Burgess, 1983; Oakes, 1985; Gamoran, 1986; Boaler, 1997a).

Responsibility for the slow pace of teaching, the strongly procedural approach, however, cannot be explained simply by the actions of one individual teacher. The students themselves had internalised a sense of their own inability in mathematics and this created a dialectic of dependency and low expectations of themselves in their relations with the teacher (see Chapter 10).

As mentioned above, the majority of students in the bottom stream in Suir (SSG Fr D) were from a working class background. Ms Scanlon's comments showed that she believed that the students' social class background influenced their attitudes to learning.

Ms Scanlon: [Some of them] will actually tell you now that they don't want to do maths, or to even finish the Leaving ... and you'll say about needing it for a job. Then they say their sisters don't have jobs.
Interviewer: Would you say then that students with a more advantaged background do better?
Ms Scanlon: The trend is for the more advantaged to do better. I think they're encouraged at home a lot more, whereas the other students, even at the parent-teacher meetings, the parents wouldn't arrive in. I haven't seen some of the kids' parents since they arrived in school. There's a lot more trouble and you want to see the parents but you just can't get to see them. The parents are not interested – so the kids are influenced from home really.

The teacher's comments on a number of individual students who were experiencing problems also provided insight into her views on how their social backgrounds influenced learning. In the following quotation we see the teacher referring the problem of one student back to the family.

Interviewer: Can you identify students in the class who would seem to have fallen back since they came into the class in first year?
Ms Scanlon: I would think Nuala ... She's been absent a good bit and I'd say she definitely has fallen back because she's very – she's quite intelligent – not very intelligent – but she doesn't make any effort whatsoever ... It would be due to absenteeism mainly. And she doesn't bother – the easy way out ... She had been in hospital but she plays up a little bit on that – maybe extended over a week. It's maybe – she's the youngest of her family and towards the end of the family... they are getting a bit slack. I had it last year as well with her – she would have been out for something else – another reason – you know, but always the same kind of ideas. She would be meant to be out for a week, she'd be out for three. That type of thing, not really genuine.

Ms Scanlon also referred to a different student with whom she had problems in relation to absenteeism, stating that 'it's a constant battle trying to keep her in'.

Speaking of a student who tended to make more demands on her time, the teacher described one girl as being a 'very volatile child'.

> *Ms Scanlon:* Yes, she would be one who makes more demands on my time. It depends on what mood Shelley is in. She has been fine, she gets on very well with me but other teachers she wouldn't. It would depend on the day. She will have a chat with me to the extent that she'll bring in dinners from her home economics class and she wants me to try it, but then other days she just sits and she's very quiet, very subdued. It depends on who she's hanging around with at lunch time and she can change.

Finally, the teacher spoke of what she expected the students in this group to be doing in ten years time.

> Shop assistant or FÁS schemes or something like that. They're not high achievers. Some of them maybe will go to third-level PLC courses in the regionals, but I couldn't see them going on to the universities and that – they're not high achievers at all.

There are now several studies that show how allocation to particular tracks or streams in school is related to students' socio-economic and social class background (Rosenbaum, 1976; Oakes, 1990; Taylor, 1993; Rees et al., 1996; Boaler, 1997a, 1997b). Our case study findings suggest that working class students are more likely to be in lower tracks than are middle class students. Moreover, the data also suggest that teachers tend to associate lower stream status and lower educational expectations with being from a working class, or what is more frequently called a 'disadvantaged' or 'low socio-economic background'.

What also emerged from the data was evidence that the learning climate in low stream mathematics classes is slow, strongly procedural, and not particularly intellectually challenging for either the students or the teacher. While the reasons for having such a learning climate are partly determined by the streaming system itself, and the expectations that it engenders among both students and teachers, it is also an outcome of the dialectic that develops within low stream classes between students and teachers.

Pedagogy for the top stream

The teacher of the top stream in Lagan (SC Fr), Ms Leydon, initially described them as 'a very quiet group and a lovely group to teach'. She also referred to a number of students in the group as being 'very highly motivated'.

The teacher explained her different teaching approaches across different tracks.

> With the higher groups you would tend just to be able to show them how to do something and they work away on their own, whereas with the weaker groups I have to do – you know do a question – show them an example and they take it down – and then the next one, you just do the first line and they do the next line. But sometimes they just can't manage on their own so you have to keep the whole class with you in the weaker groups. You sort of have to keep the whole class with you with the weaker groups, whereas sometimes in the better ones you just move on and one of them will call you over and say: 'Look, I cannot do this' or whatever.

Speaking of ways in which she believed the teaching of school mathematics could be generally improved, Ms Leydon acknowledged that one had to proceed at a fast pace to complete the syllabus; this was particularly true for the Higher level 'honours' group. While she recognised that this top stream group were 'very rushed', her comments revealed the high expectations she held for the students in the group: '… that's what makes that class that I have such a pleasure – because they are all pretty much able for it.'

The pedagogical style that Ms Leydon employed with the top stream we observed reflected her generally high expectations for the group. As noted earlier, Ms Leydon's class was undertaking a new topic for this lesson, finding the length of a circle. The teacher began the lesson with a very brief introduction:

> Right, what we're going to start with today is to talk about the length of the circle. Now we've done a bit about area and value before, but we only did, if you remember, rectangular shapes or square shapes or triangular shapes. Today we're going to talk about the length of curved shapes and the one we're going to work on is the circle.

Having stated the aim of the lesson, Ms Leydon proceeded to demonstrate the method for finding the length of a circle. This demonstration lasted just under three minutes, during which the teacher gave out a great deal of information around the method, asking just four questions of the class. There was an air of urgency surrounding this part of the lesson. It proceeded at a very fast pace. The teacher spoke very quickly and the method for the procedure was given with very little explanation. There was strong evidence of Ms Leydon's high expectations of this group. It seemed they did not need detailed explanation or time to think about what they were being told. This is illustrated in the following extract from the class.

Lesson aims (Minutes:seconds)	Activity
0:26 Topic: Length of a circle	*Teacher:* Right, what we're going to start with today is to talk about the length of the circle. Now we've Now we've done a bit about area and value before, but we only did, if you remember, rectangular shapes or square shapes or triangular shapes. Today we're going to talk about the length of curved shapes and the one we're going to work on is the circle.
0:42 Explanation/ Demonstration Terminology: Length = Circumference = Perimeter	*(Teacher goes to the chalkboard.)* *Teacher:* Now in a circle – the problem with these kind of questions is sometimes they can ask for it in three different ways. They can ask for it – one of the ways for it, is they ask for the length of the circle, the other they ask for is the circumference, right: length circumference Now both of those mean the same thing – they mean the length around the outside of the circle. And sometimes – not usually for circles – but for shapes, like them they ask you also for the perimeter. And you have to understand, when they ask for those three, that they mean the same thing, they mean the length around the outside, so as if you broke this string and opened it out how long it would be. OK. Now the way this is worked out is that it's related to the diameter:
Rule: Length of a circle worked out in relation to the diameter – i.e. its length is roughly 3 times its diameter.	The diameter of the circle is the line segment that goes across through the middle. If you worked out the length of that circle – suppose you know the diameter was 10 *(the teacher now writes 10 above the line)* the length of that circle then would work out to be a little bit longer than 3 times 10.

If you worked out the length of a circle with a diameter of 8 the length around there would work out to be a little bit more than 3 times 8.

Now the number we use for that little bit more is the number…?

1:59	Teacher asks a whole class question	*Teacher:* Have you ever heard of it before?
2:00	Class answer whole class question.	*Class:* Pi
2:02	<u>Pi:</u> $\Pi = 3.14 = \frac{22}{7}$	*Teacher:* OK it's pi and that's 3.14 or another approximation for it is 22 over 7.

$\Pi = 3.14 = \frac{22}{7}$

Now they're only approximations – they're not dead on to what this number is – but they're as close as you'll ever need to go at it. OK.

So what we're going to talk about then if you're doing the length of shapes and in each case the length is this number *(teacher points to number 3.14 on blackboard)* multiplied by the diameter but in a lot of these curved things they're more interested in working with the radius.

2:30	Teacher asks whole class question. <u>Radius</u>	*Teacher:* And what does the radius measure?
2:35	Class answer whole class question	*Class:* Half the diameter.
2:36		*Teacher:* OK. You're going to find in your tables (and we'll use the tables another day with these formulae) you're going to find in your tables that the formulae are all related to the radius. So if the length or the perimeter or the diameter or the circumference is pi by the diameter.

2:50	Teacher asks question to the class	*Teacher:* What will it be, by the radius then?
2:53	Frank answers the question incorrectly	*Frank:* Pi by r squared.
2:54	Teacher asks question again to the class	*Teacher:* It won't be pi by r squared sure it won't (shaking her head)? What would it be?
2:58	Frank gives the same incorrect answer to the question again	*Frank:* Pi by r².
3:00	Louise answers the same question	*Louise:* 2r.
3:01		*Teacher:* Yes it would be pi by 2r wouldn't it? Because the diameter is twice the radius. So if its pi times the diameter – around it would be pi times twice the radius around :

Length
Circumference
Perimeter

$$\Pi = 3.14 = \frac{22}{7}$$

$$\Pi\,(2r) = 2\Pi\,r$$

So, in your tables you will find this formula for the length, the circumference, around the circle is 2 by pi by the radius.

3:25	Teachers asks whole class question.	*Teacher:* OK. Is that OK?

Following this phase, the teacher worked through examples on the blackboard. She moved through five examples at a very quick pace, taking just over four minutes to complete these. This phase involved questioning both the whole class and individual students. There were a number of incidences here in which students mumbled answers or gave incorrect responses to her questioning. Generally when this occurred the teacher either restated the question (but did not re-phrase it) or answered it herself. This suggests that there may be a lack of understanding among the students of the methods being used. Although the teacher did check in with the class as a whole at intervals during this phase to see if they understood, asking: 'Is that OK?' and 'Is that clear enough?' many of the students did not respond to these questions and the teacher moved on.

Not only was this higher stream taught at a fast pace, it was also clear that Ms Leydon expected the students to take on any challenges they encountered. She expected them to be able to do 'hard' questions. She also gave the students responsibility for their own work, expecting them to correct their own mistakes, and to be able to see where they had gone wrong. She worked through each step of the problems they were working on, questioning the whole class and individual students. After completing part of one problem, she showed that she was not prepared to spend time on the more low level, basic elements of this particular procedure:

> OK. Now if you've got that far, you've the main part of the question done. If you don't get the right answer, then your mistake is something to do with multiplying or dividing. OK, which is not the main part of this question. But it's important that you do get this far, that's really, really important.

After setting homework, the teacher moved extremely quickly through three more examples which varied from those covered in the lesson so far. These involved finding the perimeter or length of different shapes. The three problems were taken from the textbook. Ms Leydon worked through these on the board, questioning individual students and the whole class, and inviting the class to provide suggestions regarding how to approach the problems. This process took just over eight minutes.

Another important feature of Ms Leydon's lesson was her use of praise. She praised students generally when they took initiative, such as when a student pointed out the teacher's mistake, or when another student made suggestions in relation to working out a problem. While Ms Leydon also gave some praise for correct responses to lower order questioning, this was neither as fulsome nor as frequent as her praise for initiative.

Unlike Ms Scanlon in Suir (SSG Fr D), Ms Leydon's comments suggest she had a general confidence in the ability of students in her class to understand and retain material. Remarks such as: 'You don't need to take this down' and 'Make sure you write it down in this order, so that you will have it', occurred throughout her lesson.

Like Ms Scanlon in Suir (SSG Fr D), Ms Leydon also believed that the students' social class background impacted on their learning of mathematics. Ms Leydon claimed that the predominantly middle class background of her students had a positive impact on their learning.

> I think if [students] have been given a positive feel about ability in school and in maths – like if you have a positive image about maths from home, that can make a huge difference ... Being confident is a huge part and if they stick at it and say

'I can do'. I would imagine that this top stream group are from quite a middle class background. In a foundation group you will find the opposite.

She expected most of her high stream students would proceed to third level education: 'Of that group … most of them are likely to go to college'. She also commented on their future employment prospects:

In ten years time, they would be 23 or 24 – I would say 95 per cent of them will be in paid jobs then … the girls and the boys … I would expect a few of them would end up in a maths-related career.

The findings here confirm international trends in relation to the implications of tracking. Higher track or streamed students are taught at a faster and more urgent pace (Boaler, 1997), and are exposed to more intellectual challenges and higher teacher expectations (Hacker et al., 1991; Gamoran, 1986; Boaler, 1997a, 1997c, 1997e).

Mixed 'ability' groups

A major objective of mixed 'ability' grouping is to promote equality of opportunity for all students; this is to be achieved by the adoption of approaches to teaching and learning that address the negative social consequences of homogenous grouping (Sukhnandan and Lee, 1998). Reid et al., (1981) have observed however, that the success of mixed classes depends largely on teachers' abilities to implement it successfully. To benefit from mixed grouping, teachers must ensure that they teach to the different capabilities of students in the group. Moving away from whole class teaching methods towards individualised teaching is seen to be one way of maximising the gains from mixed grouping (Gregory, 1986).

A number of studies have highlighted some of the problems associated with mixed 'ability' teaching. These have shown that teachers frequently resorted to either whole class teaching or worksheets, or set identical tasks for all students with no provision for student differences (Reid et al., 1981; Kerry, 1982a). Other research has highlighted the fact that few teachers have received any training on how to teach mixed groups (Gregory, 1986). Another problem highlighted in the literature concerns the level of teaching. Kerry (1982b) found that the cognitive demands made on students tended to be low. Hacker et al.'s (1991) study, of streamed and mixed 'ability' science classes, concluded that mixed 'ability' classes appeared to be treated as though they were low 'ability' streams. They also concluded that the teacher of mixed 'ability' classes tended to teach to the middle of the ability range.

Two of the ten class groups we observed were mixed 'ability' groups for all subjects (Nore (SSG Fr), and Lee (SSB F)) while Barrow (SSG F) has mixed grouping for all subjects except mathematics where students were set (tracked) by levels of attainment. Both Nore and Lee were single sex secondary schools: Lee was a fee paying boys' school with a predominantly upper middle class intake; Nore was a free scheme girls' school with more lower middle class intake than Lee. Nore also had a significant minority of working class students.

Because of the philosophy of mixed 'ability' grouping, it was expected that some form of individualised teaching would take place in the mixed 'ability' mathematics classrooms. In theory, the mixed classes should allow for students of different capabilities to work at different levels and at different paces. However, in line with much of the literature, we found this not to be the case. In the four mixed lessons (two lessons observed with each group in Nore and Lee respectively), we found no evidence of genuine mixed 'ability' group work. Lessons were taught at a uniform pace and level. While teachers did occasionally give a little time to one-to-one teaching, whole class teaching predominated.

However, the uniform approach adopted by teachers created problems because of the relatively wide range of mathematical skills among the students in the classes. In addition, the two mixed classes differed in a number of ways from each other in terms of the teaching style adopted. The differences in teaching style seemed to arise from the different social class profile of the two classes. To demonstrate the similarities and differences between the schools, we will examine one lesson each from Nore (SSG Fr) and Lee (SSB F).

Nore (SSG Fr) is a secondary, single sex girls' free scheme school. There were twenty-four students in the observed lesson. Two thirds of the students in the class were from a middle class background. Over half of the students (58 per cent) expected to take the Higher level paper in the Junior Certificate Examination, while 38 per cent said they would take the Ordinary level paper. The remainder (4 per cent) said they intended to do Foundation level. The class achieved a mean score of 21.9 out of 40 in the TIMSS-related mathematics test giving it a ranking of sixth among the ten schools. The attainment range (as measured by the TIMSS-related test) within the class was the second largest among the ten schools, excluding outliers. The teacher of this group, Mr Norris, is an experienced mathematics teacher. The lesson we refer to here involved learning about statistics with a focus on bar charts. It was a new topic for the class.

Comparable to findings in other studies, this mixed 'ability' mathematics lesson appeared to be taught as if it were a bottom stream class. The pedagogical style of the teacher was quite similar to that of the teachers of bottom stream classes in our study. The pace was very slow and the content level was low. In the interview with the teacher, he spoke about his general approach to teaching mathematics.

> *Mr Norris:* ... it's up to you to try and make them like it by making it interesting or by making it amusing ... by making it easy ... Revision is really important ... Retention comes from revision ... It's ridiculous to say to them: 'Go home and revise'. You have to help, and you see, in maths it's easy to do the revision with them because you have your back-up revision exercises.

The challenge Mr Norris experienced in teaching students with a wide range of different mathematical skills was apparent in some of the comments he made about the class. He indicated that he had to make conscious decisions to help students with difficulties.

> *Interviewer:* If somebody is getting lost in class? On what basis do you make the decision to go back or move on?
> *Mr Norris:* Well for example, there's poor old Sarah who came in a fortnight ago and she's lost. Now what can you do? What I can do is go back and while the others have started up the homework ... that's usually the time I go around. But if at the start of the class I find I'm hearing: 'Couldn't do the homework' and you're getting this sort of a general ... right OK, we stop. Because you do make mistakes and you do jump too quick on occasion. And we backtrack and we take it more slowly and we go over it depending on how it's going with them. And you can see the puzzlement on their faces.

Speaking about the importance of confidence in learning mathematics, this teacher commented on the way in which he attempts to instil confidence in students with different competencies.

> *Interviewer:* Do you think confidence is important in learning maths?
> *Mr Norris:* Oh yeah. Confidence is important in learning maths, that they get the thing right more often than not, and that you praise them when they do get it right. There was Mairead there now yesterday, she's very weak and she had missed out on something, and I came back to her a few minutes later and she got it. But you sort of tend to pitch your question towards the one that is able for that particular question, and sure the weak one thinks she's getting as hard a one as [the more able student]. You bring them along.

Throughout the lesson, the pedagogical practices employed by the teacher suggested that he classified students as ranging from 'weak' to 'able', and that his teaching style and pace was focused on those with lower skills in mathematics. He began the lesson with a lengthy introduction to the new topic of statistics. He explained the term in detail and gave examples of its uses in the real world. His introduction to the topic was interspersed with humour and references to the students' own lives.

> *Mr Norris:* Of course you don't find any [statistics] on TV or in the newspapers because first of all you only read the newspapers to see what's on telly, and you only watch ?
> *Class:* MTV!
> *Mr Norris:* MTV! – so therefore this doesn't really apply to us!

During the lesson he appeared to be trying to make the maths seem easy and attractive to the students: 'Our statistics today is going to be nice and easy. It's going to be bar charts.'

Mr Norris also used pedagogical practices that are more commonly associated with primary than post-primary classrooms. One of the most striking examples of these was the practice of calling on different students to read from the mathematics textbook. He did this on six occasions during the lesson, involving five students.

Mr Norris also tried to simplify and decode mathematics for the students, cajoling them with good humour into co-operating with him in class.

> *Mr Norris:* Tomorrow though we're going to do pie charts, which is circles. So tomorrow I want you to bring in ... (*teacher pauses as if awaiting a response from class*).
> *Class:* (*Giggles from some of the students.*)
> *Mr Norris:* Yes? If you're going to draw a circle?
> *Class:* Some of the students answer: a compass.
> *Mr Norris:* A compass and if you're going to make angles, your protractor. Now, unfortunately someone nicked my protractor, my little pink one. (*Teacher holds up compass to class.*) So you bring your compass tomorrow and you bring in your protractor. So if you make a note of that in your journals to show how efficient we are.
> (*Class take out journals and record it, teacher organises overheads.*)

Later in the lesson the teacher worked through more examples on the board. Again he did this at a very slow pace. He instructed the class to work out calculations in their copybooks, which mainly involved simple addition. While working out these examples, the teacher asked for a volunteer to come up and draw a bar chart on the board. He had planned in advance with the 'volunteer', that she would make deliberate errors. This was seen as a way of engaging other students with the subject.

Lee (SSB F) is a fee paying, single sex boys' school. There were twenty-six students in the observed mixed 'ability' mathematics lesson. All of the students were from a middle class background. All students said they intended to take the Higher level paper in the Junior Certificate Examination. The TIMSS-related test mean score for the group was 25.6, which was the fourth highest of all the schools. There was a reasonably wide range of mathematical competency within the class: Lee recorded the fourth highest range in the TIMSS-related test among the ten schools. The teacher in Lee was a young woman, Ms Lenehan. The lesson under consideration concerned algebra (quadratic equations). It was the continuation of a topic from a previous lesson.

The mathematics lesson with the mixed class group in Lee (SSB F) was taught in a very different way to that in Nore (SSG Fr). Contrary to findings in Nore, and in much of the literature about mixed classes, the lesson in Lee was taught as if it were a top stream group. The pace was fast and a sense of urgency prevailed.

In the interview, Ms Lenehan commented on the difficulties she experienced in teaching mathematics to a mixed group; she also commented on the difficulties confronting the students in her class.

Ms Lenehan: ... there's pressure to get grades ... pressure because you're working at a faster pace, but there's huge gaps within the class. You have some really good ones and kids that are really, really weak.

Interviewer: So it is harder to teach?

Ms Lenehan: For me it would be because you're trying to keep the good ones occupied so you're constantly working with two streams if you like. They don't as a rule do pass maths for the Junior Cert. here [in this school], but you will get maybe six that are about to do it every year but not much more than that, and that just at the last minute, they would have to follow the Higher level course [until then].

Interviewer: How does it affect them then, do you think?

Ms Lenehan: I do and don't think it's good for them. I do know that some of them ... you'll know from now ... will not be fit for a Higher level course and I'd say that possibly they would do better if the classes were streamed ... which they're not. I think it would be better for some of them.

Interviewer: Does it affect their attitude to maths?

Ms Lenehan: It probably affects their attitude to maths ... if you're not doing well at something, you take a dislike to it. A lot of them, I won't say that they're weak, I'd say they're maybe slow on doing something. Half the class may have ten questions done, then three or four might only be on question four or five. It's pure time. The course is very long. In fact the course is too long. You're hard pushed to get the course finished by the last term of school.

Although this class group in Lee (SSB F) was mixed, both students and teacher were under pressure to prepare for the Higher level mathematics paper in the Junior Certificate. While the teacher was obviously aware of what she called 'the gaps' within the class in mathematical competency, it appears that her priority was to get through the syllabus as quickly as possible and to ensure that all the students had exposure to the Higher level course.

There were a number of examples of the challenges faced by the teacher in trying to move through the work at a quick pace, while taking on board the difficulties individual students were having with their work.

In the lesson referred to below, the teacher was correcting the previous night's homework. The students had been given four questions to complete on problems involving quadratic equations. The teacher spent thirteen minutes correcting the first of these which involved expressing the following problem as a quadratic equation: The larger of two integers exceeds the smaller by three. If the sum of the squares of the two integers is sixty-five, find these integers.

The teacher corrected the question on a step-by-step basis, calling on individual students to provide the answer to each step. After each step of the procedure had been completed, the teacher checked with the class to see who had got it right up to this point. At each stage a number of students raised their hands to indicate they had not got the correct answer. The teacher then asked some of these students to explain where they had gone wrong. On three occasions, the teacher cut short the exchange with the student who was explaining his mistake, saying that she would go down to him later in the lesson. She then moved on to the next part of the procedure. We see an example of this in the following excerpt.

Time Code Activity Minutes/seconds		Content
3:17		$x^2 + (x+3)^2 = 65$
	Teacher asks whole class question	*Teacher:* Hands up who got that.
	Class reply	*Class:* Some hands go up.
3:26	Teacher asks whole class question	*Teacher:* Hands up who didn't get that.
	Class reply	*Class:* Hands go up.
	Teacher asks	*Teacher:* Where did you make your mistake?
	Marcus replies	*Marcus:* I did it a totally different way from the start.
3:30	Teacher asks same student another question	*Teacher:* What way did you do it?

3:34	Marcus replies	*Marcus:* x minus y equals 3 is equal to …
3:37	Teacher replies	*Teacher:* x minus y, you can only have one unknown. I told you that the last day, you can only have one unknown.
3:43	Marcus replies	*Marcus:* I got the right answer.
3:45	Teacher replies	*Teacher:* Yeah, but you're trying to solve these by quadratic equations. I'll take a look at the way you did it in a second, Marcus.

When the teacher moved on to correct the next homework problem, one of the students who had got the previous question wrong informed the teacher that he did not get the correct answer to the first part of the procedure and did not understand it. The teacher then spent some time trying to explain it to him. Although, at the end of their exchange the student told the teacher that he still did not really understand it, she chose to move on to the next part of the problem, calling on a different student to answer.

While the teacher made these decisions to move on during the class, she did spend time with a small number of students towards the end of the lesson. She instructed the class to begin their homework and helped those students who had been having problems. Over the two lessons, she spent a small amount (almost twelve minutes) of class time working with individual students.

Issues of social class

There was a very visible difference in the teaching and learning ethos between the mixed class in Nore (SSG Fr) and that in Lee (SSB F), differences that were not simply a function of their mixed 'ability' profile. Nore had a much more varied social class intake than Lee, which had mainly upper middle class students. While they both have a wide range of competencies, the Nore class group was treated more as a mixed class, in that both teacher and students differed in their expectations regarding the levels of mathematics they would eventually take in the Junior Certificate. In Lee the teacher, and all the students, expected they would take the Higher level paper. This seemed very much related to social class and is reflected in the comments parents in this school made at interviews as well (see Chapter 11). The parents of the boys in Lee were paying fees and this was something the teacher was clearly aware of in her teaching. Ms Lenehan acknowledged that her students get the 'push from home'.

A sense of urgency prevailed in the lessons in Lee and, although the teacher knew that some students were being left behind, she also knew that in this school they do not 'as a rule do pass maths for Junior Cert'. The teacher also knew that these children have the resources necessary to make up for deficiencies.

> I'd say due to the kids background … I'd say that the parents wouldn't take as big an interest [in other schools] as the parents do here because the parents will be in contact with you weekly/twice weekly through notes. If he couldn't understand something the parents would help them by seeing that they do their homework and that wouldn't really have happened in other schools … A lot of them also get grinds.

Thus, although Mr Norris and Ms Lenehan taught mixed classes, these were not taught in the same way. Ms Lenehan's class was in a prestigious fee paying boys' school where boys generally 'did not do pass maths for the Junior Certificate'. Mr Norris' mixed class was in a relatively low profile girls' school. While the intake was two thirds middle class, it was not upper middle class. It had what the teacher termed 'hard chaws' and 'toughies' as well as 'nice girls'. Although the teacher did not explicitly name the 'toughies' or the 'hard chaws' as working class, it was evident from the classroom data that it was students from working class backgrounds who were defined in this way. The teacher clearly believed that such students were not likely to be high achievers.

> *Mr Norris:* I tend to put the hard chaws with a nice girl, so sometimes it's hard on the nice girl but on the other hand you don't want all the toughies in the back row and you hope that they'll learn a little bit of manners, if nothing else.

The teacher in Nore (SSG Fr) was not working to the high parental expectations for all students in the way that Ms Lenehan was in Lee (SSB F). While Mr Norris' was a girls' school and Ms Lenehan's a boys' school, both student and teacher comments and our observations suggest that it was the social class rather than the gender profile of the students that seemed to be the overriding influence on expectations. One other reason for suggesting this arises from our observations in other schools. The other school in the study with a high upper middle class intake was a girls' school, Barrow, which was also fee paying. The learning climate in the classes in this school, albeit the top set for mathematics, was even faster and more competitive than that in Lee (SSB F). In contrast, the learning climate in the top stream in Liffey (SSG Fr D), a predominantly working class boys' school, was neither as fast nor as attainment oriented as that in Barrow.

Conclusion

What the data suggest is that one's experience of learning mathematics is mediated by the track, stream, set or band to which one is allocated. In common with a number of international studies, both nationally and internationally, we found that top tracks experience a more intense, work-focused and competitive learning environment than lower tracks (Boaler, 1997; Boaler et al., 2000; Burgess, 1983; Gamoran, 1986; Oakes, 1985; Lynch and Lodge, 2002).

There were important qualitative differences in the *type* and *quality* of pedagogical practices deployed by teachers in different tracks. The most striking differences were found between the bottom and top streams. In the bottom stream, the teacher's pedagogical approach was characterised by slow pace, constant repetition and an emphasis on the practising of very basic, procedural skills. The teacher's approach appeared to reflect the generally low expectations held of the bottom stream. The pedagogical approach of the teachers of the top streams was characterised by a fast pace and an air of urgency (Boaler et al., 2000). The teachers had higher expectations of the higher streams or tracks.

A dialectical relationship appeared to develop between the teachers' pedagogical style and the students' learning styles across tracks: the dependent and unconfident attitudes of the low track students to mathematics, combined with low basic skills in the subject, seemed to evoke a response from teachers that reinforced dependency. The teachers focused on developing basic procedural skills, moving slowly and systematically through the material with very low level questioning and answering. In high tracks, opposite dynamics were in operation.

However, it is not simply stream or track position that impacts on the learning climate: so does the gender composition of the class (see Chapter 6) and the social class profile of the student body. The analysis of teacher expectations and perspectives on students indicated that these were influenced by the students' social class background, a finding that concurs with international research in the field (Sorenson and Hallinan, 1986; Taylor, 1993; Wang and Ikertel, 1995; Hallam and Toutounji, 1996). In Suir (SSG Fr D) the teacher believed that the students' poor performance in school was directly related to their 'disadvantaged' family background rather than an outcome of the grouping system or teaching they had received. However, she did say that many of the bottom stream 'lacked the basic skills' of mathematics when they came to second level education. By contrast, in Barrow (SSG F) and Lee (SSG F) the teachers believed that the students' middle class backgrounds had a positive impact on their learning. The teachers of these classes indicated that they had high educational expectations for their students. This contrasted with the relatively low expectations of the teacher in schools such as Liffey (SSB Fr D) although the class observed in Liffey was a top stream within that school.

The analysis of mixed 'ability' classes gave a very clear indication of how social class and stream can interface with each other. In general we found that in mixed 'ability' lessons mathematics was taught at a uniform pace and level, and that whole class teaching predominated. There was no evidence of separate group work in the lessons. Discussions with the teachers regarding the pedagogical approaches employed in these lessons indicated that they experienced several challenges in teaching a mixed group because of the wide range of mathematical skills within them.

However, while mixed classes did occupy an interim position between top and bottom tracks generally, in terms of learning and teaching climate, their social class composition seemed to impact on whether the ethos leans towards that found in top or bottom streams. The learning climate in the mixed 'ability' class in an upper middle class school was more similar to that in a top stream, while the mixed class in a more lower middle class and working class school was similar to that in lower streams or bands in other schools. The findings here concur with other research which suggests that grouping by 'ability' is an important part of the process of social class reproduction (Lynch and Lodge, 2002).

Notes

[1] It is not possible to examine grouping in schools without recognising the complexity of the concept of 'ability'. While most research on education treats the concept of 'ability' as an unproblematic singular entity, this is far from being the case (Nash, 2001). Even a cursory analysis of psychological research on education indicates that what constitutes 'ability' is a hotly contested subject (Devlan et al., 1997; Gardner, 1985, 1993, 1997; Murray and Hernstein, 1994; Simon, 1978; Sternberg, 1998). While the IQ-generated view of ability has been largely discredited by developmental psychologists, most recently by Howard Gardner and his team at Project Zero, Harvard, the concept of fixed and immutable intelligence has a strong hold in public consciousness, including that of teachers (Fontes and Kellaghan, 1983). Students are frequently classified as 'bright' or 'dull', 'gifted', 'slow' or 'weak' without any reference to the insights of developmental psychology or education research. Moreover, students themselves have internalised and accepted these codes as we will show.

We do not subscribe to the singular definition of 'ability' or intelligence, or indeed to the view that what constitutes 'ability' is simply what is measured and tested in schools (Lynch, 1992, 1999). However, given the pervasiveness of so-called 'ability' grouping in schools, we recognise the importance of the subject as a lived practice.

Even though the students are unjustifiably labelled or grouped as 'weak' or 'able', especially when ability is assessed in narrow singular (most often, linguistic) terms, nevertheless what is defined as real is real in its consequences (Znaniecke, 1947). We have to examine the implications of so-called 'ability' grouping even though it would be more accurate to define what happens in schools as grouping based on prior attainment in specific subjects. To signify our rejection of the singular, absolutist view of 'ability', we refer to the subject throughout in inverted commas. Following Gardner, our view is that there are several intelligences or abilities rather than a singular entity called 'ability' or intelligence, and that each of these is open to development and change.

[2] The practices of *mixed-'ability' grouping, banding, streaming* and *setting* have been described in Chapter 3, page 5, footnote 3.

8

The English Classroom[1]

Introduction

The study of English as a discrete discipline gained credence in the nineteenth century with the growing interest in the 'liberal humanities'. Although it is rarely discussed in education circles, English was initially regarded as a subject that was particularly appropriate to women who wanted to enter higher education (Eagleton, 1983). The first intake of students of English in Oxford were predominantly women (and middle-class). It is not surprising therefore that English is commonly classified as a feminine-type subject in the analysis of curricula (Miller, 1996; Thomas, 1990; Reynolds, 1995; White, 1996).

Apart from its perceived femininity, the study of English was also regarded by scholars, most notably by F.R. Leavis, as being crucial for addressing moral issues, a vehicle for challenging the dehumanising influences of industrialism (Eagleton, 1983). While history has since taught us that it may be scientists rather than literary intellectuals who exercise greatest influence on how we live, and while I. A. Richards oriented the study of English to the close reading of the text, nevertheless the study of literature is still regarded by many as having a purpose beyond the critical analysis of the written word (Thomas, 1990). Literary theory has been influenced by, and party to, major philosophical debates within structuralism, feminism and postmodernism, all of which address issues of moral concern outside the realms of the literary text. Research with teachers of English shows that while some regard the study of English as being purely concerned with learning the skills of writing, reading and analysing texts, others regard it as having wider goals, such as enabling people to think critically about themselves and the way they live (Burton, 1994a; Thomas, 1990). There is also widespread support within the subject for criticism, dissent and diversity, not just about the way the subject is taught but about what should be taught (Kelleher, 2000). The level of accommodated dissent within literary theory and its related rejection of hierarchy, especially in the postmodern era, distinguishes the teaching of

English from the teaching of mathematics, especially in second-level education (Burton, 1994).

While there are undoubtedly hierarchies within English scholars, with traditionalists in particular laying great store on the classical texts, English is not characterised as being objective, value free, logical and internally consistent in the way that mathematics is. While highly regarded mathematicians such as Polya believed that the core activity of mathematical problem solving required 'judgement, originality and creativity', the practice of teaching mathematics is far more absolutist than Polya prescribed. The same does not hold true in the teaching of English (ibid).

Given the perceived differences therefore in the intellectual trajectory of mathematics and English, it seemed appropriate to choose English classes for comparative purposes in the study. Is English, a subject that was perceived by many to be less hierarchical and more feminine-oriented than mathematics, taught in a different pedagogical style? While there is a body of research suggesting that English (and other subjects) is taught in a different way to mathematics (Lindquist-Wong, 2000; White, 1996), our objective was to see if students from the same classes were taught in different ways by different subject teachers.

Ideally, we would have liked to be able to compare the teaching of English and mathematics to identical groups of students. Unfortunately this was not possible given differences in the tracking[2] of students across subjects (in particular, mathematics was more rigidly tracked than English). What was possible, was to compare similar tracks of students in second year English, at least some of whom had also been in the mathematics classes observed. What we were able to do therefore was to examine differences in the learning and teaching climates across subjects with some of the same students, and with students who were generally similar in terms of their educational attainments. Five English classes were video recorded, one each in Suir, (SSG Fr D), Liffey, (SSB Fr D), Lagan, (SC Fr), Nephin, (VCC Fr), and Lee, (SSB F). Where we had observed the top, middle and bottom tracks in mathematics, we observed the same tracks in English in each school (Table 8.1). As with the mathematics lessons, the unit of analysis was the class rather than individual students. So, while there was overlap in the membership of both the English and mathematics classes, we have not attempted to identify these particular students or to compare their experiences between the two subjects.

As can be seen from Table 8.1, there was considerable variability in the material covered in the English lessons. The material included drama, a short story, poetry, a novel, and a class discussion. The lesson in Suir (SSG Fr D) concerned an evaluation and report/functional writing based on a scene from the play 'The Field'. In Liffey (SSB Fr D) the lesson also involved functional writing which in this case was linked to a short story from the textbook 'New Odyssey'. Similarly, the English lesson in Lee (SSB F) concerned functional writing based on a poem. The subject being covered in Lagan (SC Fr) was the novel 'To Kill a Mockingbird' (comprehension). Finally, the lesson in Nephin (VCC Fr) involved a class discussion in relation to refugees in Ireland.

Table 8.1: Profile of English lessons

Name of school	Band or stream	English subject		New/ revision topic for the class
		Activity as defined by teachers	Specific topic	
Suir (SSG Fr D)	Bottom	Functional writing	Drama: 'The Field'	Revision
Liffey (SSB Fr D)	Top	Functional writing	Short story: 'Games People Play'	New
Lee (SSB F)	Mixed	Functional writing	Poetry: 'I Almost Had a Weakness'	New
Lagan (SC Fr)	Top	Comprehension	Novel: 'To Kill a Mockingbird'	Continuation
Nephin (VCC Fr)	Bottom	Discussion	Refugees in Ireland	Continuation

Key: SSG F: Secondary girls', fee-paying; SSG Fr: Secondary girls', free scheme; SSG Fr D: Secondary girls', free scheme designated disadvantaged; SSB Fr D: Secondary boys', free scheme designated disadvantaged; SSB F: Secondary boys', fee paying; SC Fr: Secondary coed, free scheme; CS Fr: Community School, free scheme; VCC Fr D: Vocational/Community College, free scheme designated disadvantaged; VCC Fr: Vocational/Community College, free scheme (where free scheme represents non fee-paying status).

In the analysis of the English lessons, we have focused on both the organisation of lessons by the teacher, and the nature of interaction between teacher and student, comparing these with our findings from the mathematics lessons.

Organisation of the lessons

The analysis of the English lessons shows that, as was the case in the mathematics classes, there was a high level of uniformity in the way material was organised and presented. All of the lessons were strongly teacher-led with low levels of student-initiated questioning. As with mathematics, a relatively small amount of time was spent on homework

Table 8.2: Percentage of time allocated to pedagogical activities in English lessons
(Figures in brackets refer to the time allocated in the corresponding first mathematics lesson)

School	Stream or band	Lesson aims %	Teacher interpreting the text (new material) %	Teacher interpreting the text (revision) %	Student practice/ reading, role play/ interpreting %	Setting homework %	Total %
				Lesson Script Stages			
Suir (SSG Fr D)	Bottom	2 (2)	0 (0)	49 (41)	42 (54)	7 (3)	100
Liffey (SSB Fr D)	Top	1 (1)	57 (38)	3 (5)	37 (54)	2 (2)	100
Lee (SSB F)	Mixed	1 (1)	48 (0)	0 (0)	46 (87)	5 (12)	100
Lagan (SC Fr)	Top	1 (1)	31 (79)	0 (0)	57 (18)	11 (2)	100
Nephin (VCC Fr)	Bottom	3 (0)	72 (0)	0 (58)	25 (40)	0 (2)	100

setting and lesson aims in each of the five lessons (Table 8.2). However, while teachers led mathematics lessons by demonstration, English teachers led by interpretation through dialogue. They led the class in interpreting the poem (Lee), the play (Suir), the narrative about refugees (Nephin), the short story (Liffey) and the novel (Lagan).

While the amount of time spent on teacher-led activities did not vary greatly between the two subjects, what did vary were the teachers' approaches to developing understanding. In English, conversation was a key mechanism for accessing knowledge in a way that did not apply in mathematics. Explanations in mathematics were linear and vertical, following predefined lines of reasoning and procedures; explanations in English lessons were more horizontal and lateral. The focus was on interpreting the text, poem or play from a range of perspectives. There was no clearly established path for analysing an issue; rather teachers examined aspects of the phenomenon under study from different perspectives, focusing on different objectives within the one lesson phase. In the second extract included below (from Lee (SSB F)), the teacher moved from a discussion of a particular character (the old woman in the poem) to an analysis of the human disposition of cynicism. Unlike the mathematics lessons, oral rather than written explanation was very much the norm, with the teacher generally making little use of the blackboard/whiteboard. In all lessons, the interpretation phases included substantial proportions of question-and-answer sessions.

An example of a teacher developing an interpretation of a short story is seen in the following extract. This is taken from Liffey (SSB Fr D), which is a single-sex boys' designated-disadvantaged school. The topic being covered in this lesson was a short story, 'Games People Play'. The teacher has spent almost one minute stating the aims of the lesson. This included statements regarding the purpose of the lesson and relating it to areas covered in previous lessons:

> Now, what we're going to do is, we're going to read bits of the story but we're going to link it up to the report writing that we're doing. Do you remember what we were doing in the functional writing? Where you had to do a report?

The teacher asked a series of questions about functional writing and has nominated a student to begin reading the story. At this stage the teacher interrupts the student reading.

Illustrative Extract from Classroom dialogue – Explanation
(Liffey (SSB Fr D) top stream)

Time Minutes:seconds		
7:12	*Teacher:*	OK. Where's this happening, before you turn over.
7:15	*Together they answer:*	On a road
7:16	*Teacher:*	OK. On a road. Where? Any ideas of what sort of place it might be? Is it in Ireland for instance? Do we know? Do we know if it's in Ireland?
7:28	*Adrian answers:*	His name is McKenna.
7:30	*Teacher:* *Alan:*	His name is..? McKenna.
7:31	*Teacher:*	McKenna. OK. Right. We're not 100 per cent sure, maybe. Maybe. Is it a city or a country area?
7.38	*In unison:* *Teacher:* *Feilim:*	Suburbs. Suburbs, how do you know? Now don't mind the illustration. How do you know? Because you can see the houses in the picture.
7:43	*Teacher:*	Well that's the illustration. How do you know Feilim? If you look at the words, any suggestions?
7:45	*Teacher:* *Feilim:* *Teacher:*	Any suggestions? What about the boys playing on the road? It's more likely isn't it? The few cars. The few cars. Well, whatever … we're not 100 per cent sure yet. What does 'exertion' mean?
8:00	*Feilim answers:*	Speed.
8:02	*Teacher:*	Exertion. Look it said here 'James stood there, his freckled face red with the exertion of the game'. What did you say? I couldn't hear you?
8:09	*Kevin answers:* *Teacher:* *Andrew:*	Speed. Speed no. Competition.
8:14	*Teacher:*	Competition. Kind of. Why was his face red? Out of breath. To exert yourself anybody? Trying very… Putting in a great effort. OK. So lets see what happens next. So this is the kind of thing you might see every day of the week. Page 76. Now, strange things happen.

8:24	*Teacher:*	Who's going to read the next bit? Thomas have a go there. Page 76.
8:38	*Thomas:*	'Give in, freckles!' Jason cried. Jason had no time to savour his victory as a pair of strong hands dragged him roughly from James. It was James' father. 'Why don't you pick on someone your own size instead of bullying my son?'
8:48	*Teacher:*	Could I ask you to read a little bit more slowly … 'Roared…'
8:51	*Thomas continues reading:*	Roared Mr. McKenna. At that precise moment Jason's parents, out for a quiet evening stroll with the dog, turned the corner from Oakdene Grove. They gaped in shock at the spectacle of Mr. McKenna shaking their Jason by the scruff of the neck. Mr. Doyle, trying to remain calm, strode forward to confront the man who appeared to be attacking Jason.
9:09	*Teacher:*	Can I stop you there just for one quick moment. What's to 'confront'. What does that mean, to confront the man?
9:12	*Dermot answers:* *Teacher:* *Gary:*	Come up and face him. To face him. Whatever. What do you think he was going to do? Ask him what was going on
9:22	*Teacher:*	Ask him what was going on. Do you think that eh, do you think that the boy was glad that his father said leave my son alone?
9:31	*Gary answers:*	No 'cos …
9:33	*Teacher:*	Who says no? (Some boys raise their hands). What do you think Declan?
9:36	*Rory answers:*	No, 'cos then he'd find out that he was fighting.
9:37	*Teacher:*	OK. (Teacher asks Andrew for his opinion since he has his hand up).
9:39	*Andrew answers:* *Teacher:* *Andrew:*	He was in front of all his, like, other friends. So how would that look? His Da had to stick up for him.
9:44	*Teacher:*	OK. So how might he feel?
9:46	*In unison:*	Embarrassed.
9:47	*Teacher:*	Embarrassed OK. eh… Do you want to go ahead there Shane. We'll get someone else to read there in a minute.

In this excerpt we can see both similarities and differences in the teachers' approaches to the English and mathematics lessons. In the mathematics lessons we found a very structured learning environment in which the teachers led the demonstrations and student involvement amounted to answering questions on particular steps of the procedures being taught. In this English lesson, this particular phase is also very much teacher-led with the students being involved mainly on the basis of answering teacher questions. What is different in this English class, however, is that the teacher is not striving to impose her own interpretation of the story on the class group, but is allowing and encouraging the students to interpret what is happening in the story through a series of whole class and individual questions. Her pedagogical style clearly reflects an epistemological approach that assumes that there is no single, definitive interpretation of the text.

Student practice in the English lessons also differed in the nature of the work undertaken. As discussed in Chapters 4 and 5, student practice in the mathematics classes involved students practising methods demonstrated by the teacher, which included the 'doing' and 'correcting' of problems assigned by the teacher. This practice was largely conducted privately by students. In the English lessons, student practice consisted mainly of students being called on by the teacher to read aloud to the class from their textbooks. This occurred extensively in all five lessons.

Other forms of student practice involved students being assigned an exercise based on the lesson topic. This occurred in two lessons (Suir and Lee). In the lesson in Suir this phase involved group work (a practice completely absent in all mathematics lessons) in which students worked in groups of two or three on an exercise. The lesson in Lee was quite similar to that in mathematics where students worked individually on an exercise assigned by the teacher. However, on completion of this, the students' work was not so much 'corrected', as was the case in the mathematics classroom – instead, it was used to generate a class discussion.

An example of how a student practice phase moved from the discussion of a particular character to the analysis of the phenomenon of cynicism is seen in the next excerpt. This is taken from Lee, a single-sex, fee-paying boys' school. The subject of the lesson here is an Elvis Costello poem, 'I Almost Had a Weakness'. At the beginning of the lesson, the teacher explained that this poem is actually a letter taken from a collection of letters put to music. It was a new topic for the class group. During the course of the lesson, the poem was read aloud by the teacher and a number of nominated students. The class built up an interpretation of the poem through a series of teacher-led questions. After this extract from the lesson, the teacher assigned an exercise that he gave the class just over five minutes to complete:

Right, so your job is to jot down in your copies, using a couple of words from the text, I want you to write a few sentences about the character of the woman involved, … What do you think she's like? Use words from the text. And then secondly when you have finished that, assemble a list of people involved in the story. In other words, who is involved here? Who is the person to whom the letter is being written? Who else will become involved in the story? Where else will the story extend?

Illustrative Extract: Lee (SSB F) Student Practice

Time
Code
Minutes:seconds

Time Code		
22:55	*Teacher:*	OK, so let's round that off for a second there. We'll put up a couple of words up here about this woman's character. So, first list, OK?
	Paul adds:	The woman involved is extremely ungrateful, throwing the flowers on the fire.
	Teacher:	OK, ungrateful for flowers (writes this on the board) Agree, disagree? Who would disagree? Paul?
23:34	*Paul adds:*	She knows they are only sending her flowers to get the money.
23:40	*Teacher:*	OK, so there's an element of grace lacking. She did get some flowers, but she sees through them to a kind of agenda. You know a hidden sort of reason for sending them. So maybe she's ungrateful. But we'll discuss later whether she's got a reason to be. So we have to put a question mark there. Rory?
	Rory adds:	The woman is very rude. Quote ' I burned the photographs of you and the kids. God, they were ugly children'.
	Teacher:	Completely rude. So now he thinks anybody. It's OK if they send him a present, you don't use it, leave it in the closet. But if they burn it and tell you they burned it, they're being rude. Right? Padraig?
	Padraig replies:	The woman is not stupid, is not easily fooled. Quote 'trying to trick a poor old woman'.
24:28	*Teacher:*	OK, we can put that on the other side of this one. Not easily fooled. (writes this on the board). Which is opposite to ungrateful for the flowers. She's both ungrateful but she's also seeing through why the flowers were sent in the first place. Colm?

Colm adds:	The old lady in the letter is very bitter. ' So you're the little bastard of that brother of mine'.
Teacher:	So from the same line we've got rude – 'you're the little bastard' and bitter because there's a spiteful tone in that. Would you agree?
	Next up, 2 more and we'll move on.
	Cathal?
Cathal adds:	She's a tired, grumpy old lady.
Teacher replies:	Tired, grumpy old lady. That's a charming way to deal with our old folks.
Cathal continues:	No, she's like tired of all her nephews and stuff, all running around, looking for money.
Teacher asks:	Right, is there a better word than tired?
Colm responds:	Worn out.
Teacher adds:	Worn out.
John adds:	Negative and paranoid.
Teacher asks:	Paranoid, OK Colm?
Colm replies:	Aged.
Teacher responds	Aged, (laugh), Aged?
	Yes.

25:47	*Teacher asks:*	Is that being older makes you tired and more sarcastic?
	Colm continues:	Sick of life.
	Teacher:	How would you describe somebody always looking for the agenda, and never trusting anyone?
	Dillon replies:	Sinister.
	Teacher:	Not sinister, a word close to that.
	James replies:	Cynical.

26:04	*Teacher:*	Cynical. Did you ever hear that word? Cynic, cynical (writes on board). A cynic – there are 2 descriptions of a cynic:
		Oscar Wilde said that a cynic was a person who knew the price of everything but the value of nothing. He's able to see the worth of something but not necessarily how good or bad it is in the overall scheme of things. My favourite definition of a cynic comes from – well me! Somebody who sees a bunch of flowers, and looks for a coffin. Because if there was a bunch of flowers, the only reason somebody would buy anyone flowers was if there was somebody dead. So that definition fits in very well with what they are doing with the flowers for this woman. She's going to be dead soon, let us ingratiate ourselves with her. So cynical means very wise in the world. It's like what you're saying, tired, fed up, grumpy. The world has thrown enough stuff at you that you know, think, I know everything that's going on in the world. Nobody is going to pull a fast one on me; I don't suffer fools gladly. So,

> cynical. OK that's a good one. If you don't have it, get that
> one down.
> Andrew?

As we can see from this excerpt, this phase of the lesson appears to have been conducted not to gather a list of 'right' answers but to generate discussion. The teacher gave an opportunity to a wide range of students to express an opinion, and ultimately to developing an understanding of different aspects of the poem. In the homework setting phase that followed, the teacher went on to explain what the class would be doing next in relation to this particular topic:

> The other thing I want you to do is to start planning. Next week I'm going to get you to write either the letter before this one or the letter after this one … Just mark that down now. Just write some notes down about what you would write. Think about your second list you did today about all the people involved, OK?

There was encouragement to plan their work independently of the teacher, and to think out and write about the characters in their own words.

Knowledge of English was clearly being generated within the classroom in a way that was quite different to mathematics. While the teachers of English did control the dialogue, and did at times seek predefined responses, the classes lacked the claims to certainty about what was 'right' and 'wrong' which was a very noticeable feature of the mathematics classes. The dialogue between students and teachers was exploratory and interpretative in English, while it tended to be grounded in certainties in mathematics – certainties about procedures and solutions, about what was 'right' and 'wrong', and about what was 'hard' and 'easy'.

Classroom interaction analysis

Overall patterns of public interactions

Public interactions taking place in the English lessons followed a pattern that was similar to the mathematics classrooms. Figure 8.1 shows that interactions were overwhelmingly teacher-led with 92 per cent of all public interactions being initiated by the teacher. The comparable figures for the twenty mathematics lessons was 96 per cent (See Figure 5.1, Chapter 5).

Teacher-initiated interactions

As was the case in the mathematics classes, analysis of the English lessons also revealed that questioning is the dominant mode of interaction between

Figure 8.1: All public interactions

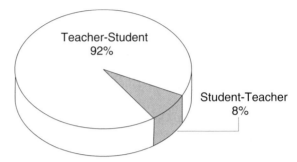

Figure 8.2: Teacher–student interactions

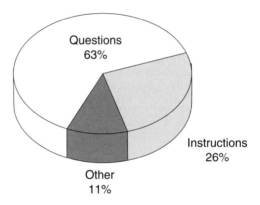

teacher and student. Figure 8.2 shows that teacher questioning is the dominant pedagogical practice in the English classroom with 63 per cent of all interactions being questions. Teacher questions comprised an even greater part (80 per cent) of teacher-led interaction in the mathematics classes. In the English lessons, 26 per cent of class time was spent on instruction compared with 14 per cent in mathematics (Figure 8.2 and Chapter 5, Figure 5.4).

Interpreting the text

While there were many similarities between mathematics and English classrooms in relation to the general character of public interactions, a more in-depth analysis of teacher-led interactions reveals some significant differences. With the exception of the English class in Lagan (SC Fr), it was very evident that in asking a question, English teachers sought an opinion, suggestion or interpretation in relation to the subject matter, as opposed to looking for the peremptory answer. While they did work on expanding vocabulary and developing a precise understanding of particular nouns, adjectives, adverbs, etc., the primary focus of classes was not on getting a single answer. In this regard, there were many incidents in which either the teacher asked the same question of a number of different students in order to glean different answers (Suir (SSG Fr D), Lee (SSB F)), or various answers were given by students to the same teacher question which was either whole-class or individually directed (Liffey (SSB Fr D); Lee (SSB F); Nephin, (VCC Fr)).

The following excerpt from a class in Suir (SSG Fr D) illustrates how the teacher develops students' understanding of the character of 'The Bird Flanagan' in the play *The Field.* In this short (1.5 minute) extract, six girls were involved. No definitive answer is sought but a series of interpretations are explored. No one interpretation is deemed to be 'wrong' or 'incorrect'.

Extract from English lesson in Suir (SSG Fr D) bottom stream

Minutes:seconds		
	Teacher:	Good afternoon everyone, today we're going to do a spot of revision on 'The Field'. Which you might remember from earlier on in the year. OK. So can anyone tell me anything about the character of the Bird?
6:00	*Teacher.*	Anyone remember anything? Deirdre?
	Deirdre:	He's very funny.
	Teacher:	What's funny about him? Can you be more specific?
	Deirdre responds:	He makes sarcastic jokes and he doesn't mean them.
	Teacher:	Right, OK, he's humorous, and?
	Deirdre:	He seems very simple.
	Teacher:	And he seems simple. OK, right, Barbara?
	Barbara:	He got his name from whistling.
6:44	*Teacher responds to answer and asks same question to Iesult.*	Yes, he is famous for whistling Yes, and Iesult?
	Iesult:	He's always scrounging drink off people.
	Teacher responds and asks same question to Olwyn	Yes he likes to scrounge drink. OK. And?
	Olwyn:	He earns a living by selling scrap on cars.
	Teacher:	Right, selling scrap on cars. He basically tries to make a few pound anyway he can, isn't that true? OK, Saoirse?

Saoirse:	He loves to rise Mamie.
Teacher:	Yes. Well. What do you mean by rising Mamie?
Saoirse:	To compliment her, like em, like the part where he says that the other man liked her, and there's like no one.
Teacher:	Right so he flatters Mamie. And there's one more hand up down there. Kellie?
Kellie:	He spies.
Teacher:	Yes he spies for the Bull, doesn't he?
Whole class responds:	Yeah.

7:30	Teacher:	Right and the Bull comes.

Sometimes teachers actually alluded to the uncertainty of the text, the uncertainty of knowing what was being told. The previously cited excerpt (Page 230) from a top stream class in Liffey (SSB Fr D) illustrates this point.

The following excerpt from a coeducational class in Nephin (VCC Fr) illustrates well the patterns of dialogue that are common in English classes, where the teacher is exploring the interpretation of the subject matter. In this excerpt, the teacher is preparing the students to do a project on the position of refugees in Ireland. The class begins with the teacher and the students reading extracts from the text on the life of an 18-year-old girl who came to Ireland from Sarajevo. Following this she asks the class to discuss her past:

Extract from English Lesson in Nephin (VCC Fr) bottom stream

Minutes:seconds

8:45	Teacher:	What would you imagine her life before the war was like?
	Robert answers:	Horrible
	Paul:	Not good.
	Teacher:	Right.
	Shane:	Before the war?
	Teacher:	Yeah, before the war.
	Laura:	Alright.

8:57	Teacher:	Yeah, what I mean is before she left the country. Why do you think she left the country?
	Few boys answer:	Because there was a war.
	Teacher:	Just a minute.
	Shane:	Because she knew there was a war starting and she wanted to get out.

9:05	*Teacher:*	And she probably had suffered. You brought in cuttings. Quite a few of you brought in cuttings about Kosovo and what is happening in Kosovo now.
9:15	*Teacher:*	So what kind of things, Paul, what did you say before, you know. Why she left her country basically? Paul?_____
9:25	*Paul answers:* *Teacher:* *Mandy also answers:* *Teacher:* *Mandy:*	And fear. Fear. She would have ended up like … Mandy? She would have ended up like them people if she…
9:36	*Teacher:* *Mandy:* *Teacher:* *Mandy:* *Teacher:* *Mandy:*	And tell me about those people. Ehh What do you call it? They don't have any food or anything like that. No food. Like they have no love from anyone. No love, security, and warmth, that's what we're talking about. Yeah, well she got out early. She got herself together.
9:49	*Teacher:*	Yes, yes. So what was the word we used for this huge crowd of people, this displacement, people moving around?
9:59	*Paula answers:*	Ethnic cleansing is it?
10:01	*Teacher:*	The ethnic cleansing, the ethnic cleansing. She didn't want to be part of the ethnic cleansing. Can anybody tell me what ethnic cleansing is? (Some students answer)
	Teacher:	Just a minute. Seamus.
10:13	*Seamus answers:* *Teacher:*	If you were, let's say if you were the Kosovans there or the Albanians. If you were Albanian then you'd have some people from another nation called the Serbs claiming the land. They'd come in and say this was a Serb civilisation. Yes, yes good boy.
10:25	*Teacher:*	Does everybody understand what ethnic cleansing means?
10.31	*Students answer:*	In unison: Yeah.

10:31	*Teacher:*	And there's another word, genocide. Do you know what genocide is?
10:37	*Seamus answers:*	The destruction of one race.
10:39	*Teacher:*	Yeah it happened in Nazi Germany. The destruction of the Jewish race and I'm afraid something similar is happening in Yugoslavia.

While the teacher in this English class is clearly using the subject matter of refugees to expand the students' vocabulary and their general knowledge of the reasons why people become refugees, and in that sense is developing basic procedural skills in English, the subject matter is not defined simply in terms of predefined procedures and responses. The teacher guides the students in their learning, but there is no established path that they must follow in arriving at their understanding. This was markedly different from the mathematics classes where the focus was on getting the right answer, and generally arriving at the answer in the 'right' way.

The moral dimensions of English

What was also interesting about the dialogue on refugees in Nephin, and the discussion in Suir on the status of women (that emerged from the analysis of John B. Keane's play, *The Field)*, was the implicit, and at times explicit, moral dimension to the analysis. English was not just about learning the skills of the language; it also provided a context for reflecting on life itself and the meaning of life for particular people. The linking of learning to philosophical or moral questions was absent from mathematics.

The following extract demonstrates how a discussion class offers scope for discussing important human rights questions in relation to refugees. The extract is taken from the part of the lesson where students had been reading the story of a girl who had come to Ireland as a refugee from Bosnia:

Extract from English lesson in Nephin (VCC Fr) bottom stream

| 17:26 | *Mandy:* | Miss, you know the way in that story her Mam is a lawyer but they won't let her use her skills and that. Well you know the way that people are doing part-time work in school. And they won't be able to do all that when they're older and now there's people coming in with that. And they're not even letting them use it. |

17:46	*Teacher:*	Yeah, yeah. That's a huge problem. What are the refugees going to do. I'd just like to say one word about that. When, you know we would come ourselves from a culture of emigration, where we had to emigrate notably after the famine, and then at later stages. But in London or America they would have no blacks or no Irish and we had to do the very menial jobs no matter what our qualifications or our intelligence. And in one sense many of the jobs are done by non-nationals that we would have had to do ourselves, you know 50 to 100 years ago in different countries. So we might be treating non-nationals the same way as we were treated a way back. But what I was going to say … I wanted to bring across the young man who is in his 20s, not able to speak English.
		But what about the girl's parents. Now, maybe the lawyer could speak English, probably could. But say that generation, the parents can't speak English. Can you imagine your parents being shoved out of Ireland and into Bosnia and trying to cope with the language there? What would happen? I mean the kids could learn it. You could learn it couldn't you. Just about. You could learn the language.
		But how would your parents feel? They wouldn't be sitting in the pub having a bit of craic with their own fellow countrymen. Do you know? Do you understand what I'm saying?
		And then we've still got … what have we got? We've got grandparents. We've old people as well. So we've all these groups of people having to struggle with different situations.
19:33	*Teacher:*	Now does anybody want to make another comment before we go and read another story from another country? (Seamus puts up his hand)
19:38	*Teacher:*	Seamus?
19:40	*Seamus speaks:*	How come we're cleaning up after NATO? Like, they started the bombing. They blew up loads of places. The Serbs ran about and now England is taking none of them in. Germany is taking a load of them in and that's not fair on Germany or Spain or France.
19:59	*Teacher:*	Are you saying that we should take some as well?

20:01	*Seamus:*	We already did, but it's not our mess. Why should we have to clean it up?
		Like, the main powers is America and is England. England and America were the first to say 'OK, we'll come in and stop this'. When they come in they slaughtered all the kings. They saved everybody. Well done. Where are they going to go?
		They apply to go to America. Oh no, we can't take you in. Fair enough. They go over to Canada. Canada has done nothing but Canada has to take them in.
20:30	*Teacher:*	Yeah well, the thing is that the preferred place for everyone to go is back to their own country. And basically, why NATO came in is because they couldn't allow Milosevic to carry on dictating and was kind of to help. Now we're not going to go into this too deep because you're only second years and it's a huge problem and there are no easy answers, James.
20:54	*Seamus:*	As soon as an asylum seeker comes over, his case would be processed. He would be given asylum. Then when the country settles down he'd be put back.
	Teacher:	Yeah.
	Seamus:	But then you see as soon as their asylum runs out they're scrambling. They're marrying Irish girls and next thing you know some of them are even drawing the dole and stuff like that.
	Teacher:	Yes, yeah. Well there is an information booklet. You see it's easy to make generalisations.
21:15	*Teacher:*	(Three or four students interrupt with comments) Excuse me, just a minute. It's easy to make generalisations. And what Ireland will have to do is kind of become more diverse culturally.

The lesson in Suir also touched on personal and social issues, in this case the dilemmas of women with children who had experienced violence in their marriages. The discussion took place in the context of discussing the character of Mamie from *The Field:*

Extract from English lesson in Suir (SSG Fr D)

Minutes:seconds

19:20	*Question 2:* *Teacher asks whole* *class:*	Right does anyone here first of all want to comment on Mamie's decision to stay with Mick Flanagan?
19:27	*All respond:*	Yes.
19:28	*Teacher asks Deirdre:*	What do you think would happen today? Would that be the case today? Deirdre?
19:31	*Deirdre responds:*	No. She'd obviously get a divorce today and she'd have the social welfare to pay for a house.
19:38	*Teacher:*	Okay, yes. Certainly years ago women after they got married they certainly didn't work in the public sector. So it was very difficult for women to leave their husbands.
19:53	*Teacher:*	So what else might happen today, apart from the fact that there are social welfare benefits and you don't have to stay with your husband if he throws you down the stairs. Iesult?
20:04	*Iesult:*	You can get a divorce.
20:06	*Teacher:*	You can get a divorce, is there anything else, any other actions that the law can take?
20:08	*Eadaoin:*	You can go to court.
20:11	*Teacher:*	You can go to court.
20:13	*Ciara:*	You can get custody of your kids.
20:15	*Eadaoin:*	You can get a barring order.
20:16	*Teacher:*	You can get a barring order. So there's lots of avenues a woman can take if she's in a difficult situation today. Anybody want to make a comment there? Saoirse?
20:28	*Saoirse asks question* *to Barbara who is* *playing the part of* *Mamie:*	You said that you had to stay because of your kids and that he loves them, but just because your kids, do you not have to be happy like? Maybe they weren't happy as well?
	Mamie (Barbara):	But like I've no life without him, like, he has the business. Back then you stayed with him when you were married to him.

Other differences

Although the number of English classes we observed was very small, it is interesting to note the absence of any reference to examinations within them. While there were several references to learning the subject matter for the purposes of doing well in examinations in the mathematics lessons, there were no such references in any of the five English lessons. Our findings regarding the use of incentives (in this case the future examination) to encourage students to engage with mathematics in particular, concur with those of Gregg (1995a, 1995b). Gregg found mathematics teachers used traditional procedural approaches, memorisation, etc., as a mechanism for coping with student disinterest in the subject matter of mathematics. Teachers felt secure in the knowledge that procedural approaches produced the desired examination success in a context where students did not appear to have an intrinsic interest in the subject of mathematics.

Another difference between the English and mathematics lessons relates to the way students answered teacher questions. Throughout the English lessons there were a number of incidences of more extended answering by the student. This contrasted sharply with the monosyllabic responses and short answers given generally to mathematics questions.

English and mathematics classes differed also in the use of group work and in making cross-curricular references. The class in Nephin (VCC Fr) began with the teacher reminding the class that the subject of refugees had already been addressed in the Civil, Social and Political Education class and that now she was following it up in English. This was one of the very few examples of the cross-curricular linking of subjects that we observed. It did not occur in any of the mathematics classes however. We also observed one example of group work in the English classes in Suir (SSG Fr D) but none in mathematics.

Language

Analysis of the language used in the English lessons also reveals differences between the two subjects. The most striking difference concerns the absence in the English lessons of certain language that was so prevalent in the mathematics classroom. While teachers used the word 'right', to affirm students in their responses, a content analysis of the transcripts found negative words such as 'incorrect' or 'wrong' were not used at all. Although teachers did use the word 'No' occasionally when students gave interpretations of particular words that were not quite accurate, there was not the same emphasis in the classes on being right or wrong in response to questions. This was especially true in interpreting texts, where many different interpretations were allowed.

The classification of subject matter in mathematics in binary codes as 'hard' or 'easy' did not feature in English classes either. When teachers introduced students to the material, the focus was not on the difficulty or accessibility of the material but rather with its relevance to the learning of particular skills, such as functional writing or report writing. Extracts from the introduction to two classes illustrates the approach:

Extract from the opening part of the lesson in Liffey (SSB Fr D) top stream

Minutes:seconds

	Teacher:	Do you remember what we were doing in the functional writing? Where you had to do a report on what? What was the report on? What was the report people were asked to do? Not the photograph but the previous one. The previous exercise in the report writing on what?
5:42	*Malcolm answers:*	The shop.
5.45	*Teacher:*	But what in the shops? What was the exercise?
5.47	*Paul answers:*	Facilities.
5.49	*Teacher:*	The shopping facilities in your area. And what were you meant to do in that exercise?
5.54	Noel answers	Write what they are now.
5.56	*Teacher:*	Well write a report.
5.57	*James:*	What could be done and what they're like now.
5.59	*Teacher:*	What they're like now plus…
6.02	*James:*	What could have been done.
6.04	*Teacher:*	What could have been done. What you'd like to see exactly.
	Teacher:	Page 75. Now this is a story called 'Games People Play' and it's about young people and adults. So will somebody read. Who wants to read? Who wants to start reading? Stephen.

Extract from the opening part of the lesson in Lee (SSB F) mixed class

Minutes:seconds

0:45	*Teacher:*	This is a piece that's going to come under functional writing, and it's also a poem. So it's kind of a double edge. So pass these back, if there are spares, pass them back across the back of the room.
1:05	*Teacher continues with lesson aims:*	OK, what we're going to do is read through this a couple of times. It will become apparent that it is actually not a poem, it's a letter, and it's taken from a collection called the Juliet letters, which is a collection of letters put to music with a string quartet by Elvis Costello. Anybody hear of Elvis Costello before?
	Students reply together:	Yes.
	Teacher adds:	He's in Austin Powers singing …
	Seamus adds:	What do you get when you fall in love.
1:27	*Teacher continues:*	That's right, 'I'll never fall in love again' Burt Bacharach. Now this one's from about 8 years ago. Anyone need a spare. (Boy gestures that he has spares). Right, just leave them down there. Okay, so we'll just read through it once and then we'll have a look at some questions. It's called 'I almost had a weakness.'

When teachers were responding to students, they tended to use terms that indicated several possible explanations or understandings rather than one. Terms such as 'possibly', 'perhaps' and 'maybe' replaced the 'correct' and 'incorrect' terms of mathematics teachers. Questions were also worded differently: 'What does that suggest to you?', 'Any of you girls got an opinion on this?', 'What do you think is happening?'.

Learning/classroom environment

In four of the English lessons (Lagan (SC Fr) was the exception) the atmosphere appeared quite different from that observed in the mathematics classes in terms of the level of student engagement. While the physical environment was similar, with students seated at individual desks arranged in rows and facing the teacher at the front, students appeared to be more engaged in the business of the English lessons than they were with that in mathematics. With few exceptions, students seemed to clearly enjoy what they were learning in the English lessons. They followed the stories very closely and seemed eager to answer questions or give opinions when called upon by the teacher. Differences between English and mathematics were especially notable in the two lower streams (in Suir (SSG Fr D) and Nephin (VCC Fr)). While students in lower tracks in mathematics in Suir displayed fear and lack of confidence in mathematics, they were highly engaged in the English lesson, actively taking part in the dramatisation of *The Field* and willing to ask questions of their peers and respond actively to the teacher's questions. In this, and in other classes, there were also very few incidences where a student gave no answer to the teacher's question, something that occurred more frequently in mathematics.

Gender differences in classroom interaction

Much of the recent research on gender focuses on differences in performance between girls and boys in public examinations. Both recent studies and earlier research indicate that girls have been achieving higher grades than boys in public examinations in English for many years nationally (see Department of Education and Science annual *Statistical Reports*) and internationally (Arnot et al., 1998; Cohen, 1998; Epstein et al., 1998; Gorard et al., 2000). In trying to understand these differences, it has been hypothesised that English is a subject that naturally appeals to girls but not to boys, hence the difference in performance. It is asserted that English is a subject that privileges narrative, and that it values personal and affective responses that appeal to girls in particular (Reynolds, 1995).

Recent research challenges this stereotypical view of the subject however, suggesting that there are fewer gender differences in the preferences for the subject of English than were originally thought. There is a growing body of evidence suggesting that girls and boys may differ in their approaches to the subject of English, and in their preferences to particular aspects of the subject (Hall and Coles, 1997; Miller, 1996; Myhill, 1999, 2002; White, 1996). Furthermore, Mac an Ghaill's work (1994) suggests the problem of gender differences in performance may have more to do with the widespread cultural approval of macho behaviour among boys; macho stereotypes denigrate literacy and related skills as feminine rather than masculine. There is also some evidence that the attitudes of teachers may reinforce gender stereotypical subject preferences (White, 1996). It may be differences in gender stereotypes, and related gender differences in preferences, that account for differences in attainment therefore, rather than any essential differences between girls and boys in the linguistic sphere.

What has not been given much attention in the research is the investigation of the learning climates of English classrooms, especially the impact of gender on learning experiences. What research there is provides little support for the claim that teachers' behaviour towards female and male students differs across subjects (Duffy et al., 2002, p. 581). Given the lack of knowledge in the field, we were interested in examining the differences in the experiences of girls and boys within coeducational classes with a view to determining whether the ethos of English classes was different to that in mathematics classes in gender terms.

Two of the five English classes that we observed were coeducational: one of these classes was in Lagan (SC Fr). It was a high stream group with twenty-six students, fifteen of whom were girls. The second class was a low stream class in Nephin (VCC Fr). There were twenty-one students in the class, nine of whom were girls. What is evident from Table 8.3 is that gender differences in interaction patterns in the two coeducational classes did not follow any clear gender trend. Neither were there any major differences between the classes in English and those in mathematics in terms of gender composition.

Table 8.3: Coeducational English classes: gender differences in class composition and in teacher-student interaction patterns

Name of school	Band or stream	Girls (n)	Boys (n)	Male: female composition ratio	Male: female interaction ratio	Ratio of teacher-student interaction per females in class	Ratio of teacher-student interaction per males in class	Gender of teacher
Lagan (SC Fr)	Top	15	11	0.73:1	2.58:1 (boys dominant)	0.67:1	1.73:1	Female
Nephin (VCC Fr)	Bottom	9	12	1.33:1	0.42:1 (girls dominant)	2.56:1	1.08:1	Female

Although both the English classes were somewhat unbalanced in gender composition terms, with the class in Lagan having more girls and the class in Nephin having more boys, the interaction ratio in the two classes was the inverse of the composition ratio. That is to say, the class in which there were more boys was female-dominated in terms of teacher-initiated interaction, while the class in which girls were in the majority was male-dominated in terms of teacher-initiated interaction. As both teachers were female, differences cannot be explained in terms of teacher gender.

The findings here concur with those in the mathematics classes where there was no clear pattern in terms of the relationship between gender composition of the class and gender interactions within them (see Chapter 6). What is noticeable however is that the interaction, per student, for girls, varied from being very high per head in Nephin to being relatively low per head in Lagan, while that for boys was more even in both classes.

Where gender differences did emerge in the English classes, they followed a pattern which was similar to mathematics in certain respects. As with mathematics, there was a greater likelihood for one or two boys to dominate the class, and some clear evidence that boys were more likely to dominate when spontaneous class contributions were requested (such as in whole class questioning). In Nephin, although boys as a whole did not dominate the classroom interaction, one boy, Maurice, was involved in a disproportionately high number of teacher-initiated interactions; he was responsible for most of the teacher-initiated interactions with boys in that class (he was inclined to be disruptive in the class so the teacher maintained his attention, and ensured the orderly continuance of the class, by engaging with him more than with other students). In Nephin also, while the teacher gave a disproportionately high level of attention to girls when initiating interaction, when students were allowed to respond spontaneously to questions (whole class questions rather than individually targeted questions), males dominated the question-answer sessions. This was particularly evident in the discussion about refugees which moved from an analysis of the human rights aspects of immigration (where girls dominated) to a discussion regarding the implications of the NATO bombing of Serbian-held areas, where boys dominated.

While boys often dominated those occasions in English classes, in particular where they could call out answers (although the teacher in Nephin tried to curb this, by asking specifically for a girl's view on one occasion), they did not always dominate. When teachers asked students to read from the text, girls were more likely to be asked to read in Nephin. Girls also received more questions in Nephin, and the questions were more evenly distributed between different girls than they were between the boys in the class. Boys were more likely to be asked to read in Lagan however, and they were also more likely to be asked questions. Unlike the teacher in Nephin, the teacher in Lagan made no reference to the need to include both genders in discussions or questioning.

Given the highly selective and voluntary nature of our case study classes, it is not surprising that there was not much evidence of disruption in either of the two coeducational (or indeed the single sex girls' or boys') classes. Where students tended to disrupt, teachers tended to keep them under control by minor reprimands or by focusing more work-related attention on them. As with the mathematics classes, it was boys who tended to be more disruptive in coeducational classes. In both Nephin and Lagan, there was just one boy reprimanded in each class, and in both cases there was only one incident of disruption.

Even though the number of case study classes observed was small, especially in the case of English, the data do suggest that interaction patterns in classrooms generally are quite similar. While boys do tend to dominate the more spontaneous interactions of the class in both subjects, there is a very low incidence of this type of interaction in both English and mathematics. Where male dominance did occur, we found that a small number of boys accounted for most of this in both subjects.

Classrooms appear to be highly idiosyncratic therefore. They are highly complex organisational spaces with the interaction outcomes being determined by the interplay of a range of social, psychological, pedagogical and organisational factors. The gender interaction patterns within them appear to be a function of the topic being taught, teacher attitudes, class composition and the pedagogical approach being employed.

Conclusion

There were many similarities between the teaching of English and the teaching of mathematics, arising in large part from the asymmetrical power relations between teachers and students that are so much a feature of all classrooms and schools, especially at Junior levels (McDermott, 1985; Lynch and Lodge, 2002). In both subjects, classroom work was generally teacher led and teacher controlled. Teachers initiated the work phases of the lesson and dominated public interaction. Both subjects also featured low levels of student-initiated questioning, with a very small amount of time being spent on homework setting and lesson aims. However, while mathematics teachers led their lessons by demonstration, English teachers led by interpretation through dialogue.

One of the most visible differences between the subjects was the manner in which the subject matter was presented to students. While mathematics was taught as a fixed body of knowledge, English was not (Burton, 1994a). The pedagogical styles employed by the English teachers fostered investigation and discussion of alternative interpretations most of the time. These teachers displayed a willingness to take different ideas and opinions on board in interpreting the text. English classes were also characterised by the absence of negatively evaluative language such as 'wrong' or 'incorrect', or of language denoting the difficulty of material as 'hard' or 'difficult'.

English was characterised by greater relativity and openness to interpretation; an exploratory, interpretative approach rather than a positivist paradigm, seemed to prevail. Whether these differences are a by-product of deep epistemological differences between the subjects or merely differences in pedagogical styles that have developed in the cultures of teaching is a matter of debate (Thomas, 1990; Burton, 1994a; White 1996). Whatever their origins, however, they led to very visible differences in the ethos of mathematics and English classrooms.

English classes also differed from mathematics in the way that learning occurred through conversation. Dialogue was a medium of learning in English in a way that it was not in mathematics. In addition, English teachers made connections between what had been learned in the past and what is currently being taught. They explained relationships between topics and provided the students with reasons as to why they were covering particular material in a lesson, or why they were being told to complete a certain exercise. There were also many incidences in which connections were being made between the subject of the text, real life situations and moral dilemmas, thereby indicating to students that English was a lens through which one could arrive at understanding of events in everyday life.

In gender terms, the differences between English and mathematics classes were not really significant, although we did find more evidence of male dominance in the five coeducational mathematics classes than in the two English classes. In both subject areas, boys tended to dominate spontaneous classroom interactions, a finding that concurs with that of Duffy et al. (2002). Dominance occurred mostly during whole class questioning.

In line with recent research findings on Irish schools, there was evidence in both English and mathematics classes that a small number of boys accounted for much of male dominance of class time (Lynch and Lodge, 2002). As the gender balance of the English classes was more even than a number of the mathematics classes, it was not possible to make any judgement regarding the impact of gender composition on interaction. It was interesting however, that boys dominated in the English class where girls were in the majority, while girls dominated in the one with more boys. Both classes were taught by women.

Notes

[1] We would like to acknowledge the kind assistance of Kevin McDermott in preparing this chapter.

[2] Tracking refers to all types of grouping of students, either on the basis of their levels of attainment in particular subjects, according to standardised tests or according to other agreed criteria in schools.

9

Learning Mathematics:
Teachers' Perspectives

Introduction

This chapter is devoted to the examination of teachers' views on mathematics. The two subsequent Chapters (10 and 11) engage in a similar analysis of the perspectives of students and parents on the subject. The analysis in each case is based on data from questionnaires, semi-structured interviews and focus groups.

Listening to the views of teachers, students and parents was important for two reasons. First, knowing the perspectives of teachers and students deepens our understanding of what we observed in the classrooms. Second, the inclusion of parents' views provides us with a more complete understanding of the learning process; it offers an important insight into the connections between school and home learning.

In this chapter the views of the ten teachers involved in the study are examined. The analysis focuses on their responses to a number of attitudinal statements, their views on mathematics as a subject (in general terms and in the context of the Junior Certificate curriculum and examination), their approach to teaching the subject, and their experience with the observed class group. The chapter closes with a discussion of the main findings.

Examining the teachers' perspectives on their classroom work not only deepens our understanding of the teaching of mathematics generally, it also gives insights into how teachers define and interpret gender relations in mathematics (Fennema, 1996a). Listening to teachers also helps us understand the interplay between teacher beliefs about teaching, and their teaching practice in classrooms. While some studies suggest that teachers' beliefs about mathematics teaching influence their interaction (Clark and Peterson, 1986; Shavelson and Stern, 1981; She, 2000), others have high-lighted the inconsistencies between teachers' philosophy and their practices (Gregg, 1995b; Raymond, 1997). The constraints of time and resources, and the pragmatism of students in relation to schooling and examinations, have all been found to explain the inconsistency between teaching philosophy and teaching practice.

Teachers' perspectives on mathematics

As national data on Irish teachers' perspectives on mathematics was available from the Third International Mathematics and Science Study (TIMSS), our findings are presented in comparison with these. Figures 9.1 and 9.2 present the results of the teachers' responses to the questionnaire items about the nature of mathematics and teaching mathematics. The first column presents the responses of the ten mathematics teachers in our study to each item, while the second column presents the national results of the Irish mathematics teachers who participated in the TIMSS 1994-95 study (Beaton et al., 1996).

Figure 9.1: Percentage of mathematics teachers who agree or strongly agree with statements about the nature of mathematics and mathematics teaching

(Case-study teachers vs. TIMSS Irish mathematics teachers)

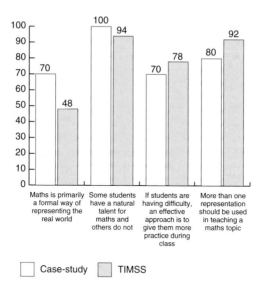

The teachers involved in the case-study expressed a more formal view of mathematics than teachers did nationally. While less than half of Irish mathematics teachers (48 per cent) surveyed for the TIMSS study claimed that mathematics was primarily a formal way of representing the world, seven of the ten teachers in our study held that view (Figure 9.1, Beacon et al., 1996). This was the only area, however, in which the group differed greatly from the national sample of mathematics teachers. Both sets of teachers shared similar views of student capabilities in mathematics, and of approaches to the teaching of mathematics. It is noteworthy that all of the teachers in the case study, and more than nine in ten of the mathematics teachers surveyed nationally, held strongly essentialist views about mathematical abilities: they believed that some students have a natural talent for the subject while others did not. There was also widespread agreement among teachers about the benefits of students practising procedures during class, a view that resonates strongly with their formal view of the subject.

Figure 9.2 outlines the attitudes of teachers to the cognitive demands of mathematics. It documents in particular the skills the teachers regarded as 'very important' for succeeding in mathematics. As with Figure 9.1, the views of the teachers in the case study are compared with those of teachers nationally.

Figure 9.2: Percentage of mathematics teachers who think that particular abilities are very important for pupils' success in mathematics in school (Case-study teachers vs. TIMSS Irish mathematics teachers)

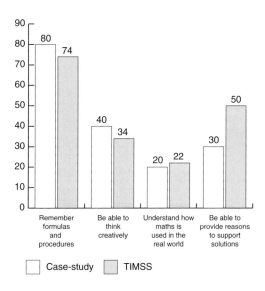

There was a high level of congruence between the views of the teachers in the case-study, and the views of teachers in the national TIMSS study, as to the attributes that were required for success in mathematics (Figure 9.2). The only area of any great difference was in the importance attributed to being able to give reasons to support solutions; the teachers in the case-study attributed even less importance to this than teachers did nationally.

In the international TIMSS study, mathematics teachers in Ireland attributed more importance to memorising formulae and procedures than teachers in other countries (74 per cent rated it as important in Ireland compared with 40 per cent in most other countries). The teachers in the case-study expressed similar views to teachers nationally, with eight of the ten regarding the memorisation of formulae and procedures as very important for success in mathematics.

In the TIMSS study, the majority of mathematics teachers internationally expressed the view that it was very important for students to be able to think creatively, to understand how mathematics is used in the real world and to be able to provide reasons to support their solutions. These skills were not rated highly in Ireland in the national study. Equally, the findings in Figure 9.2 show that the teachers in our study do not attribute a high level of importance to these skills. In the context of labour market expectations that students are able to apply mathematics to solve practical problems, Beaton et al., (1996, p. 139) expressed surprise at the low ranking attributed by teachers in countries such as Ireland to understanding and thinking creatively in mathematics.

Overall, our case study teachers, and Irish teachers generally, seemed to regard mathematics in traditional ways. It was seen as a formal way of representing the world, and as a subject at which students were either naturally talented or not. While most believed that varied teaching methodologies and practice at the subject improved learning, learning itself was most often equated with the memorisation of formulae and procedures rather than thinking creatively. Relatively few believed that being able to provide reasons for solutions or understanding how mathematics is used in the real world were very important.

These findings suggest that Irish mathematics teachers have what Burton terms (1992, 1994a, 1994b, 1995, 1996a) an absolutist rather than a relativist view of the subject of mathematics. This absolutist or objectivist view has been shown to have an impact on pedagogical practice; the focus is on procedures and formulae, on the how rather than the why of mathematics (Dossey, 1992).

Pedagogical practices

Figures 9.3 and A.9.1 present teachers' self-reports of their level of usage of particular methodologies in their Junior Cycle mathematics lessons. Each teacher was asked to specify the extent to which they vary their pedagogical practices by Higher, Ordinary and Foundation level. These findings provide a context for the qualitative accounts that follow.

From the findings outlined in Figure 9.3 we can conclude that the teachers in the case study schools were most concerned with showing

Figure 9.3: Teachers' reports about teaching mathematics: events happening 'every lesson' or 'most lessons'
(Base: All teaching particular level)

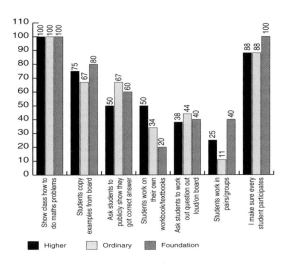

students how to do maths problems. Teachers' accounts of their work in this respect confirm the findings from the video analysis material (see Chapters 4 and 5) where there was strong evidence of demonstration-led teaching. Given the importance of teacher-led demonstration, it is not surprising that teachers report that most lessons also involved students copying examples from the board. It is clear therefore that the objectivist view of mathematics held by the case-study teachers impacted on their work, leading to a focus on procedures and formulae.

The teachers also report that they actively attempt to involve all students in the lesson. They claim this is particularly the case at the foundation level where they believed that involvement was necessary to maintain the students' concentration and motivation. Teachers' claims regarding involving all students in the lessons were not borne out in all classes. There was a considerable difference in levels of student involvement across classes, with single sex girls' classes being the most inclusive and boys' only classes the least inclusive, regardless of the level at which the subject was being taught (see Chapter 6)

The claims of teachers regarding the public nature of mathematics work in class resonates with what we observed in the lessons and reported in Chapter 5. While appraisal is also often conducted publicly, the teachers admit that they are less likely to ask students to do questions out loud or on the board. Mathematical problems tend to be broken down into small parts with a range of students being asked to offer solutions at different stages. Our observation of the lessons showed that teachers tended to transcribe each step onto the chalkboard; in only one school (Blackstairs VCC Fr D) was there any evidence of students completing entire problems themselves.

Finally, work by students either on their own or in small groups is reported to be infrequent, especially in Ordinary and Higher classes. Once again, the claim that group work is infrequent is confirmed by our analysis of the lesson videos. However, contrary to teacher claims, we did not observe any more group work in the lower stream classes, where Foundation mathematics was being taught, compared with higher streams.

Teacher reports of homework organisation concur with our classroom observations (Figure A9.1). Irrespective of whether the class is studying mathematics at Foundation, Ordinary or Higher level, most of the teachers assign homework in each lesson. Equally, the normal practice is for this homework to be corrected in the next lesson. Only in the case of Higher level mathematics is there a practice, albeit occasional, of students correcting each other's homework. Finally, teachers of Foundation level mathematics report that they frequently allow students to start their homework in class. As explained in the interviews below, this allows teachers time to circulate and observe students' progress and help them with any difficulties. Teachers reported that such students were less likely to have access to help outside of school and doing homework in class afforded them the opportunity to get help from the teacher on a one-to-one basis. In our observations however, we found evidence of both high and low track classes commencing their homework in class.

The data would suggest therefore that while there is a high level of congruence between teachers' accounts of their pedagogical practices and their actual practice, there are also inconsistencies. The main differences arose in relation to the levels of inclusiveness reported and the amount operating in practice, and between teacher accounts of how they accommodated the needs of Foundation level students and what they did in the classrooms. Teachers reported themselves to be more inclusive of all students and to be more accommodating of the needs of Foundation level students than they were in practice.

Person-centred and depersonalised accounts of mathematics teaching

We asked teachers to describe in their own words their approach to teaching maths. While all the teachers depict their pedagogical approach in traditional terms, their actual accounts can be further divided into two main categories, namely person-centred and depersonalised accounts. In the person-centred accounts, teaching was adapted to suit the particular needs and experiences of the students. References were made to improving the quality of the students' learning experience by using humour, encouragement and patience, and by including examples with which students could identify.

Teaching is depersonalised in the other accounts. The main emphasis is on the procedures for transmitting knowledge from teacher to student, with little or no reference to the cultural context of the learning situation. Students tend to be defined in homogenous terms, most often as part of a particular 'ability group'.

Five of the ten teachers in the study describe their approach to teaching mathematics in a person-centred way. These teachers refer to ways of making the learning of mathematics more meaningful, relevant and enjoyable. In the first excerpt included here, the teacher of a top-stream class in a girls' fee paying school mentioned the importance of humour, and of making learning fun and satisfying:

Ms Brennan: I hope my approach to teaching maths is through explanation number one. My second thing is – and it may not have been obvious when you were videotaping me – but I try to be good humoured in a big, big way. I try to make it light hearted and enjoyable because I, over the years, experienced shocking drudgery from teachers, total disinterest and also *confusion* at times! I really did! So I try to make it enjoyable and I try to make them see that it's fun and that you can get lots of satisfaction out of getting something out or out of conquering something that you thought was impossible. And the bit of praise is good and I also want them to think I love it (*with a laugh*). I try to make it happy and I try to make it simple and I do try to explain and I don't give them much written work in class. I try to have it all board work and the class responding. They do the written work at home. (Barrow SSG F)

Similarly, the teacher of a top-stream boys' class in a designated disadvantaged secondary school points to the importance of personalising the lesson, of getting around the class and getting to know individual students.

Mr Little: I'd like to think that it's very personal and personable, in so far as I try to accommodate the various elements within the group that I'm teaching, as in from the top to the bottom. And to be a little bit aware of their own needs and hopefully to devote enough attention into the various levels to keep the very good ones ticking over and motivated, and yet to keep the weak fellas on board. If anything I would go more for the weaker fellas than the stronger fellas. In that approach it's always to the child – it is like it's child-centred. I like to get around and *see* what they're doing every day. One of the reasons why I do a lot of rambling and roaming around the class is to identify those who have problems, to see if I can remedy the problem there and then. If I can I will. That's an integral part of my teaching approach. If there's a problem that needs further remediation, I would normally ask the guy to stay back normally at lunchtime. It's a hands on full job and I really get to know them that way. (Liffey SSB FrD)

The next excerpt involves a teacher of a bottom stream coeducational group in a designated disadvantaged community college. This teacher's report of her approach to teaching mathematics shows her awareness and understanding of the educational and social difficulties experienced by a majority of the students. In this context, the teacher emphasises the importance of encouragement, patience and not being critical.

Ms Malone: I suppose my approach is a bit of exposition, a lot of getting them to do stuff, rather than me doing it. I'd say I spend much less time talking than they spend working on it, and I try to get them to think. Now I think in certain situations … I don't do that initially because I think you have to get them to some basic skills first and to be happy with it, and to be comfortable with it, and then to try and get them to think things out for themselves. I suppose encourage – I don't know how I describe it really, I try to encourage and bring out their natural intelligence I suppose and try and be patient. That's very important in maths. Like I think it's very easy to get very impatient and then if that communicates itself you have destroyed five weeks of work. I have on occasion said something, say something harsh because I was in a bad humour and think I have destroyed five weeks of building up – just with one sentence and you kill yourself then and think – that was really stupid. (Mourne VCC Fr D)

The final excerpt involves a teacher of a top stream in a coeducational community college, also designated disadvantaged. The approach involved the teacher establishing rapport with the students through a combination of personal friendship and making the subject matter relevant to their lives. It is noteworthy that in making the material relevant to their lives the teacher used only male oriented examples (soccer scores, matches and teams). The video analysis shows that this teacher's lesson was also very male oriented in practice (see Chapter 6). The teacher described ways of involving the students in the lesson, by bringing them up to the board and getting the students (rather than the teacher) to nominate the person to go to the board.

Mr Butler: In the classroom I would try and bring myself to the level of the students and in a lot of cases I would talk to them about their interests. I would try to get their interest and hold their interest by basing a lot of maths problems on their experiences outside school. If we were doing bar charts or pie charts we would talk about scores of matches and Premiership games, number of goals scored and players. If we're doing relations and functions you can do soccer players on a particular team. When you're involved outside with teams it's a huge benefit and I still think I have a fairly good relationship with our past students and with students generally. When you meet them out you stop and chat, particularly the senior students in the school. I would base a lot of problems on their experiences rather than lecture to them. (Blackstairs VCC Fr D)

Turning now to the less person-centred accounts by the remaining five teachers, references to the particular social context of teaching are absent. With the exception of differences by 'ability', students are discussed as if they are a homogenous group.

Most teachers made some reference to the tight time frame for completing the Junior Certificate course. However, some laid more emphasis than others on having to tailor their pedagogical approach to meet the requirements of the curriculum and national examination system. They claimed they had to progress through the curriculum at a fast pace to ensure that all the topics in the Junior Certificate course were covered for the examination.

In this first excerpt, the teacher of a bottom stream class in a girls', designated disadvantaged secondary school describes teaching in the context of a tight schedule. Her approach to teaching is influenced also by her belief that all the students in the class are of low 'ability'. Students are described as being in need of a lot of help and guidance from the teacher.

Interviewer: How would you describe your own approach to teaching maths?
Ms Scanlon: Very traditional, I would think. I have a course to do and I have this much maybe set out for myself for one year, maybe a couple of chapters to do and that has to be done within a certain timeframe. I tend to give this class [bottom stream most likely doing Ordinary or Foundation] in particular a lot of … give them homework and get them started and then come up around then to have them working on topics with me.… With another group I'd push them more and more. I know I can get more out of them so I'd push them and get them to think, to try and relate topics. If I was doing – for instance – the honours maths course and I was doing differentiation, I would try and get them to think back to the line, to the equation of a line and link it in and get the tangent to something and they can think that way. But once you get a class like this one you have to really push to get <u>any</u> information out of them and they can't relate topics at all. (Suir SSG Fr D)

The students in the next excerpt are in a mixed group in a fee paying boys' secondary school. In this context, the teacher refers to the need to teach at a slower pace to ensure that the 'weaker ones' can understand.

Interviewer: How would you describe your own approach to teaching maths?
Ms Lenehan: Normally what I do – it obviously depends on the topic – but again it would just be – I'd do maybe three or four examples and then let them try an example. Or else sometimes I'd get them up to the board to do stuff, it totally

depends on the topic what you do. In a topic where you know some of them are going to get it straight away, and I know that some of them aren't, I'd need to go through each, line by line, so the weaker ones will pick it up. I'd start and explain it and then do an example – maybe they'd do one. I'd practice and then we'd continue. (Lee SSB F)

Similarly, the teacher of a top-stream coeducational group in a secondary school described how she would alter her teaching approach in the context of a 'good group' compared with a 'weak group'.

Interviewer: How would you describe your own approach to teaching maths?
Ms Leydon: I would say I'm very traditional – it's very traditional. I would tend – I would try and aim at what their homework is going to be. I would know at the beginning of the class what they're going to have to do tonight. If it's a good group you can work away and give them five questions for homework. But if it's a weak group I may have to decide: okay those first three questions are going to be for homework and they'll manage those and I'll do four, five or even six with them. I'll do the harder ones. What I would tend to do a lot is just give examples, explain the example or ask them maybe to do an example with me on the blackboard, where they tell me what to write down and then they do an example on their own. It's quite traditional. (Lagan SC Fr)

This next excerpt contains an explicit reference to the importance of repetition; this was a pedagogical practice that was apparent in several mathematics lessons, particularly with bottom stream classes. The teacher involved in the following interview is tutoring a middle stream coeducational group in a community school.

Interviewer: How would you describe your own approach to teaching maths?
Ms Ennis: Traditional enough I suppose but I would try to break it down into very small steps. It depends on the group I have. If I'd a good class and I knew they were going to be an honours group I would try and elicit more from them than me just giving it to them. While I would still do an example – like in that class you observed I did an example and said: 'What do you spot?' and 'Tell me what you see'. If I had an honours group I would push them a little bit. I would try and get the answer from them rather than me telling them. I think when you are explaining things you need to be very repetitive – you need to say something over and over and over and over. Especially with Foundation – it would really be one to one and doing it over and over and over. (Errigal CS Fr)

In the final excerpt the teacher describes his approach to teaching as didactic. It is an impersonal account: there is no reference to the individual needs of the particular students involved. The students referred to in this interview are a bottom stream coeducational group in a community college.

Interviewer: How would you describe your own approach to teaching maths?
Mr Nally: Uuum – didactic – which, I think is the only way to teach maths really. I'm not into discovery teaching where maths is concerned I'm afraid … Very much the way I was taught myself. Very much explain the theory, do it on the board, show an easy one, show a hard one, then: 'On yer bike' *(with a laugh)*. (Nephin VCC Fr)

Knowledge of alternative pedagogical approaches

Whether they were person-oriented or not, each of the teachers' self-reports of their pedagogical practices indicated an allegiance to traditional approaches to teaching mathematics. Following this discussion, we asked the following question:

> The general approach to teaching maths could be described as explanation of the concepts, followed by demonstration of the procedures, followed by student practice. Have you ever experienced any other style of teaching maths, either in your own education, during your teacher training or in your career?

Only one of the ten teachers in our study had ever experienced any other type of pedagogical approach. The teacher involved taught a top stream, girls' class in a fee paying secondary school. This teacher had previously worked in Britain and was exposed to a different pedagogical approach there. She was not very positive, however, about her experience of teaching with less traditional methods; she believed they were suited to neither top stream students nor to the syllabus in Irish schools.

> *Ms Brennan:* Teaching in the British system was very, very practical. Now I'm very scathing of that!
> *Interviewer:* What do you mean by practical?
> *Ms Brennan:* You had kits for all sorts of things. I mean, if you were doing three dimensional shapes you spent your time building tetrahedra and that. We don't do that – we tend to make sketches of them here. A lot of it is very time wasting and repetitive and I think that if you have children who are mathematically talented to some degree it's a waste of time … I suppose it would be possible to move away from the traditional style of teaching, provided that the syllabus changes. But the syllabus that we have is so structured we have to stick to chalk-and-talk methods or we're never going to prepare the student. Perhaps in fourth year, in transition year, there's definitely room there for examining other areas in mathematics. (Barrow (SSG F)

The remaining nine teachers in the study explained that they were taught in traditional ways themselves. They had not experienced an alternative approach throughout their teacher training or their teaching career. This is explained in the following excerpt by the teacher in a single sex girls' secondary school.

Ms Scanlon: That's probably the way I was taught myself. I would reverse the order sometimes. I would give the demonstration, then go back on the theory behind it. I generally give a kind of idea how to do it firstly and then we go back on the theory. That way they can apply it more, see what's happening rather than look at the theory because that [the theory] just turns them off. (Suir SSG Fr D)

Teachers' views on learning

Making Progress: Encouragement and 'Innate Mathematical Ability'

To explore teachers' views of learning, we asked if they could identify particular students who had 'made progress' over the course of the school year, and equally, if they could identify individual students who 'had fallen back' during this time. Six of the ten teachers were able to identify students who had made progress. One teacher could not identify any student who had made progress, while three reported that they were unable to answer the question.

The teachers who identified students who had made progress over the school year generally explained this in terms of active confidence building and encouragement on the part of the teacher. Importantly, however, progress was seen to be contingent on the particular student(s) having 'natural mathematical ability'.

In the excerpt that follows, the teacher of a middle streamed coeducational class in a community school identified one particular girl as having made progress during the year. When asked to identify the reasons for her progress the teacher pointed to a pedagogical approach that included confidence building and encouragement. However, the teacher believed that progress was possible only because the student was not naturally 'weak' at mathematics.

Interviewer: So to what would you attribute her progress?

Ms Ennis: I would say I have given them a bit of confidence – even some of the boys – they would perhaps last year have said, they have this thing if they don't get the answer right they're wrong and they're no good. So I would try to encourage them that it's the amount of work you put down on paper, it's not necessarily the answer.

Interviewer: So, in other words you are saying that you think the teacher and the teaching approach is very important in a student's progress.

Ms Ennis: Yes, but I couldn't bring someone who is very weak – I could never bring them up to an honours standard – ability of course comes into it.

Interviewer: So you don't think it is possible to make that kind of progress?

Ms Ennis: No – not if they're terribly, terribly weak. But you would have children who would experience difficulties and consider themselves a failure and I can get them and give them that little bit of confidence ... (Errigal CS Fr)

Another teacher of a top stream coeducational class in a designated disadvantaged community college mentioned two particular students (a boy and a girl) as having made progress during the course of the year. In this case, a pedagogical approach that included attention, encouragement and praise was identified. Here again, progress is seen as contingent on students' having 'innate mathematical ability'.

Interviewer: Do you know why these students made progress?

Mr Butler: I don't know – they give me … or I'd have the feeling that if they were allowed to drift they probably would have gone back down a little bit. Giving them a little bit of attention and let them know you're monitoring their progress from all the other classes, and give them a little bit of encouragement where they are having difficulty and a bit of praise. Let them know that you are aware that they have scored well in class tests and that they are improving. That seems to help them.

Interviewer: Do you think then that students can change over time either for the better or worse?

Mr Butler: They can change if you allow them to change. With maths we find if they have the ability you can work on that ability and you can improve their results with a bit of individual attention and praise and a bit of encouragement and especially if you can monitor everything they do. And where they get questions right, praise them for it. But on the other hand, if they don't have that *innate mathematical ability* then some of them are not going to improve, they would probably end up not improving. You can recognise that at an early stage. Like if you get to know students well in first year, some of them just won't have it with maths – they're not going to change. They'll change a bit alright. They will get enough to pass by working repetitively on examination questions. They will probably pass the Junior Cert. But when they come to senior cycle – where they change around questions – they won't know what to do, they won't be able to cope. If they don't have that something, that innate ability, they just won't acquire it, it just won't happen. (Blackstairs VCC Fr D)

A teacher of a single sex top stream group in a fee paying, secondary school was unable to identify particular students who had made progress. Her inability to identify particular students was in the context that they are all 'very academically talented and particularly good at maths and had all progressed very well'. Speaking generally, she pointed to 'inherited ability' but also encouragement as key in terms of mathematical achievement.

Interviewer: What do you think makes a difference in terms of success at learning maths?

Ms Brennan: I think mathematical ability and I think ability to a greater extent is *inherited*. But you can improve a lot with extra help and one-to-one tuition and I've seen that happen.

Interviewer: Would you recognise mathematical ability fairly quickly when a student comes into your class?

Ms Brennan: Yes, generally, but it may not develop with some children as quickly as others. I've seen children at 11 and 12 who weren't all that brilliant you would think and then they do very very well later on ... a student performance can change considerably over time. Very much so. Encouragement is a huge part of it. (Barrow (SSG F)

Falling behind: 'Lack of effort, lack of interest and/or lack of ability'

Five of the ten teachers were of the view that some students in the observed class had 'fallen back' in terms of mathematical learning over the course of the year. Lack of progress was generally explained in terms of the students' own behaviour or attitude to mathematics: here behaviour included absenteeism, lack of effort, a negative attitude towards mathematics and, in the case of one particular girl, an interest in boys. It is notable that while teachers attributed improvement in part to teacher effort or praise, student failure was explained entirely in terms of their behaviour or deficiencies.

In the following excerpt, the teacher of a bottom stream single sex girls' class in a designated disadvantaged secondary school identifies one particular girl whose progress had deteriorated over the course of the year. This, she maintained was due to absenteeism, and had resulted from a lack of interest by her family in her education. Her decline was considered to particularly regrettable as the girls in question was seen to be 'quite intelligent'.

Interviewer: Can you identify students in the class, if any, who would seem to have fallen back?
Ms Scanlon: I would think Nuala. She's the girl in the second row in the extreme left. She's been absent a good bit and I'd say she definitely has fallen back because she's very – she's quite intelligent – not very intelligent – but she *doesn't make any effort* whatsoever. It would be mainly due to absenteeism and she doesn't bother – always the easy way out.
Interviewer: And is there a specific reason for the absenteeism?
Ms Scanlon: She has been in hospital but she plays up a little bit on that – maybe the youngest of the family and towards the end of the *family* and *they are getting a bit slack.*
Interviewer: Did that just happen this year do you know?
Ms Scanlon: No, I had it last year as well and she would have been out for something else – another reason – you know – but always the same kind of idea. She would be meant to be out for a week and she'd be out for three. That type of thing – not really genuine. (Suir SSG Fr D)

A teacher of a single sex boys' mixed class in a fee-paying secondary school believed that a negative attitude towards mathematics, resulting from poor mathematical ability, was the main reason why students had 'fallen back'. Like most other teachers she defined lack of 'ability' at mathematics as being 'weak' at the subject:

> *Interviewer:* Can you identify students, if any, who have fallen back?
> *Ms Lenehan:* There would be maybe 3 of them … it's easy to see the *weaker ones* at this stage. I'd say Tony, Sean, and James would be quite weak but would actually get it in the end, so Tony and Sean would be the two main ones.
> *Interviewer:* How would you explain this?
> *Ms Lenehan:* I'm not saying that you're either good at it or you're not, but if you're not good at it then there's a negative attitude towards it. Maybe you're blocking out part of it but I'd say it would be more easy or it would be easier I would say for someone who was middle of the road ability-wise to get waylaid by other things going on in the school. (Lee SSB F)

Another teacher of a bottom steam coeducational class in a community school identified a female student whose performance had deteriorated over the school year. Pointing to her grades in first year as evidence of her 'potential', the teacher attributed her decline to socialising with boys and the area where she lives.

> *Interviewer:* Can you identify students, if any, who have fallen back?
> *Mr Nally:* Well – Aoife, she has fallen back, way back. She was an excellent student in first year and then went deadly downhill. I saw her grade then and its now 43 per cent. She was getting 60 and 70 in first year. In everything – like for business and maths – she was great. But I know why – it's because she's socialising – very heavily into boys.
> *Interviewer:* So you think it's because she's socialising?
> *Mr Nally:* Oh, definitely, and with the wrong types. Completely. With kids who have been suspended and continuously suspended and going to be expelled. That kind of individual. Very, very – just lives in that area and she can't help it. She's sucked into it … And Aoife was such a lovely kid. But now she's – she's coarsened. Her language has disimproved, things like that. I told her mother – she was aghast at the time but nothing happened. She's out till all hours at night she tells me. Walking the streets – that kind of thing. (Nephin VCC Fr)

While teachers attributed students' improvements in mathematics to having the 'innate ability', or to the encouragement and support given by the teacher, they attributed a deteriorating mathematical performance to the student's and/or parents' disinterest, or to the student's lack of 'ability'. Teachers spoke of lack of ability mostly in terms of being 'weak' at the subject.

Teachers operated two distinct codes of interpretation, therefore, when explaining a student's performance in mathematics. An improving performance was interpreted in terms of both teacher effort and a student's natural ability. Declining performances were also attributed to 'lack of ability'. However, they were also explained in terms of the student's lack of effort or interest, or the lack of parental interest. Teachers did not appear to hold either themselves or the school system responsible for declining performances in mathematics.

Teacher perspectives on gender differences

When asked whether there were gender differences in success rates in mathematics, there was considerable variability in teacher opinions. Three teachers agreed that there were gender differences while four disagreed. A further three teachers reported that they did not know.

In the five coeducational schools, two teachers claimed there were gender differences while three disagreed. Only one of the five teachers in the single sex schools claimed there were gender differences in success levels in mathematics: one said there were none, while the remaining three said they were unable to comment as they had never taught in a mixed setting (Figure 9.4).

Figure 9.4: Teachers' perspectives on whether or not there are gender differences in how successful students are in learning mathematics
(Base = 10 teachers)

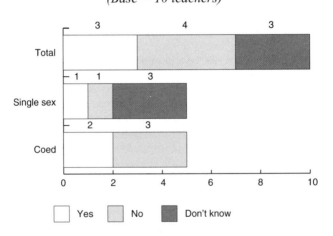

The three teachers who maintained that boys and girls differ in terms of success in learning mathematics attributed this to 'natural differences' between the two groups. One such teacher maintained that boys and girls differ in their aptitude for certain mathematical topics. The teacher was teaching a top stream, coeducational class in a secondary school.

Interviewer: Do you think there are gender differences in how successful students are in learning maths?

Ms Leydon: Yes. I think that, maybe certain topics suit certain genders better. Yes, I think that there are certain topics, I think that girls can work through algebra problems better. I think that girls suit the methodical questions whereas the lads suit the ones to do with area – the ones to do with trigonometry, the visual level, and the ones to do with seeing something. Also when we come to do probability, the lads might come quicker to those but the girls would do better maybe working through problems. (Lagan SC Fr)

Another teacher, Ms Malone, who was teaching a bottom stream co-educational class in a designated disadvantaged community college, expressed a similar view. In her opinion, gender differences in approaches to mathematics was an important issue: she suggested that girls are typically methodical while boys attempt to find the easiest and quickest way. She also suggested, however, that boys were 'a bit more quick witted' at the subject.

Interviewer: From your own experience – and not just from your own class here – do you think there are gender differences in how successful students are in learning maths?

Ms Malone: I think there is a different level, not always, but often a different *type* of ability between girls and boys. But in my experience – and particularly in recent years – the level of achievement … I've had as many girls as boys doing the honours maths for the Leaving Cert or doing the higher level. Indeed I've had more doing the higher level for the Junior Cert – I have more girls than boys. Having said that, I would find the boys to be a bit more quick witted generally. There are exceptions, but in general more quick witted and wanting the easy, quick way. The girls are more methodical, wanting to know how to do it, understand how to do it and do it like that, quite happy to do the long way if they can follow each step and get it out at the end. Whereas the boys, and James and Connor – they would be typical – would leave out four steps. They're really not that bothered if they get the wrong answer: 'Ah, sure I only made a little mistake, it doesn't matter, it's of no great consequence'. The girls are much more perfectionist – they would want to get the right answer and have it done properly, and the boys are not as much interested. That's a generalisation but they're not as much interested in doing step-by-step and showing the steps. (Mourne VCC Fr D)

Ms Lenehan, who was teaching a single sex boys' class in a fee paying secondary school, believed that there were innate gender differences in mathematical ability. In this case, success in mathematical learning was attributed to the innate ability of boys and to hard work on the part of the girls. Ms Lenehan was the only teacher to express a strongly gender stereotyped view of mathematics.

Interviewer: Do you think there are gender differences in how successful students are in learning maths?

Ms Lenehan: Yeah there is – my experience would be that girls would have to work harder. The fellas would have been good at maths or really bad but the girls would have to try harder to do well. What I find is the fellas have been better at maths than girls – if they're good at maths and they are doing a higher level – fellas are more mathematically minded whereas the girls would have to work. (Lee SSB F)

As noted above, four of the ten teachers in the study maintained that gender differences do not exist in terms of success in learning school mathematics. They claimed that when gender differences arise they are due to conditioning rather than 'natural ability'.

The first excerpt illustrating this viewpoint involves a teacher of a middle stream group in a coeducational community school. This teacher maintained that girls are frequently labelled as failures at mathematics; what then happens is that this becomes a self-fulfilling prophecy.

Interviewer: Do you think there are gender differences in how successful students are in learning maths?

Ms Ennis: I think, you know, it's hard to answer that. Often I would find it and I would get girls from another teacher – like you don't have them in first year and you have them in second year – or you just have them in third year, this happens. I would find that they come in with very poor skills at maths and so they don't have the confidence. You have to build up and try and give them confidence and say: 'You can do this thing' after all and all of this. Like a girl I have in another class and only recently I found out that last year the teacher had sent her for remedial maths. She's in there now doing algebraic division with me and she's doing it and she's delighted with herself. I would think that it is confidence. You'd wonder why she was put out, was she labelled in some way? (Errigal CS Fr)

Another teacher of a bottom stream, coeducational class in a community college expressed an identical view.

Interviewer: Do you think there are gender differences in how successful students are in learning maths?

Mr Nally: There is a difference but I think it is societal. In that school I was talking about, great and all as it was, they had no honours maths class for girls, that was conditioning. (Nephin VCC Fr)

What the interviews with teachers suggest is that there was considerable uncertainty and ambivalence among teachers regarding the interface between gender and mathematical competency. While four of the ten teachers said that there were no gender differences, three believed that girls and boys had a different approach to mathematics. In the latter case, the differences were generally not interpreted in hierarchical terms however. Only one teacher expressed a definite belief that boys had more natural talent at mathematics than girls. Three teachers said they did not know enough to comment on the matter.

There is no single gender code that prevails among teachers therefore for interpreting gender relations in mathematics. Teachers appear to be operating out of a series of gender codes reflecting the increasingly problematised interpretations of femininity and masculinity that co-exist in contemporary society (Arnot, 2002). Only one of the ten teachers expressed a stereotypical perspective on gender relations within mathematics, with most either claiming there were no differences, being unsure, or suggesting that such differences as did exist were in approaches to the subject rather than in performance.

Teacher perspectives on social class differences

There was greater unanimity among teachers regarding the impact of students' social class backgrounds on the learning of mathematics. While three teachers expressed no opinion, six of the ten claimed that a student's social class background was important in terms of learning mathematics; only one teacher held a contrary view (Figure 9.5).

Figure 9.5: Teachers' perspectives on whether social class background influences students' success in mathematics.
(Base = 10 teachers)

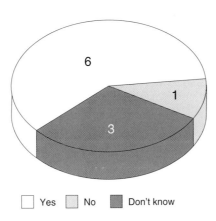

What teachers focused on mostly was parental knowledge of, and interest in, the education system. Parents of students from an economically disadvantaged background are generally described as having little knowledge of, and interest in, their children's education. A strong cultural deficit view of working class parents prevailed among teachers; the students' poor performance was attributed to the cultural poverty of their families. This finding concurs with other research on teachers' views of social class differences in performance (Lynch and O'Riordan, 1998).

A teacher in a single sex girls' school articulated the cultural deficit view most clearly. She was teaching a bottom stream class in a designated disadvantaged secondary school. The girls' lack of interest in learning was attributed to the lack of parental interest and student ambition:

> *Interviewer:* Do you think that social class background is important in terms of learning in maths?
>
> *Ms Scanlon:* Definitely – you'll actually see it in the class, when you go into the [observed] class – about five out of seventeen in the class, five of them will have *no interest whatsoever.* They'll actually tell you that they don't want to do maths, they don't want to finish their Leaving Cert. You know at this stage – and you'll say: 'What about for getting a job?' and they say that their sisters don't have jobs, you know, they will say that to you. It definitely does. And there might be one or two who will be from a poor social background who would be striving to get on in the class.
>
> *Interviewer:* So generally speaking then are you saying that the social class difference is a major factor in terms of motivation to learn – you mentioned there that a minority will try hard?
>
> *Ms Scanlon:* The minority – maybe one out of thirty.
>
> *Interviewer:* Overall then, you think that students from a more advantaged background tend to do better?
>
> *Ms Scanlon:* Yes – I think they are encouraged at home a lot more whereas the other students ... even at the parent teacher meetings, the parents wouldn't arrive in. I haven't seen some of the kids' parents since they arrived in the school. They'd be a lot more trouble and you want to see the parents but you just can't get to see them, the parents are not interested and the kids are influenced from home. (Suir SSG Fr D)

The teacher in a top stream single sex boys' class in a designated disadvantaged secondary school expressed a similar view. In this case the teacher explained how belonging to a particular social class can have a negative impact on a child's education. First, he pointed out that if parents are not educated they are generally not in a position to be actively involved in their child's education, particularly in terms of helping with homework. He also maintained that such parents often have an unrealistic perception of the effort that is required for good results. Indeed, at a broader level, he claimed that without first hand experience of education, parents tend not to attach any great importance to learning. Finally he suggested that shortages, in terms of space and resources (such as computers and books) at home mean that out of school work is often difficult.

Interviewer: Do you think that social class background is important in terms of learning in maths?

Mr Little: Yes. Absolutely. No hesitation. Learning has to have a few things. You have to have support, you have to have background and you have to have very supportive parents. If you haven't got background where learning can go on, you're up against it, you're back to the resources that the school can provide, as is the case here. If they don't learn here [in school], they won't learn and if they go home there's five, six and seven or eight children in a three bedroom house and they don't have quality time on their own to do their studies. A lot of *parents don't have an educated background* – they think if their child does twenty minutes work that they're great. Whereas if you were watching 'The Leaving' [television programme] last night there some of them putting in six or seven hours and weekends are kind of gone – nine hours Saturday and nine hours Sunday. That's what you're talking about. You need motivation. [It is] not so much [about being from] an ignorant background. You're talking about people who are not aware of what is necessary and therefore there are different standards being set by the parents and the teachers. I can empathise with the parents and say: 'OK, right, I can see where you are coming from' but as regards what they are prepared to put in, it's very limited ... so there definitely is a background thing to it. (Liffey SSB Fr D)

The converse of this is articulated by another teacher in a fee paying, all boys' secondary school. Here, the vast majority of students have highly educated parents in professional jobs. According to the teacher this results in pressure to do well by the parents and a concomitant high degree of emphasis on learning.

Interviewer: Do you think that social class background is important in terms of learning in maths?

Ms Lenehan: Oh, yes – these guys are working not just to their peers but the guys that went before them – their peers who do great, they're on the rugby team. They are all working to that. Because the majority of parents are in high class jobs, there would be a lot of solicitors, doctors – the parents would be in good jobs. So I suppose that would come back to the parents focusing on learning from the start. In the other school I taught in before this it was a totally different set up. Like here where you'd have 75-80 per cent doing higher for the Leaving Cert, in the other school it would be more like 7-8 per cent. I'd say it's probably due to the kids' background. They would be from totally different backgrounds. I'd say *the parents there [previous school] wouldn't take as big an interest as the parents do here*. The parents here will be in contact with you weekly or twice weekly through notes or if he couldn't understand it they'd let you know. The parents would help them, by seeing that they do their homework, and that wouldn't have really happened in the other school. (Lee SSB F)

One teacher believed however that there was a connection between social class background and stream or band position. She suggested that the tendency to place working class children in low tracks was part of the problem: low track placement became a self-fulfilling prophecy, depressing students' expectations and performance. The teacher who expressed this view was teaching a middle stream coeducational group in a community college.

> *Interviewer:* Do you think that social class background is important in terms of learning in maths?
> *Ms Ennis:* [What] I think [regarding] social class differences is, the damage is done often before they get here. You would find *people from the higher social groups are getting into higher streams* and I think *the damage is done before they get here.*
> *Interviewer:* When you say damage what do you mean?
> *Ms Ennis:* They are already labelled – I think anyway. I think that in the national schools – whether they're perhaps not attending school and they miss out on basics or maybe the parents aren't as interested – I think that they lose confidence before the people got here a lot of the time. I'm not saying the teachers have labelled or damaged them but I feel that you often get a kid coming in here in first year and you wonder how they got through eight years and not know how to add and subtract and multiply and divide. You wonder how did that happen … so I think they've lost their confidence before they even come in here. And if they don't get the basics there, then they come in to us and they're gone in terms of confidence. And if they come in from the top stream you see they are eager and confident, they have that … whereas if you get a weak stream in first year, aah, it's more of the same to them. They are slouched, they don't come in looking … like the ones in the better class … they come in and they are ready to go and they are all delighted to be here. Whereas the other ones they'd be negative about the teachers right from the beginning and you have to try then to turn that around. I think home has an awful lot to do with it as well.
> *Interviewer:* Would you think it is important that parents have a lot of input?
> *Ms Ennis:* I would, yes.
> *Interviewer:* In practice – how?
> *Ms Ennis:* I would think that just being interested in – like there's my little fella now, there's a girl in his class and – sort of – the parents would be known to have very little interest in school blah, blah, blah. And my little fella comes home and is saying 'Such and such gave trouble in school today', she did this, she did that, she did the other, she threw this on the floor – there's problems already. He would tell me: 'She colours outside her lines, she can't colour inside her lines' and so already there's a dynamic there that something has started. And he comes home and I say: 'What did you do today?' and he usually says: 'Nothing'. And I say: 'Now come on' – I think [it matters] to have the parents interested, and to be there to support them. (Errigal CS Fr)

While some teachers realise that students were disadvantaged by their social class in terms of the resources and opportunities available to them, and in terms of parents' own limited knowledge of education, most also held quite strong cultural deficit views of economically, disadvantaged parents. All but one teacher attributed primary responsibility for students' poorer attainment in mathematics to lack of parental knowledge of, and interest in, education. They did not suggest that the school could or should compensate for this deficit. One teacher suggested, however, that labelling of students in primary school and streaming might also explain their lower attainment.

Conclusions

The interviews with the teachers in the case-study show that they generally regarded mathematics as a formal way of representing the world, and as a subject where 'innate ability' plays an important role in determining learning outcomes. While most believed that varied teaching methodologies and practice at the subject improved learning, learning itself was most often equated with the memorisation of formulae and procedures, rather than thinking creatively, being able to provide reasons for solutions, or understanding how mathematics is used in the real world. The views of our case-study teachers were found to be broadly in line with those of mathematics teachers in the national TIMSS research (Beaton et al., 1996).

Our findings also lend support to the claims of those who suggest that teachers' views of teaching influence their pedagogical practices (Clark and Peterson, 1986; Shavelson and Stern, 1981; She 2000). We found a high degree of consistency between teacher reports of their pedagogical style and their pedagogical styles. Teachers reported that much of their time in mathematics lessons involved demonstration of procedures and monitoring of students' progress; this was consistent with the findings from the video analysis of their teaching practice. Correspondingly, their reports that the main activities in mathematics lessons involved students copying examples from the board and answering teacher questions were also borne out in practice. Teachers also recognised in their accounts of their work that students rarely initiated interaction in class, and that there was little general discussion of mathematical topics. Overall, the data (from the teachers) confirmed that the didactic approach to teaching mathematics was the norm for the ten teachers in this study, both in theory and in practice.

However, like Gregg (1995b) and Raymond, (1997), we did not find teachers to be wholly consistent between their philosophy and their practice. In our case, we found that teachers were less inclusive and less accommodating of differences than they claimed themselves to be. In most classes, only a minority of students participated publicly in class work with the teachers. This was especially the case in boys' classes while single sex girls' classes were the most participatory; within coeducational classes, a small number of boys also tended to dominate the public work of the class. There was also an inconsistency between teacher accounts of how they accommodated the needs of Foundation level students and what they did in the classrooms. Teachers reported themselves to be more accommodating of the needs of Foundation level students than they were in practice. Finally, despite claims by some teachers that they arranged for students to work in pairs or groups, we did not find evidence of this in practice in mathematics classes regardless of stream or band. The disjunction between teachers' philosophy and practice is understandable however, given the cellular nature of teaching (Lortie, 1975), and given the speed and intensity of the teaching process (Good and Brophy, 2000). Teachers work in autonomous units, largely divorced from peer contact and observation. The lack of peer review and evaluation does not encourage reflexivity about practice, or indeed about the relationship between philosophy and practice. The speed and intensity of the teaching process also offers little opportunity for reviewing the interface between theory and practice.

Teachers generally attributed students' improvements in mathematics to having an innate ability and being encouraged and supported by the teacher. On the other hand, teachers did not hold themselves responsible for any observed deterioration in students' mathematical performance. Here students' own attitudes, behaviour or lack of ability were deemed to be the main causal factors.

While earlier studies of teacher attitudes to gender differences in mathematics found that teachers held quite stereotypical views of female and male capabilities and approaches, (Fennema et al., 1990), our interviews suggest a more complex picture of gender perceptions among teachers. Teachers were quite hesitant and ambivalent in their interpretation of gender relations, with only one of the ten holding clear stereotypical views. Teachers were almost equally divided between those who thought that there were no gender differences in success rates in learning mathematics (four), those who did not know (three) and those who said there were differences (four). Where differences were identified they were not, with one exception, presented in simple hierarchical terms, although one other teacher did seem to support the traditionally gendered view of mathematical capability. Girls and boys were seen as having different approaches to the learning of the subject, not as being more or less capable at the subject. The findings regarding the ambiguity and uncertainty expressed by teachers concur with those of Francis (2000) who found evidence of a decline in gender stereotyped expectations among students in their subject preferences. Our findings also lend support to Arnot's (2002) and Connel's (1997) claims that concepts of femininity and masculinity are becoming increasingly fractured and diverse in the post-modern era.

Teachers were more unanimous in their views on social class. Six of the ten teachers claimed that students from 'poor' backgrounds were disadvantaged in learning mathematics by their parents' lack of knowledge of, and especially interest in, education. On the other hand, the greater resources (educational and material) available to upper middle-class students were regarded as crucial to their educational success. Only one of the ten teachers claimed that schooling procedures (labelling students from particular backgrounds and placing them in low streams/tracks) contributed to their lower attainment. It is evident, therefore, that a 'cultural deficit' view prevailed in relation to understanding lower attainment levels among working class students, a finding that concurs with other Irish research on teacher attitudes to students from working class backgrounds (Lynch and O'Riordan, 1998). However, some teachers were also aware of the resource related privileges of upper middle-class students especially, and of the impact of school policies and practices in relation to student placement in lower and higher streams or bands.

Appendix to Chapter 9

Figure A9.1: Teachers' reports about homework: whether events happen in 'every lesson' or 'most lessons'.
(Base: All teaching particular level of mathematics)

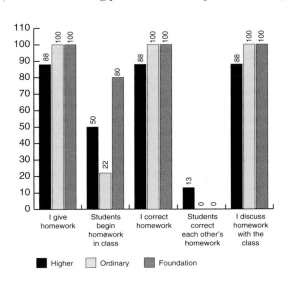

10

Student Perspectives on Learning Mathematics

Introduction

In this chapter, student perspectives on the learning and teaching of mathematics are analysed. Accounts of the students' attitudes and experiences are based on questionnaire and focus group data. The students' general attitude and self-image in relation to mathematics, their experience in the classroom, and their expectations in relation to the Junior Certificate and later education, were examined in the questionnaires. These issues were explored in depth in the focus groups with a number of targeted students within each of the classes.

As there is considerable international evidence to show that students' attitudes towards, and performance in, mathematics are strongly influenced by their mathematical experiences, and in particular by the way mathematics is taught in school (Dick and Rallis, 1991; Johnston, 1994; Ma, 1997; Reynolds and Walberg, 1992; Boaler, 1997a, 1997b), we examined students' perspectives on mathematics, and in particular their experience of learning mathematics in class. Our focus on gender is informed by the considerable research evidence regarding gender differences in both attitudes to, and experience of, mathematics (Beaton et al., 1996; Jones and Smart, 1995a, 1995b, including recent evidence that these may be changing and not as stereotyped as formerly perceived – Forgasz and Leder, 2001; Leder and Forgasz, 2000).

In the analysis, we also devoted attention to the differences in attitude and experience between students in different tracks and from different social class backgrounds given the evidence that both impact on students' experience of learning mathematics (Boaler, 1997a, 1997c, 1997e; Zevenbergen, 2000; Dunne, 1999).

What is required for success in school mathematics?

Students were asked to indicate their level of agreement or disagreement with six statements about what is required for success in school mathematics. Figure 10.1 shows the level of students' agreement with each of the statements. 'Having a good maths teacher' received the highest level of agreement among the students. Most students also agreed that 'study at home' was important for success in mathematics, while somewhat fewer believed that success was contingent on 'liking the subject' (Figure 10.1).

With the exception of one school, few students regarded 'good luck' as a requirement for success. Similarly, students in the majority of the classes (six out of ten) did not agree that success in mathematics necessitates 'learning the textbook off by heart'. However, good memorisation was considered to be important by the students in the remaining four classes. All but one of the classes that believed 'luck' or 'learning off' was crucial for success were low streams, while the fourth was a top stream in a school where most students took Ordinary or Foundation level mathematics (Figure 10.1).

While teachers considered 'innate ability' as important for succeeding in mathematics, students were more divided in their views and no particular pattern is discernible. Students tended to regard success in mathematics as being an outcome of good teaching and study, rather than any of a given mathematical ability.

However, there were gender differences between students regarding what was considered important for success at mathematics. Boys were more likely than girls to consider natural talent and memorisation as prerequisites for success, and to a statistically significant degree. Within three of the five coeducational classes, the tendency for boys to attribute more importance to natural talent also held true (Lagan (SC Fr); Errigal (CS Fr); and Blackstairs (VCC Fr D)).

Importance of doing well in school mathematics

Students were asked to indicate the extent of their agreement or disagreement with a number of statements as to 'why you need to do well in mathematics'. The findings would suggest that the students are quite positive about the value and importance of mathematics. A majority believed that mathematics is required for everyday life, for employment and for further education purposes; they regarded mathematics as an important subject that had both a short and long term value. This contrasts with the small proportion of students who only viewed success in mathematics as necessary because it was compulsory and/or because it would please their parents (Appendix 1, Figure A10.1).

Figure 10.1: Students' views of requirements for success in school mathematics

(Base: 237)

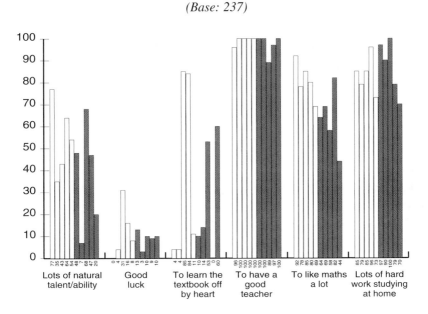

Key: Single sex schools: (white bars) and **Coeducational schools:** (grey bars)

1. Barrow (SSG F)	4. Liffey (SSB Fr D)	7. Errigal (CS Fr)	10. Nephin (VCC Fr)
2. Nore (SSG Fr)	5. Lee (SSB F)	8. Mourne (VCC Fr D)	
3. Suir (SSG Fr D)	6. Lagan (SC Fr)	9. Blackstairs (VCC Fr D)	

Note: Same key applies to all six statements.

Gender differences in attitudes to mathematics, classroom experience
and academic expectations

Having observed students in classes, we wanted to explore their own views on their classroom experience of learning. We wanted to understand their subjective experience of mathematics, and in particular to explore gender differences in perceptions of mathematics learning. To achieve this objective, we administered questionnaires to all of the students present in the observed classes using Likert type scales (Oppenheim, 1966, pp.120-159). Five areas were examined:

1. **Attitude to mathematics**: perceptions of school mathematics, that is, how difficult, useful, interesting, enjoyable or boring mathematics is perceived to be and whether it is listed as a first or second favourite or least favourite subject (MATHATT scale);

2. **Academic image in relation to mathematics**: self-assessed 'ability' in school mathematics in the context of the particular class and wider peer group (MATHIMG scale);
3. **Positive classroom interaction with teacher**: perceptions of frequency of interaction with the mathematics teacher and the level of reward for achievement in this class (MATHPTI scale);
4. **Negative classroom interaction with teacher**: perceptions of correction/sanctioning in mathematics class – mainly for work poorly done or bad behaviour (MATHNTI scale);
5. **Academic expectations**: perception of likely performance in the Junior Certificate Examination and in future education[1] (EXPECT Scale). [2]

The mean scores for each gender group on each of the scales are presented in Table 10.1 below, while differences between girls and boys in single sex and coeducational schools are outlined in Tables 10.2 to 10.6. A more detailed analysis of the findings for each school is presented in Appendix 3 of Chapter 10, Tables A10.3 –A10.7.

Table 10.1: Gender differences in attitudes to mathematics, mathematics self-image, classroom experience of mathematics and educational expectations

	Girls	Boys	Total
1. MATHATT	1.26	1.33*	1.29
2. MATHIMG	.98	.94	.96
3. MATHPTI	1.27	1.67*	1.45
4. MATHNTI	.53	.71*	.61
5. EXPECT	1.87	1.99*	1.93

* Significant, p < 0.01

What is clear from Table 10.1 is that girls have more positive views of mathematics, more positive views of their classroom experiences in mathematics, and higher educational self expectations than boys generally. In four of the five areas (Scales 1,3,4,5) the differences were statistically significant. The only area in which boys had a more positive perspective was in terms of mathematics self-image. However, the difference between girls' and boys' self image was not significant.

Girls within coeducational schools also had more positive classroom experiences than boys and higher educational expectations; however, they had a lower mathematics self-image, and slightly less positive attitude towards the subject. The only significant difference between girls and boys in coeducational schools was in the more positive classroom interaction experiences reported by the girls (Table A10.3).

Both social class background and track or stream position also appeared to impact on attitudes and experiences. There were statistically significant differences between middle-class and working class students in terms of educational expectations, and between higher and lower streams in terms of both expectations and mathematics self-image. Both middle-class and higher stream students reported more positive attitudes on four of the five scales (the exception in both cases was classroom sanctioning which was reported to be higher among the top tracks and among middle-class students: Tables A10.2 and A10.5).

Attitude to mathematics

Table 10.2: Gender differences in attitudes to mathematics (the MATHATT scale: overall average = 1.29**)

Overall scores by gender	Girls: 1.26	Boys: 1.33
Gender differences within coeducational classes and between single sex classes	SS Girls: 1.21 SS Boys: 1.38*	Coed girls: 1.32 Coed Boys: 1.28

*p < .001
**The lower the score the higher the liking for mathematics.

What is evident from Table 10.2 is that girls have a more positive attitude toward mathematics than boys overall. Girls in the single sex schools held the most favourable views of mathematics, followed by boys, and then girls, in the coeducational schools. The boys in the two single-sex secondary schools were the least likely to express positive attitudes towards the subject. Yet the boys in question were not in low tracks (where students generally held more negative attitudes and lower expectations, see Table A10.6). One of the classes was mixed in a fee paying school (Lee (SSB F)) while the other was a top stream class in a school of designated disadvantage status (Liffey (SSB Fr D)).

Turning to gender differences within the schools, boys held more favourable attitudes towards mathematics in two of the five classes. These are both bottom stream classes in community colleges; the first comprises equal numbers of girls and boys (Mourne (VCC Fr D)) while the second has an over-representation of boys (Nephin (VCC Fr)). In one of the five coeducational schools, girls had more favourable attitudes toward mathematics; this was a top band in a secondary school with equal numbers of boys and girls (Lagan (SC Fr)). In the remaining two schools, there were no differences in the mean scores (Table A10.8).

Overall therefore, while girls generally held more positive attitudes to mathematics than boys, such views are mediated by social class, stream/track position and, as we will see later in this chapter, the style and attitude of the teacher.

Mathematics self-image

In general, boys had a slightly higher mathematical self-image compared with girls, although the differences were not significant (Table 10.3). Boys in the coeducational schools had the highest self-image followed by the girls in the single sex schools. The girls in the coeducational schools had the lowest self-image in relation to mathematics.

Table 10.3: Gender differences in mathematics self-image (the MATHIMG scale: overall average = 1.04**)

Overall scores by gender	Girls: 0.98	Boys: 0.94
Gender differences within coeducational classes, and between single sex classes	SS Girls: 0.95 SS Boys: 0.97*	Coed Girls: 1.01 Coed Boys: 0.92

*p < .001
**The lower the score the higher their academic self-image in relation to mathematics.

Within the coeducational schools, boys had a higher self-image in four out of the five schools. Gender differences were statistically significant in two of these schools (Mourne (VCC Fr D) and Nephin (VCC Fr), Table A10.9). In the remaining coeducational school, girls were shown to have a higher self-image relative to both boys and to their peers in the other four schools; this is a top-stream class in a community college (Blackstairs (VCC Fr D), Table A10.9).

Classroom experience: positive reinforcement and negative sanctioning

Two scales were constructed to examine positive and negative aspects of classroom interaction. The positive scale measured students' perceptions of the frequency of their interaction with their mathematics teacher and the level of reward/praise for their achievements in class. The negative scale indexed negative interaction with the teacher. It specifically referred to sanctioning/correction for particular behaviour, including work-related and non-work related behaviour.

Girls reported more positive interactions with teachers in their mathematics classes compared with boys, and to a statistically significant degree. Girls in the single sex schools reported substantially more positive classroom experience than boys in single sex schools in particular (Table 10.4).

Table 10.4: Positive interaction in mathematics classrooms: (the MATHPTI scale: overall average = 1.60**)

Overall scores by gender	Girls: 1.27	Boys: 1.67*
Gender differences within coeducational classes and between single sex classes	SS Girls: 1.15 SS Boys: 1.76*	Coed Girls: 1.38 Coed Boys: 1.59

*p < .001
**The scale ranges between 0 and 3. The lower the score the greater the level of perceived positive interaction/reward.

Within the five coeducational schools, girls reported higher levels of positive interaction with their mathematics teachers than boys although the differences are not statistically significant. The differences between girls and boys were statistically significant in only one of the five schools; this was a middle stream class in a community school (Errigal (CS Fr), Table A10.10).

Given gender differences in the reporting of positive interactions, it is not surprising to find that girls also reported receiving less negative attention than boys, and to a statistically significant degree. In this case, it was girls in the coeducational classes that reported the lowest level of sanctioning in mathematics classes, while boys in single sex schools reported the highest levels of negative attention (Table 10.5).

Table 10.5: Negative interaction in the mathematics classroom (MATHNTI scale: overall average = 0.62**)

Overall scores by gender	Girls: 0.53	Boys: 0. 71*
Gender differences within coeducational classes, and between single sex classes	SS Girls: 0.55 SS Boys: 0.84*	Coed Girls: 0.51 Coed Boys: 0.60

*p < .001
**The scale ranges between 0 and 3. The lower the score the lower the level of perceived negative interaction/sanction.

Within the five coeducational schools the findings were mixed. In two of the five schools, the girls reported receiving low levels of negative attention; one was a middle band in a community school (Errigal (CS Fr)) while the other was a bottom band in a community college (Mourne (VCC Fr D)). The opposite applied in two other schools, both of which were community colleges; the first involved a top band (Blackstairs (VCC Fr D)) while the second involved a bottom band (Nephin (VCC Fr)). Finally, in one of the schools there were no gender differences in the mean scores with both boys and girls reporting high levels of negative interaction. The class involved was a top band in a secondary school (Lagan (SC Fr), Table A10.11).

Although girls generally reported most positive interaction, the variability in the character of classes in which interaction was most positively perceived, suggests that individual teachers play an important role in determining classroom climate as well. This hypothesis found support in the interview data which we discuss later in this chapter.

Academic expectations

Students were also asked to comment on their educational expectations for themselves, and on those of their parents and teachers. Girls held higher academic expectations for themselves, to a statistically significant degree, compared with boys. Girls in the single sex schools had the highest academic expectations, followed by boys in the single sex schools. Boys in the coeducational schools had the lowest expectations.

Differences in expectations between single sex and coeducational schools must be interpreted however in the light of the differences in the types of schools in the study. While there was an equal number (two out of five) of designated disadvantaged schools in both the single sex and coeducational groups, there were more middle-class students in the single sex sector (79 per cent of the students in single sex schools were middle-class compared with 52 per cent in coeducational schools (see Table 7.2, Chapter 7)). The differences between coeducational and single-sex schools may, therefore, have much to do with the social class background and related track expectations of students in different types of schools, rather than with the gender composition of the schools.

Within the coeducational schools, girls had consistently higher educational expectations than boys. The difference was greatest in the designated coeducational school involving a bottom stream class (Nephin (VCC Fr), Table A10.12).

Table 10.6: Gender differences in educational expectations (the EXPECT scale: overall average = 1.9**)

Overall scores by gender	Girls: 1.87	Boys: 1.99*
Gender differences within coeducational classes, and between single sex classes	SS Girls: 1.98 SS Boys: 2.10*	Coed Girls: 2.14 Coed Boys: 2.23

*p < .001
**The scale ranges between 0 and 3. The lower the score the higher the self-expectation.

Discussion

The data indicates that girls generally had more positive attitudes to mathematics, had higher expectations of themselves, and more positive classroom experience of learning the subject than boys. These findings suggest that girls' attitudes to mathematics and their learning experiences of the subject may be more positive than originally perceived (Leder and Forgasz, 2000). It also concurs with findings by McDonnell (1995) demonstrating girls' generally more positive attitude to schooling. However, boys had a slightly higher mathematics self-image than girls, a finding that concurs with that of Hannan et al., (1996).

The attitudinal differences between girls and boys generally towards mathematics were reversed in the coeducational schools where girls had slightly less positive attitudes. Girls in coeducational schools also had the lowest self-image in relation to mathematics compared with girls in single sex schools and boys in coeducational, or single sex schools.

Girls in coeducational classes had significantly more positive classroom experiences than boys, however, and somewhat higher expectations. Girls in coeducational classes also had far fewer negative interactions than boys in their own class, and than boys in single sex classes (the group with the highest level of negative interaction). It was girls in single sex classes that had the highest expectations and the most positive interactions of all groups. However, they had somewhat more negative interactions than girls in coeducational classes.

Differences between students were not confined to gender however. They were also related to both social class background and track placement. While there were no significant social class differences between students in their attitudes, self-images or positive interactive experiences of mathematics, middle-class students reported more positive attitudes and experiences in all three areas. Middle class students also had significantly higher educational expectations although they reported significantly more negative experiences of mathematics (Table A10.2).

Differences across streams mirrored those across classes, with the top streams reporting more positive attitudes, self-images, classroom experiences and expectations. The differences between the social classes were significant in relation to both self-image and expectations, with middle-class students having the higher mathematics self-image and expectations (Table A10.2 and Table A10.5).

Overall, therefore, the data indicates that the relationship between gender and attitudes to, and experience of, mathematics, is complex and is mediated by social class and track position. As we will see below, it also lends support to Ma's (1997) claims that perspectives on mathematics are influenced by the way in which the subject is taught by individual teachers.

Profiling mathematics learning: 'positive' or 'negative' experience

While there was a general tendency for girls, top stream classes, and middle-class students to hold the most positive views of mathematics overall, the profile of the schools with the most positive perspectives shows that teacher practices also impact on attitudes to the subject (Figure 10.1 and Table 10.7). Although students in the three bottom streams (Suir (SSG Fr D); Nephin (VCC Fr); Mourne (VCC Fr D)) did not have positive attitudes to mathematics or positive self-images, expectations or learning experiences, students in one of these, Nephin, had more positive attitudes to mathematics than the boys in the mixed class in Lee (a socially select, feepaying boys' school). Even their mathematics self-image was only marginally lower than that of the boys in Lee. The students in Nephin also had more positive attitudes and self-images than the top stream in Liffey (SSB Fr D). The classes in which low levels of negative interactions with teachers were reported (Barrow (SSG F) and Errigal (CS Fr)) were also those where attitudes and self-image were most positive.

A profile of positive mathematical experience

One of the most striking findings from the focus group material is that the majority of the students did not have the necessary vocabulary to discuss mathematics as a subject and had little interest in discussing it. These findings concur with cross-national data from Picker and Berry (2001) suggesting that mathematicians were 'largely invisible' to lower secondary school students, and that they held quite stereotyped and negative views of mathematics. When students did discuss the subject, most of their experiences were expressed in terms of particular teachers rather than mathematics per se. This finding also concurs with international research (Dick and Rallis, 1991; Johnston, 1994; Ma, 1997) which suggests that

Table 10.7: *Ranking of schools in relation to attitudes to mathematics and experience in class*

Rank of School out of 10 (1 = most positive)

Case Study Schools – Rank order	Perceptions of Mathematics		Experience with the Class Teacher		Academic Expectations	Maths JC Level (Majority)	TIMMS-related Test % Grade C or above (School Rank)	Streamed (s)/ Mixed (mix)	
	Attitude to (1 –2)	Self Image (0-2)	Positive Interaction (Rewards) (0-3)	Negative Interaction (Correction)* (0-3)					
Barrow (SSG F)	1	1	1	2	1	Higher	1	S	Top
Nore (SSG Fr)	4	8	3	5	3	Higher	6	Mix	Bottom
Suir (SSG Fr D)	9	10	5	7	8	Ordinary	9	S	Top
Liffey (SSB Fr D)	8	6	6	6	9	Ordinary	5	S	Bottom
Lee (SSB F)	7	4	10	9	2	Higher	4	Mix	Top
Lagan (SC Fr)	10	9	9	10	4	Higher	2	S	Top
Errigal (CS Fr)	2	2	2	1	6	Ordinary	7	S	Middle
Mourne (VCC Fr D)	6	7	4	8	7	Ordinary	9	S	Bottom
Blackstairs (VCC Fr D)	3	3	7	3	5	Higher	3	S	Top
Nephin (VCC Fr)	5	5	8	4	10	Ordinary	8	S	Bottom

Case Study Schools – Rank order	Mean Score	Mean Score	Mean Score	Mean Score	Mean Score	Level subject is taken by Majority	TIMMS-related Test % Grade C or above	Streamed (s)/ Mixed (mix)	
Barrow (SSG F)	1.05	0.67	0.89	0.47	1.64	Higher	96	S	Top
Nore (SSG Fr)	1.24	1.08	1.14	2.40	1.75	Higher	38	Mix	Bottom
Suir (SSG Fr D)	1.50	1.25	1.22	0.64	2.18	Ordinary	0	S	Top
Liffey (SSB Fr D)	1.40	1.02	1.32	0.61	2.21	Ordinary	48	S	Bottom
Lee (SSB F)	1.35	0.92	1.52	1.06	1.67	Higher	62	Mix	Top
Lagan (SC Fr)	1.56	1.09	1.58	0.77	1.79	Higher	87	S	Top
Errigal (CS Fr)	1.14	0.87	1.60	0.26	2.02	Ordinary	18	S	Middle
Mourne (VCC Fr D)	1.29	1.05	1.63	0.69	2.17	Ordinary	0	S	Bottom
Blackstairs (VCC Fr D)	1.20	0.90	1.70	0.49	1.92	Higher	81	S	Top
Nephin (VCC Fr)	1.28	0.99	1.93	0.57	2.42	Ordinary	10	S	Bottom
Overall average	**1.29**	**0.96**	**1.45**	**0.61**	**2.11**				

*In relation to teacher correction, rank order 1 implies students report receiving the highest level of negative interaction while rank order 10 implies the lowest level.

Key: SSG F: Secondary girls', fee-paying; SSG Fr: Secondary girls', free scheme; SSG Fr D: Secondary girls', free scheme designated disadvantaged; SSB Fr D: Secondary boys', free scheme designated disadvantaged; SSB F: Secondary boys', fee paying; SC Fr: Secondary coed, free scheme; CS Fr: Community school, free scheme; VCC Fr D: Vocational/Community college, free scheme designated disadvantaged; VCC Fr: Vocational/Community college, free scheme (where free-scheme represents non fee-paying status).

students' views of the subject are strongly influenced by their classroom experience of learning it. Although students were able to identify particular areas of mathematics where they experienced a difficulty, they were generally unable to pinpoint the reason for the problem: problems were often described in terms of something 'not clicking' or 'not getting it'. While interviews with students provided some insight into their feelings about mathematics, they were limited at times by an inability to name issues of concern.

Introduction

Of the ten case-study classes, three were largely 'positive' about learning mathematics.[3] The schools in question included an urban fee paying all girls' secondary school (Barrow (SSG F)) and two mixed community colleges in a large and a small town respectively (Blackstairs (VCC Fr D) and Errigal (CS Fr)). Blackstairs was also a designated disadvantaged school.

There were a number of similarities between the students in Barrow (SSG F) and Blackstairs (VCC Fr D): both were top stream classes (with a majority assigned to the Higher level Junior Certificate course in mathematics) and students in both achieved high scores in the TIMSS-related test. In terms of social background however, the students were very different: Barrow is a socially selective school while Blackstairs has students from diverse social backgrounds. However, in Blackstairs the particular top stream class has an over-representation of students from a middle-class background compared with all students in the school (see Chapter 4). By contrast with the other two schools, the students in Errigal are in a middle stream class, with the majority assigned to the Ordinary course in mathematics for the Junior Certificate. As the data in Table 10.6 show, less than 20 per cent of these students achieved a grade C or above in the TIMSS-related test, compared to 96 and 81 per cent respectively, for Barrow and Blackstairs.

Students in the class in Barrow were the most positive about their mathematics classes and education generally. Of the ten schools, they rank highest in terms of attitude to mathematics, experience of learning mathematics and academic expectations for the Junior Certificate and their future education. In addition, of the ten classes in this study they achieved the highest mean score in the TIMSS test. As we will see below, interviews with the students confirmed findings from the questionnaire data regarding their positive perspective.

In Errigal, the students were extremely positive despite a relatively low average achievement in the TIMSS-related test, and their placement in the

Ordinary level mathematics class (Table 10.7). From the focus group discussions, it was clear that the 'teacher factor' was critical in shaping their current attitude to, and experience of, learning the subject. Finally, the students in Blackstairs were very positive about mathematics (in terms of attitude and self-image) and reported a low level of negative interaction with their teacher. Of the three schools in the 'positive' experience category, their score on the level of reward received for achievements in class was lower than both the average score and that recorded for the other two schools.

Using material from focus group discussions, the reasons why students in these classes are positive about mathematics, and their schooling generally, are explored.

The 'good teacher': 'clear', 'patient', 'good-humoured' and 'fair'

When asked about their current experience of learning mathematics, the students in the focus group in Barrow (SSG F) were very positive. As is the case generally for the students in this study, responses about learning are articulated in terms of the teacher rather than in terms of curricular content, learning resources or the forthcoming Junior Certificate Examination.

> *Interviewer:* How do you find maths this year?
> *Liz:* Ms Brennan makes maths interesting. She adds little funny things. It is her sense of humour. She keeps you interested. (Barrow SSG F)
>
> *Barbara:* I just think she is very good at teaching and explaining. I think it also helps when you are graded on ability. It makes it easier when you don't have people who need it to be explained millions of times. (Barrow SSG F)

In Blackstairs (VCC Fr D), all six students in the focus groups[4] had a very positive view of their mathematics teacher. The following extract indicates that the girls liked the teacher, Mr Butler, (and the subject) not solely due to his skilled teaching but also because he treated the students with sensitivity and respect.

> *Interviewer:* So how are you finding maths this year?
> *Jackie:* I think Mr Butler is a good teacher. He goes fast but then he really explains things. I suppose you have to get a certain amount done by the end of the year.
> *Patricia:* When we came into his class first, the way he would bring people up to do questions on the board and that, that was quite unnerving at first. But he explains it really well so most people know how to do it when they are called up.
> *Jackie:* Yeah, like you feel that everybody is watching you. And then he would say: 'Is that right?' and you are hoping they will say 'yes'. And then if nobody does, it's: 'Oh no!'.

Interviewer: So it is unnerving?

Aine: If you got it wrong, he would say: 'Are you sure that is right?' and usually you would look at it again and then you would usually realise where you have gone wrong, like say with just a minus or plus. Then if you still can't do it he will come up and show you – like he will rub out the bit you got wrong and show you how to do it.

Interviewer: So you think it is a good or bad method, overall then?

Jackie: I think it makes you concentrate more. If you are not concentrating and you are called up you feel really stupid. So when he says: 'You are going up to the board', everyone is thinking: 'That might be me'. So I think you definitely listen and take in more.

Interviewer: So what else do you think about maths class with Mr Butler?

Jackie: While he doesn't really praise or go on if you got it right, he will just kind of say that you got it right. You kind of feel good because of the way he says it.

Interviewer: What about if you hadn't your homework done or that – would he give out to you?

Patricia: You would bring in a note if you hadn't it done or you couldn't do it or something. You wouldn't just not do it. But usually he wouldn't embarrass you. He would probably speak to you on your own. But he never says names to embarrass you. Like sometimes he says that the class is so big he would say that there are a few in the class who are not paying full attention, or something like that. And it would unnerve you in case it was you and you would pay more attention. But he would never say names.

Interviewer: What about how he explains things – how do you find that?

Patricia: He would show you the hard way and then he would show you the easy way. He would show you the easy way from the hard way – like you take that from that. Then he will go into why you do that. You know like quadratic functions and why you do that is that and then he would go into a big long explanation of it. Then he would say: 'Now you don't have to do it that way, just do it this way because it is a shorter and easier way'. (Girls group)

This excerpt revealed aspects of skilled teaching from the point of view of the students, including thorough explanation and involvement of students through board work. In addition, the responses implied a rapport and mutual respect between teacher and students. Turning to the responses of the three boys in Blackstairs (VCC Fr D), it is evident that there are many similarities between the two accounts.

Interviewer: So how do you find maths this year with Mr Butler?

Robert: Good. I think the way he does it really brings you out of yourself. He did it the very first day. He says it helps each other to know each other. And in the class nobody has a grudge against him or anything so it is far easier to learn. He has a good way of teaching. It gets through to you. And it makes the class more enjoyable.

Interviewer: And would you say that the boys and the girls both think like this in the class?

Robert: Yeah – they are both the same. Much the same anyway. Like there are the same kind of grades coming out from both.

Interviewer: So in general you think Mr Butler's way of teaching maths is good?

Brian: Yeah – sometimes he shows us two ways of doing maths – but he shows us what he thinks is the better way.

Christopher (interrupts): He normally goes away from the book like. Normally the book has harder ways and he shows us an easier way.

Brian: Yeah. He would show us two ways and he would ask: 'Which do you find easier, which would you prefer?' and then we would do it that way. He never takes an example out of the book – like he never just reads it out. He takes things out of his head. Actually he would tell us to close the books while he is explaining something and he wouldn't let us write it down until afterwards so that we can pay attention and understand what he is doing.

Robert: It's good then – we have these hardback copies and we take down the explanation of a sum and an example and that. We use these for revision – like it is hard to revise maths, it's hard to study maths. But he directs how we do our written work and then it is easy to find things and it is not confusing. Like it can be confusing otherwise. You would get to know what was in the copy, you would learn it off and usually it would stick to you. You usually get it into your head anyway because usually when you are doing a topic it is usually for a week and you would stick at it and by the end of the week you sort of have it. (Boys group)

The views that emerged in the course of the two focus group discussions are largely consistent with the positive picture that emerged from the quantitative data. Other data from Blackstairs (VCC Fr D) show that the students' rating of the level of reward for achievements in mathematics class was below the average: 1.70 compared to the overall average of 1.45 (Table 10.7). This finding may relate to the students' description of the teacher's style; achievements were acknowledged at a whole class rather than individual level. In all other aspects, however, the students in Blackstairs (VCC Fr D) were very favourably disposed toward the mathematics teacher.

In Errigal (CS Fr), the boys reported that they had made a lot of progress in mathematics since they came into the post-primary school. They reported that this happened since they came into Ms Ennis' class in second year.

Gerard: She explains it more. She puts really good notes on the board.

Interviewer: Do you find the notes helpful?

Gerard: Yeah, they are really good because you can go back on it again and it is really clear to understand how she did it.

Sean: Anytime you do it the wrong way in your copy you write in the right way beside it in red pen and you can see exactly what you are doing.

Declan: It's easy to spot then where you went wrong. Anyway she always explains it again if you go wrong and then it is easy to understand.

Interviewer: When you get it right does she praise you?

Gerard: No, not really. She might say: 'That's good'. But nothing more than that really.

Interviewer: What about then if you don't get it right – would she ever give out?

Gerard: No she wouldn't make fun of you. She's nice like that – fair like.

Interviewer: Do any of you mind when you are asked to answer questions out loud in front of the class?

Boys all answer: No. (Boys group)

The girls in Errigal (CS Fr) have had the same mathematics teacher since they came into post-primary school. In the following excerpt, they describe how they came to like Ms Ennis' teaching style.

Interviewer: So how do you find maths this year?

Geraldine: I was scared of Ms Ennis in the beginning.

Interviewer: Why was that?

Geraldine: Oh, I don't know. In first year we were put outside for looking out the window and if you got something wrong you had to say where you went wrong and my mind would go blank. But this year she is really nice.

Agnes interrupts: I liked her last year.

Geraldine: I liked her but it took me a while to get used to her.

Rose: I really liked her too.

The girls went on to explain how Ms Ennis is considered to be an effective mathematics teacher in their school.

Agnes interrupts: She is a very good teacher. You see, I'm not too good at maths and I was afraid that I wouldn't get a great teacher that wouldn't explain it very well but I was delighted that I got Ms Ennis. So were my parents.

Geraldine: I know a girl in third year and she was put in another class (not Ms Ennis' class) and her mother asked that she be moved in with Ms Ennis because she is a better teacher.

Rose: She is a brilliant teacher.

Interviewer: It sounds from what you say that she has really developed a reputation in the school as a 'good' maths teacher?

Students: Yeah. Definitely. (Girls group)

The girls explain that the teacher monitors their progress closely, asking frequently about homework and work set in class if anyone 'got it wrong'.

Interviewer: How do you feel then if you have to explain what you got wrong?

Geraldine: OK, yes, fine! Like she is really good, she doesn't make you feel bad just because you made a mistake.

Rose: She'll do something until you understand it. She won't mind like.

Marjorie: She's not a teacher that would make you nervous.

Rose: She'll spend the whole class. She will just make sure that you get it right.

Agnes: I got something wrong there a while ago and she asked me did I understand it. I was afraid to say no but she kept us in for 10 minutes until I understood it. Like she is very good like that.

Geraldine: At the end of first year we were supposed to be divided into Higher level and Lower level but whatever happened it wasn't done. Anyway I didn't care if I didn't do the Higher level. I just prefer to stay with Ms Ennis than to [move to another teacher and] do the Higher level.

Students: General agreement with Geraldine's last point.

Rose: Everyone wants to stay in her class. A lot of people come begging at her door to be taken into her class. Like my sister now, she's in fifth year, she was in with another teacher and then she changed to her class and she says she really understands her better than she did the other teacher.

The girls continued in their praise of the teacher. Rose volunteered an example of why they like the teacher: 'If someone didn't do their homework she will just say that homework is for your own benefit but that it is your life' but 'she won't show you up'. They agreed that she was 'fair' and not 'sexist', by comparing her with another teacher.

Interviewer: What do you mean exactly when you say she is fair and that she is not sexist?

Geraldine: Last year we had this woodwork teacher. If you went up with a piece of woodwork and said 'Look' or whatever, he'd go: 'Well that's good *for a girl'*. We were treated different to the boys.

Rose: Yeah, I left woodwork just because of him. (Girls group)

Mathematics as a subject seemed to be defined and interpreted in terms of the person who taught it. The students who were most positive about mathematics were also very positive about their teachers describing them as 'good teachers', clear in their explanations, patient in their approach, good-humoured, not sarcastic, and fair to all students.

Fear of being wrong

Despite the overall positive experience, an issue that arose spontaneously in the focus group discussions related to help seeking. Students were reluctant, even fearful, to ask for help in mathematics class. This issue was raised by the students themselves, in the context of a discussion about their experience of learning mathematics throughout their primary and post-primary education. Students said they generally preferred to ask their parents and/or other siblings for help at home, or alternatively to ask one of their friends or classmates. Help from home or friends appeared to be less threatening than the prospect of asking the teacher in front of the entire class. Students were fearful of being wrong and looking 'stupid' in class.

The fear of asking for help in class was expressed in the two top stream classes (namely Barrow (SSG F) and Blackstairs (VCC Fr D)) but not in the middle band class in Errigal. In Blackstairs it was only the girls who referred to their need for outside help. The competitive atmosphere in the top stream classes, something we observed in the video analysis, did not seem to lend itself to any display of weakness or inadequacy, and the girls appeared to be somewhat more sensitive to this.

The following excerpt from a class in Barrow illustrates the point:

Catherine: Sometimes if I didn't understand I wouldn't ask her. I would feel it was a stupid question. I would ask my Dad instead.

Barbara: Well if I had a problem I would wait until maybe towards the end of the class because usually she does the sum out on the board and she would do it step by step, so you understood. If I had a problem I would probably ask her, but it would depend. I would say to the girl beside me: 'Do you understand that?' and if she says 'Yes' then I wouldn't ask.
Interviewer: So you would go by the person beside you?
Barbara: Yeah. Everyone in the class is amazing at maths. There is a lot of pressure as well, there are some people who are just amazing. You feel that you have to keep up and everything – there is a lot of pressure to do really well.
Liz: I think Ms Brennan tries to take some of that pressure off. But then sometimes she would say also: 'You are all meant to gain As' all the time!' (Barrow SSG F)

This same issue arose in the discussions with the girls in Blackstairs (VCC Fr D). Although the girls were comfortable in asking the teacher for help, in that he invited and welcomed questions, they did not like to feel embarrassed in front of everyone in the class. In the context of this particular class, most of the help was likely to come from friends or classmates rather than family:

Interviewer: Do you always ask Mr Butler questions when you don't understand what is going on?
Aine: We *can* ask him. But the thing is you wouldn't want to ask him because the class is so big. If everyone else understands it you would be embarrassed to ask.
Jackie: He always encourages us to ask. And like if you ask a question he will always answer it. But you can feel a bit weird asking.
Interviewer: Was this the case in primary as well?
All three girls: Yes!
Interviewer: Was it just maths or did it happen in other subjects as well?
Patricia: In every subject. If you needed help your friends would usually show you.
Interviewer: And what would happen if all your friends were stuck as well.
Aine: That wouldn't usually happen. If a lot of people got stuck, then someone was bound to say: 'I don't understand it' and then others would join in and say: 'Me too'. And then he would go over the lot again.

The most positive views on learning mathematics were expressed in two top streams and in one mixed class. In each class the teacher's competence in explaining mathematical material, and their caring, non-critical and supportive approach to student learning, led to a positive response to the subject overall. Although students were positive, students in the top stream classes were also quite fearful in class, partly of the teacher, but mostly of being seen as 'stupid' by their peers if they asked an inappropriate question. Fear of being 'wrong' was part of the sub-text of the top set mathematics classes. It led certain students (especially girls) to seek help outside of class rather than within it.

A profile of negative mathematical experience

Introduction

Students in three of the case-study classes were mostly negative about their experience of learning mathematics. Of these three, one was exceptionally negative. The class in question was in Lagan, a coeducational secondary school located in a large town. It was a top track group assigned to the Higher course for the Junior Certificate. Most of the students (87 per cent) achieved a grade C or higher in the TIMSS-related test; overall in the TIMSS-related test, the class achieved second place relative to the ten schools in this study.

The second school where there was considerable negativity, Lee (SSB F), is a fee paying, all boys' secondary school located in an urban area. The school is socially selective in its intake with the vast majority of the students from an upper middle-class background. All students are assigned to the Higher course for the Junior Certificate and are taught in mixed 'ability' classes. Most of the boys in the class (62 per cent) achieved a grade C or higher in the TIMSS-related test, putting them in fourth rank-order place overall (Table 10.7).

The third class in this 'negative' category is the top stream in a boys' secondary school located in an urban area (Liffey SC Fr D). The school is designated disadvantage and a majority (76 per cent) of students are from a working class background. The principal and the teacher both described the school as having an over-representation of students with low levels of academic achievement, and they attributed this mostly to unsupportive family backgrounds. In addition, the principal made reference to a particularly high incidence of 'social problems' in the geographical area in which the school was located. The norm in this school was for *none* of the Junior cycle students to follow the Higher course in mathematics for the Junior Certificate. The observed top stream class was an exception and the teacher expected that a number of the students were likely to take the Higher paper in the Junior Certificate Examination. However, this did not happen and the Junior Certificate results were disappointing in the teacher's view. In the observed class, almost half (48 per cent) of the students achieved a grade C or above in the TIMSS-related test, placing them fifth among the ten schools in the study (Table 10.7).

The class in Lagan (SC Fr) had the most 'negative' reports of mathematics, which seemed surprising in the context of their high achievement. Yet this negativity was expressed, by a large proportion of the students in the class, in response to an open ended question in the questionnaire.

In this question we asked students to record any opinions or experiences they felt were not catered for in the questions asked. Approximately one third took the opportunity to do so and the negative comments were divided between dissatisfaction with the principal and with the mathematics teacher. While most students in the other nine schools in the study took the opportunity to include some positive comments about various aspects of their school, or their mathematics teacher, this did not happen in Lagan. Two reasons emerged for overall student negativity, the attitudes of the principal which were regarded as being too controlling, and the approach of the mathematics teacher which was not regarded as being sufficiently attentive to the students' learning needs. It was not related to the subject per se.

> I don't like the principal or some other teachers in this school. They are too strict on things like uniform and they are unfair to some students. The vice-principal is sound. (Male student)

> I don't like the principal because he gives out and doesn't listen to your side. Also generally girls are treated differently to boys in most subjects including maths. (Female student)

> The school is okay but the principal is too strict. Maths sometimes is really boring and difficult. (Female student)

> I think that despite us learning all the time in CSPE and other classes that we should listen, and be listened to, it is funny how the most important person in the school [i.e., the principal] doesn't! (Male student)

> The maths teacher today put on an act. Also I think she explains things too quickly. And why on earth do we have to do algebra? (Female student)

Critical teachers, competition, speed and fear of being wrong

What emerged most strongly from the focus group with the mathematics class in Lagan (SC Fr), was an experience of 'pressure' and 'competition'.

Although both girls and boys expressed such concerns, it was the girls who articulated it most clearly.

Interviewer: How do you find maths this year?

Anne: I like maths this year when I can do it. It often happens that I cannot … then I get kind of down about it.

Pauline interrupts: Yeah. Exactly, I feel like that too…

Anne: I think Ms Leydon explains it but she goes *too fast.* There is a lot of pressure to do well.

Pauline: I like maths but this year it has been a real challenge. Ms Leydon is a good teacher. Like she knows her stuff and she is good at keeping control. Like last year our teacher did not explain things very well. But then we were in a mixed class and it was easier to get top of the class. Because we were doing easier stuff that everyone is expected to know it was easier to get it. Ms Leydon's class is very competitive and you are expected to know it first time. You are almost *afraid* to say that you got the answer wrong and that you will look stupid in front of everyone else.

Interviewer: Where did the competition thing come from do you think?

Pauline: Some people in the class are awful brainy. Some of the boys, but some of the girls too. Like there is one girl and she is really brainy and very determined as well. It makes it more *competitive* because it feels like if you don't know it you shouldn't be there – actually Ms. Leydon often reminds us about that and she will say: 'You better pay attention and keep up because you may not see this again until the Junior Cert'.

Anne interrupts: If you got something wrong she will keep on at you until you do …

Pauline: Yeah, like I remember that happened to me. I didn't know something or I got something wrong and I honestly didn't have a clue. She just kept asking me about it. She kept on at me and *I was nearly reduced to tears* about it in the end. And *I rarely ask questions* since.

Interviewer: That must be difficult?

Pauline: Well it has improved a bit. Since the parent teacher meeting it is easier to ask questions. I think a lot of parents told her that we were finding it tough and that she goes *too fast.* She has slowed down *a bit* since. She also says a lot more now: 'If you don't understand, ask me.'

Sinead: She goes *too fast.* Even though she had slowed down lately she still goes too fast I think. There is so much to cover in maths. Like even if you revise it will never be as thorough an explanation again – so if you don't get it as you go along it is a problem really.

Interviewer: Do you ask questions if she is going too fast for you and you need more explanation?

Sinead: I don't really like asking questions. If I don't understand I usually ask a friend to help me.

This 'pressure to perform' was emphasised further when the issue of praise for work well done was raised:

Pauline: Ms Leydon wouldn't, I wouldn't say she would *praise* you as such. If you are doing well it is just expected. If you have a record of being good then you know that she will automatically think: 'Oh she is good at that'. With those people she might say 'Good' but nothing more really.

Anne: Sometimes when she gives back tests she might say 'Good'. But she will also say 'That was bad' or 'You should have done much better'.

Interviewer: Is that privately or in public?

Anne: In front of everyone. If you don't do well she will say that you should have asked her if you didn't understand it. I don't think she should say it like that in front of the class.

When asked about criticism, all of the girls agreed that she wouldn't 'give out' but she would say that they should have asked for help:

Pauline: When you get something wrong she tells you that you should have asked a question. Sometimes she will say: 'Ah come on, you can do this' and then everyone turns around and has a look at you. That is why people are *afraid* – they are afraid they will be put on the spot if they ask a question. (Girls group, Lagan (SC Fr))

The responses by the boys are consistent with the latter reports, albeit somewhat attenuated. The fast pace of the lesson was mentioned but was not associated with 'pressure' and 'competition' to the same degree.

Interviewer: How do you find maths this year?

Vincent: I think she explains it quite well. She keeps your interest like. Having said that *she goes fast* enough alright. I'd say that sometimes people are slow to ask a question or ask for help because *you wouldn't want to be seen as the one who would ask.*

Peter: It's OK. Well it's OK as long as you keep up with what is going on. If you don't understand then it's tough, like I would say most *people don't like to ask questions.* Then if you get it wrong she gives out and says you should have asked the question. I'd mostly ask somebody at home or sometimes I'd be able to figure it out myself.

Joe: I usually understand what she is doing at the time. But then sometimes I forget how to do it or I get mixed up. Like in algebra some of the equations look the same and I can't see what way to do it.

Interviewer: Is there anything that would help you to remember?

Joe: Just to go back over it a lot. Like lots of practice and revision as well. But we go through things *so fast* that – just say with an equation, I think that if you knew why you were doing it that way you would probably remember it better.

An indirect reference to pressure was made when talking about the teacher's use of praise.

Fergal with a laugh: No she wouldn't praise you. *You are just expected to get it right.* She may say 'Good' but that's all.

When the issue of the teacher's use of criticism was raised only one of the four boys responded.

Peter: People don't usually mess in her class. Like she has good control.
Interviewer: Apart from messing, what about if you get something wrong?
Peter: Well she might look sort of annoyed or tell you that you should know it. She would try and get you to work out the problem there and then.
Interviewer: What is that like?
Peter: I don't know – you feel under a bit of *pressure* I suppose. (Boys group, Lagan (SC Fr))

The discussion became much more animated when we moved on from the issue of maths to the boys' general attitude to the school. All four boys reported that they did not like the principal because he was too strict and unfair. Three of the four boys related particular incidents with the principal; the general feeling was of 'being blamed in the wrong' and that 'he would not listen to your side'. Similarly, the girls also identified that the principal was 'very strict' in relation to uniform and rules about how to walk in the school.

Although the students in Lagan (SC Fr) were high achievers in a top stream class, the data from the questionnaires and the focus group discussions suggest that the 'teacher factor' was instrumental in generating negativity about mathematics. Negative feelings were explained in terms of being afraid to ask a question or give a wrong answer. Students felt they were under pressure, and that the material was being presented too quickly. At its strongest, the negativity was described as feeling that one was not entitled to be in the class if one was unable to keep up.

An interesting comparison can be made between this school and Barrow (SSG F) (discussed under 'positive experience' above) where the work ethic, pace and competitive atmosphere are similar. While the core ethos in each mathematics class is similar, the difference appears to be in the teacher's teaching style or delivery. In Barrow (SSG F) the use of humour is mentioned by the teacher and students, while this is noticeably absent in the accounts given by the students in Lagan (SC Fr). In addition, negative comments or sanctioning for mistakes were mentioned frequently by the students in Lagan (SC Fr) only. Lagan (SC Fr) provides a good illustration of the co-existence of high achievement and negative attitude and experience, while Barrow (SSG F) demonstrates almost the opposite. Although students in Barrow (SSG F) also felt under pressure, this was counterbalanced by a combination of teacher support, good humour and praise.

While overall attitudes to mathematics were quite negative in Lee (SSB F), they were a good deal more negative among the low achieving boys in the class. The low achieving students involved in the first group articulated quite negative views about mathematics.

Interviewer: How are you finding maths this year?

Conor: She really knows her stuff. And she says if you don't understand something to put up your hand. But then if you do she says: 'There is the example on the board' even if you don't get it!

Interviewer: So you would like more help?

Conor: Yes. Definitely. She really flies through it on the board. I think it would be better if she just came down to you. I find it easier to understand when she talks to you directly yourself.

Interviewer: What about asking your neighbour? Would you ever do that?

Conor: No.

Jonathan: I think she is good. She comes down to you the odd time to explain something. Like she would do it if there was time. But she is going *really fast* trying to get the course covered. Like it is a really long course for honours and you have to go fast. I suppose it would be better if she could go into more detail in explaining things but it is probably not possible to do that and still get everything finished.

Stephen: She is a good teacher. But as Jonathan said she tries to get the chapters done *as fast* as she can so she can finish the whole course on time. She should slow down really and spend a bit more time helping people that have problems. Sometimes she will ask who doesn't understand and she will say that she will come back and help them, like say at the end of class or when we are doing work or started our homework, but then she often forgets or doesn't get around to it and that. Like I think there is no point going on unless you understand it.

Interviewer: And would any of you ask for help at home or from someone other than the teacher?

Conor: My Dad, he's reasonable at maths, but he doesn't really explain it that well. He goes too fast. My mum's not good at all. I don't like asking my Dad for help.

Jonathan: I usually ask in class so I don't really need to ask anyone. The odd time my Dad but he does things a different way sometimes.

Stephen: I ask my Dad. Not often though. Like you are taught one way in school and when you go home he'll probably show me a different way. Then in class the next day I won't have a clue.

Jonathan: I think our parents were taught a different way. In maths class too I hate the way she always shows us the harder way. She says that it is so we can understand it better. Then she might show us an easier way. Then in the tests I get mixed up about what way to do it.

In our discussion about the use of praise and criticism by the teacher, the boys convey further negative attitudes. Overall, they report little or no praise for achievement or successes but a considerable amount of criticism for mistakes or misdemeanours.

Turning to the high achieving students in the second focus group from

Lee (SSB F), our analysis revealed fairly positive views about their experience of learning mathematics this year. The excerpt shows that while they are positive about the teacher's pedagogical approach there is little evidence of a rapport between students and teacher. In fact, students reported being ridiculed if they did not understand. Opportunities to ask for help are not always taken, with evidence that the choice is sometimes made to ask someone else or work it out on their own.

Interviewer: So what do you think of maths this year?
Dermot: It's enjoyable. The subject is good. So I don't mind it. The teacher is good.
Shane: Yeah, she is.
Larry: She knows her stuff.
Interviewer: Do you find maths challenging?
Dermot: It's not challenging, just fun to do. I just like doing maths.
Shane: Yeah. It's easy so you just do it!
Interviewer: So is that the way then? If you can do it you like the subject?
Larry: No. I can do Irish but I hate Irish.
Dermot: It's more the teacher than the subject.
Interviewer: So getting back to your maths teacher – do you think she is a good teacher then? You like her?
Laughter from the three boys
Dermot: No, we're not saying she's likeable!
Interviewer: So why do you think she is a good teacher?
Dermot: Well if someone has a problem she explains it. She will spend more time with those that didn't get it and be more patient. But if you were capable to put in the work and you didn't get it, she'd push you a bit further because she knows what you are capable of. There are other teachers in the school in other subjects and if you ask them what way to go about something they wouldn't explain it as thoroughly. She has a better method.

While students praised the teacher's method for explaining mathematics, they were cautious about asking questions.

Shane: Normally *I'd ask people in my class* to explain something before I'd ask the teacher or else I would just look at the answer and try and figure it out. Sometimes if you do ask the teacher she makes a big deal of it and sometimes she spends too long on it.
Dermot interrupts: It's a quicker process to ask someone else or just figure it out yourself.
Interviewer: One thing we noticed from being in the class is that you don't seem to mind putting up your hands to say you have a problem or you got something wrong?
Dermot: It's a good class. So no one takes it personally.
Shane interrupts: If you asked a question because you didn't understand, there might be someone who was jealous of you. There was a guy in my old school and if I asked a question he'd be saying: 'Why are you asking questions? You're supposed to be a brain, you're stupid'.

Larry: Most people in the class now are fairly good. So if only a few people don't understand she'll go down to them but if nearly everyone doesn't understand she will do it all over again.

When asked about positive reinforcement, the boys unanimously agreed that the teacher did not praise them for work well done.

Larry: She only praises people who are not good at maths but the people who are good at maths she would never praise. There are some people who are really bad at maths and she might praise them. I suppose this is to build a bit of confidence, you know. (Group 2, Lee (SSB F))

The students in Mr Little's class in Liffey (SSB Fr D) convey a general satisfaction with their teacher in terms of his pedagogical approach. Notwithstanding this, the students appeared quite alienated from learning, mainly articulated in terms of 'hating maths' and 'not being any good at it'. This applies particularly to the low achieving boys in the group: they spontaneously refer to, and are quite focused on, having performed badly in the Christmas test and are quite open about their low self-image in relation to maths. This is the only school where a 'disruptive' student participated in the focus group discussions.

Interviewer: How are you finding maths this year?
Ian: It's good. Mr Little is good. If you don't understand something he will explain it. He also goes around and helps you if you need it.
John: Yeah, we had this teacher last year and he used to make us go up to the blackboard.
Interviewer: And how did you find that?
John: Embarrassing! Especially when you got things wrong.
Robbie: He used to call me up to the blackboard and I would have just gone back to my seat and he would call me up again.
Interviewer: Why did he do that?
Other boys in the group interrupt saying that Robbie was always messing. Robbie laughs and looks proud.
Liam: I think Mr Little is good. Like if we get a question, a hard question, you know like an honours question, and we get it right he will say: 'Ask who got it right'. If a lot of people got it right he looks happy not like some of the others who just want to give out and get at you. When he is going around the class, when he looks at our homework, or if he gives us stuff to do in class, he will put a big smiley face on your copy if you did it right.
Robbie: Sometimes he starts roaring and shouting and bangs the desk.
Boys start chatting and laughing about a classmate that got thrown out of the class.
Interviewer: Getting back to maths. Is there any topic or part of the course you are having any difficulty with?
Robbie (with Liam joining in): All of it is hard. Like when it comes to the test.

I know it while we are doing it but then I forget. He starts a new thing every few days and it is hard to remember. You learn how to do it one way and then you get told to do the sum and then there's always a new way added in.

Liam: And you don't even know how to do one sum and he moves on to another one.

Interviewer: Do you do a test after finishing a topic or just at Christmas and summer?

John: I done bad at the Christmas test.

Robbie: I failed my Christmas test.

Ian: I did bad too.

Interviewer: Was it the same for you Sean?

Sean: Yes. I did bad. I knew all the sums and then at Christmas I don't know what it was. I knew some of the sums but I was just sitting there looking at it. Like we got a lot of formulas for the sums and I wouldn't know which ones to use.

John: I thought I did good in it but when I got the results back I failed it.

Interviewer: And did you get a chance to discuss it with Mr Little?

Ian: Yes. We went over it in class.

Robbie: I'm dreading the summer test. We're after doing loads this year. We have only started revision and we are starting the tests next week. I hate maths.

Liam: I hate it too. I'm crap at it.

Interviewer: Which comes first do you think, hating it or not being good at it?

Robbie: Hating it.

Liam: I'm not good at it. That's why I hate it.

Interviewer: So maybe you are not giving it a chance if you are hating it so much?

Robbie: It's just hard to take in everything.

Interviewer: So maybe more attention would help or more explanation?

Pat: I don't think so. I think that if you're not good at maths, you're not good at maths and you can't do anything to make yourself good at it.

Interviewer: You think that?

Boys all agreeing: Yes.

John: I hate when the teacher comes down.

Interviewer: Why is that?

John: I just do. I hate the whole thing about maths. I can't do them. I prefer to ask the fella beside me. I hate the way he comes down all the time.

Some of the other boys seem to agree with this.

The reasons why students were negative about mathematics varied across the three classes. In both Lee (SSB F), and especially Lagan (SC Fr), the approach of the teacher to the subject was the key factor. When the teacher moved too fast without adequate explanation, used ridicule or got annoyed when the student had difficulties, or if s/he was not positive in orientation, students tended to be negative about the subject. In the class in Liffey (SSB Fr D), however, it was the students' sense of failure in mathematics that led them to view mathematics negatively.

Fear of being wrong

A reluctance to ask the teacher for help also emerged in the context of our discussions with the 'negative' students. This was particularly evident in relation to Lagan (SC Fr), the most 'negative' of the classes in this study. In this case it was mentioned specifically in relation to their current experience of learning mathematics.

> *Pauline:* I find that it is easier, definitely easier, to ask my mum. Or sometimes, I might ask one of my friends. My *mum* is brilliant though. She would sit down with me and she has a way of saying it to me that I won't feel stupid.
>
> *Interviewer:* What's the difference between asking her and asking the teacher?
>
> *Pauline:* Well Ms Leydon tends to go very fast and you don't want to stop her and say I don't understand it. And because you didn't understand it by that time from way back it is worse. She would probably get annoyed and expect you to know what came before.
>
> *Interviewer:* So would that apply to all of you?
>
> *Anne and Sinead agree that this is the case.*
>
> *Sinead:* It's just hard to be the one to say you don't understand if you think everyone else does. You don't want Ms Leydon to think you are not able for it. People are afraid to be put on the spot. It can be really embarrassing.

While the boys' group in Lagan (SC Fr) reported the importance of 'asking for help when you don't understand', they did not express their reluctance to ask the teacher as clearly as was the case for the girls.

> *Vincent:* I don't think that people always ask when they need it. It is important though, to ask questions when you don't understand.
>
> *Interviewer:* Would you always ask yourself?
>
> *Vincent (laughs):* Not always. No. I'd try to figure it out myself first and then I'd ask my older brother or someone else at home. Not very often though. Only if I couldn't figure it myself.
>
> *Peter:* I don't think people always ask either. Sometimes when people ask she starts asking them a load of questions, so I would say that that would put them off.
>
> *Interviewer:* Would the rest of you agree or disagree with that?
>
> *Fergal and Joe agree that this is the case but do not contribute any further comments on the issue.*

Negative views of mathematics were evident in classes that were different in both track, academic track and social profile. The most negative views were expressed in a top track, coeducational class that was predominantly middle-class. The two other classes were boys' classes, one in a fee-paying school and the other in a designated disadvantaged school, the former being a mixed class while the latter was a top track. While negative views in the latter school seemed to be more associated with

students' own sense of failure in mathematics, in the two other schools it seemed more related to the teaching style and learning climate. Students were most negative in classes that were very competitive, classes in which no student wanted to 'be the one to ask a question'.

Fear of being 'wrong' or 'being put on the spot', was not only expressed among students that were negative about mathematics classes however, it was expressed by students who had a positive view of both the teaching of mathematics and the subject itself. Our findings regarding students' sense of being intimidated in mathematics classes concur with similar findings in a cross national study by Picker and Berry (2001) and with those of Boylan and Lawton (2000) regarding students' sense of vulnerability in mathematics classes. There are also indications from Boylan, Lawton and Povey's (2001) research that girls fear the public shame of being wrong in class more than boys, and from Boaler's (1997e) research that the competitive ethos of high stream classes facilitates anxiety around the subject of mathematics itself.

Discussion and conclusion

Most students believed that success in mathematics was dependent on having a good teacher, studying hard and liking the subject. Students did not attribute as much importance as teachers to 'natural talent' or 'innate ability' in learning mathematics. While most students regarded mathematics as an important subject in school, the reason it was seen as important was because of its usefulness, in terms of employment, third level education and everyday life.

Analysis of student data revealed considerable differences across the classes in general attitudes to, and experience of, mathematics. They differed in terms of mathematics self-image, their perceptions of class-room interaction, and in their academic expectations for the future. Six classes were broadly classifiable as either being positive (three classes) or negative (three classes) in their experience of mathematics. The remaining four classes occupied an interim place between these two positions.

While one might expect students who were high achievers in mathematics to be the most positive about the subject, we did not find this to be the case. Although the most 'positive' class was the highest performing group in the TIMSS-related test, the most 'negative' class was also a high-achieving group (second in rank-order of the ten schools). In addition, while two of the 'positive' classes were in the top-stream in their year group, this was also the case for two of the most 'negative' classes. Moreover, students who were largely negative about mathematics often described their teacher as 'good' in terms of explaining material clearly.

The focus group discussions highlighted the importance of the style of individual mathematics teachers in determining attitudes to, and experiences of, the subject. This finding concurs with international research suggesting that students' view of the subject is strongly influenced by their classroom experience of learning it (Dick and Rallis, 1991; Johnston, 1994; Ma, 1997). All students spoke about mathematics in terms of their *teacher* and rarely mentioned other issues like the curriculum, the examination system or resources for the subject. There were three teacher practices that seemed to contribute to negative views on mathematics: when teachers taught at a very fast pace, when they were critical of students who made errors or sought help, or when they pressurised students to achieve without giving positive support. Students' accounts of mathematics classes were also more negative when the teacher lacked good humour, or rarely praised or encouraged students in class. Students who were positive about their experience of learning mathematics described their teacher as a 'good' teacher with a strong knowledge of the subject, capable of explaining the material and interacting with them in a humorous, supportive and non-judgmental way. Even in these 'ideal' circumstances, however, students were often reluctant to look for help from the teacher, seeing family or friends as a less threatening source of help. A fear of being seen to be 'wrong' was an overriding concern of students in all types of mathematics classes, a finding that concurs with that of Boylan and Lawton (2000), Boylan, Lawton and Povey (2001) and Picker and Berry (2001).

The relationship between gender and attitudes to, and experience of, mathematics was quite complex and not as stereotypical as has been reported in past studies (Forgasz and Leder, 2001; Leder and Forasz, 2000). While girls had more positive views of mathematics and their classroom experiences than boys, and significantly higher aspirations for themselves educationally, the impact of gender was mediated by social class, stream position, teacher style and students' level of attainment in the subject. Students who had positive teaching experiences, who were successful at mathematics, and who were in higher tracks (these also tended to be middle-class) were more positive regardless of gender. Moreover, boys had a Higher mathematics self-image than girls, although differences here were not significant.

Within coeducational classes, the only area in which there was a significant difference between girls and boys was in their classroom experiences; girls reported more positive experiences than boys. While girls also had slightly higher educational expectations, boys had slightly higher mathematics self-image, and more positive attitudes towards the subject.

One of the most important findings from the focus group discussions with students related to the learning climate of mathematics classes generally. Several students (in top tracks especially, but also in other classes) expressed fears about asking questions or seeking explanations in class. Students of both genders (albeit girls somewhat more than boys) spoke of their fear of appearing 'stupid' in mathematics. They said they did not ask questions as they were afraid of being criticised, either by their peers, or, in some cases, by their teachers. Students seemed to feel exposed and vulnerable in mathematics, and they tried to hide their lack of understanding from peers and the teacher. They reported seeking help from friends, siblings or parents, rather than the teacher.

Our findings regarding students' sense of fear and vulnerability in mathematics classes has been reported in a number of other recent studies (Boylan and Lawton 2000; Boylan and Povey 200; Picker and Berry 2001). Our findings regarding the competitive ethos of top tracks, especially as seen by girls, corroborates Boaler's (1997) earlier findings in the UK.

Appendix 1 to Chapter 10

Figure A10.1: Students' views of 'why they need to do well' in school mathematics

(Base: 237)

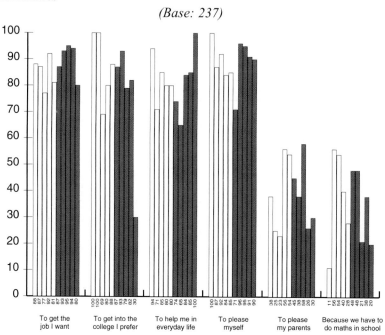

Key: Single sex schools: white bars and **coeducational schools:** grey bars

1. Barrow (SSG F)	4. Liffey (SSB Fr D)	7. Errigal (CS Fr) 10. Nephin (VCC Fr)
2. Nore (SSG Fr)	5. Lee (SSB F)	8. Mourne (VCC Fr D)
3. Suir (SSG Fr D)	6. Lagan (SC Fr)	9. Blackstairs (VCC Fr D)

Note: Same Key applies to all six statements.

Appendix 2 to Chapter 10

Construction of attitude scales

In the course of the research it was necessary to construct a number of indices or 'scales' in relation to students, particularly in terms of their attitudes and aspirations. The main results from our survey of the different attitudes, beliefs and aspirations of the boys and girls surveyed are presented below.

The attitude scales used are Likert scales (Oppenheim, 1966, pp. 120-159).

(i) *Attitude towards maths (MATHATT)*

Responses to the following nine items were used in this scale. The scored responses were aggregated in the following way to give a scale that ranged in total value from 9 to 19. To control for non-response, the total score was divided by the number responded to by each student giving the final score with values ranging from 1 (very high liking for maths) to 2 (low liking for maths). The overall reliability was very high: Cronbach's Alpha = .8151.

Item	Statement	Response/Score	
1 Measy	'Maths is an easy subject'	Very easy/ easy = 1	Quite difficult/ difficult = 2
2 Museful	'Maths is useful'	Yes = 1	No = 2
	interesting'		
4 Mdiff	'Maths is difficult'	No = 1	Yes = 2
5 Menj	'Enjoy maths I do at school'	Always/most of the time/sometimes = 1	Hardly ever/never = 2
6 Mlife2	'Maths is important to everyone's life'	Strongly agree/ agree = 1	Strongly disagree/ disagree = 2
7 Mbore2	'Maths is boring'	Strongly agree/ agree = 1	Strongly disagree/ disagree = 2
8 Mfavsbj	'Maths is my favourite subject': 1st /2nd mention	Yes = 1	No = 2
9 Mlfavsbj	'Maths is my least favourite subject': 1st or 2nd mention	Yes = 1	No = 2

(ii) Maths self-image (MATHIMG)

This is a three-item scale with an Alpha of .82. It indexes the student's image of her or his own mathematical ability relative to that of peers. The items below were aggregated for each student and divided by the number of valid responses. Thus the values of the scale range from 0 (very high maths self-image) to 2 (low maths self-image).

Item		Statement	Response/Score		
1	Mustand	'This year so far, I understand the maths'	Very often = 0	Often = 1	Few times/ Never = 2
2	Mable	'Do you think you are good, bad or okay at the maths you do in school?'	Good = 0	Okay = 1	Bad = 2
3	Mprognow	'Thinking of everyone in your maths class this year, where would you place yourself'	Top/well above average = 0	Just above average/ average = 1	Below average/ well below average = 2
4	Aheadcc	'I'm usually well ahead of others in my maths class'	Strongly agree = 0	Agree = 1	Strongly disagree/ disagree = 2
5	Mvable	'In maths I can do just about anything I set my mind to'	Strongly agree = 0	Agree = 1	Strongly disagree/ disagree = 2
6	Magegp	'I am as good at my maths school work as most other people of my age'	Strongly agree = 0	Agree = 1	Strongly disagree/ disagree = 2

(iii) Positive Teacher Interaction (MATHPTI)

This is a six-item scale with an Alpha of .73. It indexes the student's image of her or his interaction with the maths teacher. The items below were aggregated for each student and divided by the number of valid responses. Thus the values of the scale range from 0 (very positive) to 3 (negative interaction).

	Item	*Statement*	*Response/Score*			
1	Mwkgood	'Over the past 2 weeks in maths class I have been told my work is good'	Very often = 0	Often = 1	A few times = 2	Never = 3
2	Maskqs	'Over the past 2 weeks in maths class I have been asked questions in class'	Very often = 0	Often = 1	A few times = 2	Never = 3
3	Mpraise1	'Over the past 2 weeks in maths class I have been praised for answering a difficult question'	Very often = 0	Often = 1	A few times = 2	Never = 3
4	Mpraise2	'Over the past 2 weeks in maths class I have been praised because my written work is good'	Very often = 0	Often = 1	A few times = 2	Never = 3
5	moffans	'This year so far, I offer to answer questions without the teacher asking me to do so'	Very often = 0	Often = 1	A few times = 2	Never = 3
6	mpayatt	'This year so far, I pay attention and work hard in the class'	Very often = 0	Often = 1	A few times = 2	Never = 3

(iv) Negative Teacher Interaction (MATHNTI)

This is a four-item scale with an Alpha of .63. It indexes the student's image of her or his interaction with the maths teacher. The items below were aggregated for each student and divided by the number of valid responses. Thus the values of the scale range from 0 (less negative) to 3 (very negative).

	Item	Statement	Response/Score			
1	Mtoldoff	'Over the past 2 weeks in maths class I have been given out to because my work is untidy or not done on time'	Very often = 3	Often = 2	A few times = 1	Never = 0
2	Mignored	'Over the past 2 weeks in maths class I have wanted to ask questions but have been ignored'	Very often = 3	Often = 2	A few times = 1	Never = 0
3	Mmess	'Over the past 2 weeks in maths class I have been given out to for misbehaving in class'	Very often = 3	Often = 2	A few times = 1	Never = 0
4	Mueqatt	'My maths teacher pays more attention in class to what some students say than to others'	Strongly agree = 3	Agree = 2	Disagree = 1	Strongly disagree = 0
5	Mhardtk	'I find my maths teacher is hard to talk to'	Strongly agree = 3	Agree = 2	Disagree = 1	Strongly disagree = 0

(v) General academic expectations (EXPECT)

This is a four-item scale with an Alpha of .74. It indexes academic expectations for the future. The items below were aggregated for each student and divided by the number of valid responses. Thus the values of the scale range from 0 (less negative) to 3 (very negative).

Item		Statement	Response/Score			
1	Perfjct	How well you are expected to do in the Junior Cert by – your teachers	Very well = 0	Well = 1	Just below average = 2	Well below average = 3
2	Perfjcy	– yourself	Very well = 0	Well = 1	Just below average = 2	Well below average = 3
3	Perfjcm	– your mother	Very well = 0	Well = 1	Just below average = 2	Well below average = 3
4	Perfjcf	– your father	Very well = 0	Well = 1	Just below average = 2	Well below average = 3
5	Hedt	What in your opinion is the highest certificate or qualification you are expected to get by – your teachers?	University degree = 0	3rd Level Certificate Diploma = 1	Leaving Cert = 2	Junior Cert = 3
6	Hedy	– yourself	University degree = 0	3rd Level Certificate/ Diploma = 1	Leaving Cert = 2	Junior Cert = 3
7	Hedm	– your mother	University degree = 0	3rd Level Certificate/ Diploma = 1	Leaving Cert = 2	Junior Cert = 3
8	Hedf	– your father	University degree = 0	3rd Level Certificate Diploma = 1	Leaving Cert = 2	Junior Cert = 3

Item	Statement	Response/Score			
9 Postjct	What do you think you are expected to do after the Junior Cert by – your teachers?	Definitely stay at school to do the Leaving Cert = 0	Probably stay at school to do the Leaving Cert = 1	Look for a job straight away = 2	Do a vocational, training or FÁS Course = 3
10 Postjcm	– your mother	Definitely stay at school to do the Leaving Cert = 0	Probably stay at school to do the Leaving Cert = 1	Look for a job straight away = 2	Do a vocational, training or FÁS Course = 3
11 Postjcf	– your father	Definitely stay at school to do the Leaving Cert = 0	Probably stay at school to do the Leaving Cert = 1	Look for a job straight away = 2	Do a vocational, training or FÁS Course = 3

Appendix 3 to Chapter 10

Analysis of relationships among scales measuring attitudes to and experience of mathematics in school, and independent variables

A correlation analysis was conducted to examine the relationships amongst the five scales outlined above, namely attitude to maths (MATHATT), self-image in relation to maths (MATHIMG), positive teacher interaction (MATHPTI), negative teacher interaction (MATHNTI) and academic expectations (EXPECT). The results of this analysis are presented in Table A10.1 (below). All of the variables are inter-correlated to a statistically significant degree, with the exception of the two classroom interaction variables (MATHPTI and MATHNTI) and the variable describing their academic expectations for the Junior Certificate and beyond.

The results show that the strongest positive relationship is that between attitude to mathematics (MATHATT) and self-image about the subject (MATHIMG). Both of these variables are correlated with the positive classroom interaction variable (MATHPTI); the strongest positive relationship being between attitude to mathematics and positive classroom interaction. In addition, a strong positive relationship was found between attitude to mathematics and negative classroom interaction; this implies a more positive attitude to mathematics is strongly related to less classroom sanctioning/correction for mistakes and misdemeanours.

Not surprisingly, our analysis showed that there is a strong positive relationship between mathematical ability and academic expectations, and to a statistically significant degree. In addition, such a positive statistically significant relationship also exists between mathematical ability and mathematical self-image.

We will now briefly discuss the inter-correlations among the Likert-scale variables and our independent variables. The independent variables referred to are as follows:

Social class: middle-class (Group I, II and III) vs. working class (IV, V).
Gender (overall): girls vs. boys
Gender (within coeducational schools): girls vs. boys
Maths achievement (TIMSS-RELATED): fail vs. grades A/B
Ability grouping: Top (Barrow (SSG F),22, 31, 56) vs. bottom stream (Suir (SSG Fr D), 51 and 57)
Within-group 'positive' mathematics learning experience: Barrow (SSG F) vs. 46; Barrow (SSG F) vs. 56 and Errigal (CS Fr) vs. 56
Within-group 'negative' mathematics learning experience: Lagan (SC Fr) vs. 22; Lagan (SC Fr) vs. 24 and Liffey (SSB Fr D) vs. 24

In relation to social class differences (Table A10.2), as defined by middle-class versus working class, the results reveal that middle-class students have significantly higher expectations than their working class counterparts. However, working class students are less likely to report classroom sanctioning relative to the middle-class students, and to a statistically significant degree.

Taking all students, girls are significantly more positive in all aspects, with the exception of maths self-image (although not statistically significant: Table A10.3). Looking at gender differences within coeducational schools, the results show that girls are significantly more likely to report rewards for achievements in their maths classes (Table A10.4).

Returning to mathematical performance, we compared the mean score difference on the above items between those who failed and those who obtained a grade B or above. Not surprisingly, we found a strong positive relationship between high mathematics achievement and both mathematics self-image and academic expectations (Table A10.5).

In relation to ability grouping, we compared the mean scores of students in the top compared to the bottom stream (Table A10.6). Overall, the top stream was accorded more positive scores on all items, except classroom correction where no differences were found. Statistically significant differences occurred in relation to mathematics self-image and academic expectations.

Table A10.1 Correlations among Likert-scale items

	MATHATT	MATHIMG	MATHPTI	MATHNTI	EXPECT	Ability‡
MATHATT	1.00	.631*	.520*	.404*	.195*	−.113
MATHIMG	.631*	1.00	.461*	.228*	.262*	−.297*
MATHPTI	.520*	.461*	1.00	.292*	.118	.032
MATHNTI	.404*	.228*	.292*	1.00	−.029	−.013
EXPECT	.195*	.262*	.118	−.029	1.00	−.503*

‡Ability refers to mathematical ability measured by TIMSS-RELATED test.
* Significant, $p < 0.01$

Table A10.2 Differences in Likert-scale item means by social class

	Middle-class	Working class	Total
MATHATT	1.28	1.30	1.29
MATHIMG	.92	.99	.96
MATHPTI	1.42	1.46	1.45
MATHNTI	.67	.55*	.61
EXPECT	1.94	2.26*	2.11

* Significant, p < 0.01

Table A10.3 Differences in Likert-scale item means by gender within coeducational schools

	Girls	Boys	Total
MATHATT	1.32	1.28	1.29
MATHIMG	1.01	.92	.96
MATHPTI	1.38	1.59*	1.45
MATHNTI	.51	.60	.61
EXPECT	2.14	2.23	2.11

* Significant, p < 0.01

Table A10.4 Differences in Likert-scale item means by mathematics achievement scores measured by score in TIMSS-RELATED test 1 (lowest) to 40 (highest)

	Fail	Grade 'A'/'B'	Total
MATHATT	1.32	1.23	1.29
MATHIMG	1.12	.80*	.96
MATHPTI	1.32	1.43	1.45
MATHNTI	.53	.60	.61
EXPECT	2.44	1.91*	2.11

* Significant, p < 0.01

Table A10.5 Differences in Likert-scale item means by ability grouping

	Top stream	Bottom stream	Total
MATHATT	1.33	1.35	1.29
MATHIMG	.90	1.10*	.96
MATHPTI	1.33	1.46	1.45
MATHNTI	.64	.64	.61
EXPECT	1.84	2.50*	2.11

* Significant, p < 0.01

Table A10.6 Differences in Likert-scale item means within 'positive' experience of mathematics in school (Barrow (SSG F), Errigal (CS Fr) and Blackstairs (VCC Fr D))

	Barrow (SSG F)	Errigal (CS Fr)	Total
MATHATT	1.05	1.14**	1.29
MATHIMG	.67	.87*	.96
MATHPTI	.89	1.14*	1.45
MATHNTI	.47	.26	.61
EXPECT	1.76	2.27**	2.11
	Barrow (SSG F)	**Blackstairs (VCC Fr D)**	**Total**
MATHATT	1.05	1.20**	1.29
MATHIMG	.67	.90*	.96
MATHPTI	.89	1.60**	1.45
MATHNTI	.47	.49	.61
EXPECT	1.76	2.06**	2.11
	Errigal (CS Fr)	**Blackstairs (VCC Fr D)**	**Total**
MATHATT	1.14	1.20	1.29
MATHIMG	.87	.90	.96
MATHPTI	1.14	1.60**	1.45
MATHNTI	.26	.49*	.61
EXPECT	2.27	2.06*	2.11

* Significant, p < 0.01

Table A10.7 Differences in Likert-scale item means within 'negative' experience of mathematics in school (Lagan (SC Fr), Liffey (SSB Fr D) and Lee (SSB F)).

	Lagan (SC Fr)	Liffey (SSB Fr D)	Total
MATHATT	1.56	1.40	1.29
MATHIMG	1.08	1.02	.96
MATHPTI	1.70	1.58	1.45
MATHNTI	.77	.61	.61
EXPECT	1.92	2.38**	2.31
	Lagan (SC Fr)	Lee (SSB F)	Total
MATHATT	1.56	1.35**	1.29
MATHIMG	1.08	.91	.96
MATHPTI	1.70	1.93*	1.45
MATHNTI	.77	1.06	.61
EXPECT	1.92	1.84	2.11
	Liffey (SSB Fr D)	Lee (SSB F)	Total
MATHATT	1.40	1.35	1.29
MATHIMG	1.02	.91	.96
MATHPTI	1.58	1.93*	1.45
MATHNTI	.61	1.06*	.61
EXPECT	2.38	1.84**	2.11

** Significant, $p < 0.01$

* Significant, $p < 0.05$

Table A10.8: Attitude to mathematics: average scores of girls and boys in ten case-study schools on the MATHATT scale (overall average = 1.29). The lower the score the higher the liking for mathematics.

	Barrow (SSG F)	Nore (SSG Fr)	Suir (SSG Fr D)	Liffey (SSB Fr D)	Lee (SSB F)	Lagan (SC Fr)		Errigal (CS Fr)		Mourne (VCC Fr D)		Blackstairs (VCC Fr D)		Nephin (VCC Fr)	
School average scores	1.05	1.24	1.50	1.40	1.35	1.56		1.14		1.29		1.20		1.28	
By gender	G	G	G	B	B	B	G	B	G	B	G	B	G	B	G
	1.05	1.24	1.50	1.40	1.35	1.62	1.49	1.15	1.14	1.27	1.30	1.21	1.20	1.21	1.44

Overall scores by gender

Girls: 1.26   Boys: 1.33

Single sex versus coed by gender

SS Girls: 1.21   Coed Girls: 1.32
SS Boys: 1.38*   Coed Boys: 1.28

*p < .001

Table A10.9: *Mathematics self-image: average scores of boys and girls in ten case-study schools on the MATHIMG scale (overall average = 1.04). The lower the score the higher their academic self-image in relation to mathematics.*

School average scores	Barrow (SSG F)	Nore (SSG Fr)	Suir (SSG Fr D)	Liffey (SSB Fr D)	Lee (SSB F)	Lagan (SC Fr)		Errigal (CS Fr)		Mourne (VCC Fr D)		Blackstairs (VCC Fr D)		Nephin (VCC Fr)	
	0.67	1.08	1.25	1.02	.92	1.09		0.87		1.05		0.90		0.99	
By gender	G	G	G	B	B	B	G	B	G	B	G	B	G	B	G
	0.67	1.08	1.25	1.02	.92	1.02	1.13	0.81	0.90	0.83	1.29*	1.00	0.81	0.82	1.38*

Overall scores by gender

Girls: 0.98 Boys: 0.94

Single sex versus coed by gender

SS Girls: 0.95 SS Boys: 0.97* Coed Girls: 0.01 Coed Boys: 0.92

*p < .001

Table A10.10: Positive interaction in mathematics classrooms: average scores of boys and girls in ten case-study schools on the MATHPTI scale (overall average = 1.60). The scale ranges between 0 and 3. The lower the score the greater the level of perceived positive interaction/reward.

School average scores	Barrow (SSG F)	Nore (SSG Fr)	Suir (SSG Fr D)	Liffey (SSB Fr D)	Lee (SSB F)	Lagan (SC Fr)		Errigal (CS Fr)		Mourne (VCC Fr D)		Blackstairs (VCC Fr D)		Nephin (VCC Fr)	
	0.89	1.22	1.52	1.58	1.93	1.70		1.14		1.32		1.60		1.63	
Average															
By gender	G	G	G	B	B	B	G	B	G	B	G	B	G	B	G
	0.89	1.22	1.52	1.58	1.93	1.73	1.68	1.44	1.01*	1.33	1.31	1.68	1.51	1.66	1.55

Overall scores by gender

Girls: 1.27   Boys: 1.67*

Single sex versus coed by gender

SS Girls: 1.15   Coed Girls: 1.38
SS Boys: 1.76*   Coed Boys: 1.59

*p < .001

Table A10.11: Negative interaction in the mathematics classroom: average scores of boys and girls in ten case-study schools on the MATHNTI scale (overall average = 0.62). The scale ranges between 0 and 3. The lower the score the lower the level of perceived negative interaction/sanction.

	Barrow (SSG F)	Nore (SSG Fr)	Suir (SSG Fr D)	Liffey (SSB Fr D)	Lee (SSB F)	Lagan (SC Fr)		Errigal (CS Fr)		Mourne (VCC Fr D)		Blackstairs (VCC Fr D)		Nephin (VCC Fr)	
School average scores	0.47	0.59	0.64	0.61	1.06	0.77		0.26		0.69		0.49		0.57	
By gender	G	G	G	B	B	B	G	B	G	B	G	B	G	B	G
	0.47	0.59	0.64	0.61	1.06	0.78	0.77	0.32	0.24	0.84	0.53	0.48	0.50	0.52	0.66

Overall scores by gender

Girls: 0.53

Boys: 0.71*

Single sex versus coed by gender

SS Girls: 0.55
SS Boys: 0.84*

Coed Girls: 0.51
Coed Boys: 0.60

*p < .001

Table A10.12 : Average scores of boys and girls in ten case study schools on the EXPECT scale (overall average = 1.9). The scale ranges between 0 and 3. The lower the score the higher the academic expectation.

School average scores	Barrow (SSG F)	Nore (SSG Fr)	Suir (SSG Fr D)	Liffey (SSB Fr D)	Lee (SSB F)	Lagan (SC Fr)		Errigal (CS Fr)		Mourne (VCC Fr D)		Blackstairs (VCC Fr D)		Nephin (VCC Fr)	
	1.64	1.75	2.18	2.21	1.67	1.79		2.02		2.17		1.92		2.42	
By gender	G	G	G	B	B	B	G	B	G	B	G	B	G	B	G
	1.64	1.75	2.18	2.21	1.67	1.84	1.74	2.11	1.98	2.21	2.12	1.93	1.91	2.42	2.12

Overall scores by gender

Girls: 1.87   Boys: 1.99*

Single-sex versus coed by gender

SS Girls: 1.98   Coed Girls: 2.14
SS Boys: 2.10*   Coed Boys: 2.23

*p < .001

Notes

[1] See *Appendix 2 of Chapter 10* for the full details on the scales and *Appendix 3 of Chapter 10* for a discussion on the relationship between each of the scales, and between independent background variables and various attitude scores.

[2] The scalability of the items included in each scale was checked using Factor Analysis and Likert Scaling techniques and the reliability of the scales was tested using Cronbach's Alpha; this statistic ranges in value from 0.0 to 1.0 and measures the extent of co-variation amongst items in the scale. For our purposes a value of .80 or over is very high and those between .60 and .80 are highly acceptable. Alpha is within this range for all five scales used here. The methodological issues pertaining to the construction of these five scales are discussed in Appendix 2 of Chapter 10.

[3] 'Positive' here refers to a positive attitude to mathematics, a strong self-image in relation to mathematics, perception of a high level of reward from the mathematics teacher for achievements and a low level of sanctioning for mistakes or misdemeanours. In addition, it includes high academic expectations in relation to the Junior Certificate Examination and more generally in relation to their future education.

[4] We had two focus groups from this class, one with three boys and the other with three girls.

11

Parent Perspectives

Introduction

While teachers and students are the key players in the schooling process, parents also exercise considerable influence on their children's education. Many studies have highlighted a strong association between social class and parental involvement in education in particular (Coleman et al., 1965; Lareau, 1989; Gewirtz et al., 1996; Reay, 1998; Crozier, 2000). Other research has highlighted the strong association between parents' educational levels and their knowledge of, and integration into, school affairs (Bourdieu, 1996; Useem, 1992; West et al., 1998). The work of Lareau and Shumar (1996) has shown how differences in parents' educational skills, their occupational flexibility, and access to social networks advantage some parents to the detriment of others. Both Lareau and Shumar's work, and that of Gewirtz et al. (1995), also demonstrate the way in which working class parents are disadvantaged in managing their relations with the institution of the school, and how little the school does to overcome this disadvantage.

To understand the way in which parent perspectives impacted on learning, it was decided to interview parents of the students observed in the mathematics classes. The interviews were semi-structured and based on the parents' own experience of schooling generally and mathematics in particular. The parents of twenty-eight students were chosen for interview. They were selected across schools and streams to represent the range of students in the study. In all therefore thirty-seven parents were interviewed. For nine of the twenty-eight pupils, both parents were interviewed; in the case of fifteen children, the mothers only were interviewed; the remaining four interviews were with the father only.

We identified three different types of parent in terms of knowledge of the education system, education level, and levels of intervention with their child's school. We called these Insiders, Outsiders, and Intermediaries. While our classification of parents broadly parallels those of Gewirtz et al.'s (1995),[1] it differs in that this study was not solely concerned with school choice. It also examined parents' levels of intervention in schools, and their knowledge of school process generally, and mathematics in particular.

Differences in the cultural capital of parents

The research of Bourdieu and his colleagues in France (1977; 1986; 1997b) has underlined the importance of cultural capital in the education process. It has highlighted in particular the way in which parents of different social classes are either advantaged or disadvantaged in the forms of cultural capital to which they have access via their habitus (home experience). Their work has also shown how schools only grant recognition and legitimacy to particular forms of cultural capital, thereby advantaging some parents and marginalising others.

In this study it was very evident that parents differed in the cultural capital that they possessed (education credentials, knowledge of how education worked, confidence etc.), and in the social capital (networks of power and privilege) and economic capital (money and related resources)[2] to which they had access. Insider parents were characterised by their in-depth knowledge of the education system, their own high levels of education and their high level of intervention with regard to their children's education. They were deeply integrated into the education system. Outsider parents, in contrast, were 'outside' the system, possessing lower levels of knowledge of the education system, lower education levels themselves and low degrees of intervention. Some parents occupied an Intermediary position between the Outsider and Insider groups, so while they had sufficient knowledge to make them aware of certain aspects of the educational system, they lacked the deep knowledge of the Insider parents. They did not have enough knowledge to control their children's learning environment or to regulate it when it was not working. They also lacked both the financial and cultural resources of the Insiders.

Another defining difference between parents related to their knowledge of the discourses of education itself. The Insiders were familiar with the professional discourse of education. They knew the language of education and could discuss their views on different issues at length. On the other hand, the Outsider parents' perceptions revealed a basic unfamiliarity with certain aspects of schools and education. A number of them did not appear to have the language to discuss certain issues. Many of the Intermediary parents also appeared to lack experience in contemporary discourses of education.

The following table presents the main characteristics of the parent groups.

Table 11.1 Profile of parents

Social Class group and Formal Education	Insiders (n=6)	Intermediaries (n=13)	Outsiders (n=9)
% Middle-class	100.0	63.0	22.2
% with University degree (at least one parent)	83.3	30.1	0.0
Type of school			
% Free scheme/VOC/Comm	0.0	100.0	100.0
% Fee paying	100.0	0.0	0.0
Coeducational vs. Single sex			
% Coeducational	0.0	76.9	44.0
% Single sex	100.0	23.1	56.0
School type			
% Secondary	100.0	46.2	56.0
% Community school	0.0	15.4	11.0
% Vocational/Community college	0.0	38.4	33.3

As we can see from Table 11.1, all of the parents in the Insider category were from a middle-class background; eight out of the thirteen Intermediary parents were middle-class, while in the Outsider group, just two of the nine sets of parents were from middle-class backgrounds. Both parents held a university degree in six Insider families, with one exception. In the Intermediary group, four families had at least one parent with a university degree, while none of the Outsider parents had a third level degree. Only one set of parents in the Intermediary group had children in a designated disadvantaged school, while seven of the nine sets of parents who were Outsiders had children in such a school.

In the following discussion we analyse parental differences in approaches to education. We examine the relationship between parents' education and levels of intervention, and differences between parents in their knowledge of subject policies in schools, and knowledge of their children's progress at mathematics. We also examine parent views regarding the teaching and learning of mathematics.

Insiders

While the interviews with parents were taken primarily to examine their views on mathematics education, it was necessary to explore their views on education and schools generally to set the context for this analysis.

Given the constitutional rights of Irish parents to choose what type of education they want for their children, one of the first issues we examined was parental views on school choice. A further reason for examining school choice was because of its impact on mathematics learning. As is evident from Chapter 2, second level schools vary considerably in their approach to the teaching of mathematics. While almost all students do Higher level mathematics in some schools, very few or none do the Higher level course in others. Having the resources and knowledge to choose schools therefore influences the type of mathematics one's child is likely to learn.

School choice

School choice has become one of the dominant ideologies of new right education in the UK, and in other English speaking countries since the 1980s (Dale, 1997). Although school choice has always existed in Ireland as a constitutional right, its educational implications have never been critically analysed. We decided to examine parents' views of school choice not just because of its impact on course choices in mathematics, but also because it sets the context for understanding parent views on schooling generally and mathematics in particular.

Insider parents demonstrated both a strong inclination to choose a school other than their local one, and a strong capacity to utilise the possibilities of choice. They possessed the economic and cultural capital needed to gain inside information on the schools. One parent's succinct phrase summed up a general view of Insider parents in relation to choice: 'I will seek out the best school I can get.' (Lee SSB F)

Many parents began the process of choosing a second level school when their children were very young. In a number of cases there appeared to be an established pattern of transfer from certain primary schools into certain secondary schools, so strategic decisions were being made very early in the child's life. Getting the child's name down on time was crucial to the success of the educational strategy. We can see an example of this in the following excerpt:

> *Mrs O'Brien:* She went to Montessori school in School X and then she went into the Junior School at Barrow.
> *Interviewer:* So you knew for years that she was going to go to the Secondary there?
> *Mrs O'Brien:* That is right – we had her name down. (Barrow SSG F)

The inside knowledge, which certain parents possessed with regard to the education system, played an important role in school choice. Before the final choice of school for their child was made, the parents carried out extensive research to find the 'right' school. This research involved visiting a number of schools, studying prospectuses, talking to staff, attending open days, observing pupils and consulting with friends.

Interviewer: How did you go about getting information on the schools?
Mr Keogh: It was probably word of mouth, and we would go and have a look at the prospectus and reputation of the school. It is really the reputation of schools. (Barrow SSG F)

Mrs Connelly: From our own experience, I mean different people come at schools from different angles, and a school can give you their principles which is good, and you either like them or you don't. I think you have to see people, even just to go into the school and see the kids moving around. I mean, they are all very happy, chatting and they all know each other and the size of the school is another factor. We would have looked for a smaller rather than larger school. I mean both my husband and I were in small schools. It has certainly worked for us. I'm a bit of a control freak and I like to be on top of things but word of mouth and meeting children who have gone through the school certainly gives a good impression. Every school has its ups and downs, what some people look for may not be what you would look for so, I suppose you need a combination. You certainly need to find out what the school is about from themselves. (Lee SSB F)

Their privileged position as Insiders enabled the knowledgeable parents to confidently enter schools and seek appointments with the relevant staff. They were also able to interpret and 'decode' the information they were receiving. In this regard, the parents demonstrated an ability to discriminate between schools in terms of their policies and practices.

Interviewer: How did you choose this particular school?
Mr Keogh: We probably looked at School Y because she always was a very hard working girl … at primary, she worked hard and then she obviously excelled … so we thought at that stage that we would send her to a school with more than the academic. So we looked at Barrow which seemed to be the better balance so we wanted a better balance. It is an extraordinarily good school, it is the best school. (Barrow SSG F)

Insider parents were very clear about what they wanted when choosing a school for their children. While all mentioned the importance of the school's reputation and referred to 'seeking out the best school', it became clear that for most of the parents one of their primary concerns was finding a school that best 'suited' their child – a process which Gewirtz et al. (1995) refer to as 'child-matching'. In this process we see further evidence of the parents using their inside knowledge to seek out the best school for *their* child. The best school was one that would yield good academic results and that would help generally in the personal development of the child. This is illustrated in the following extract from an interview with the father of a pupil in a fee paying boys' school.

> *Interviewer:* What did you look for in your choice of school for Shane?
> *Mr Barrett:* [I looked for what was] … fit for him. He is bright, quite assertive. Always been very comfortable with adults, likes being the boss – ideas and discussions and talks – he is intelligent and bright and fundamentally he needs to be challenged. We felt that this was a school that would stretch him, academically, but also, and even more importantly, in terms of his personal development that he wouldn't find himself to be arrogant, in the sense of 'Oh, I am the best of everyone around here'. He would be with people where it would be normal to be quite good at things, and where that wouldn't be – em, he wouldn't become complacent and arrogant about that. And where he would see there is a wider dimension than just achieving the A or the B or whatever. We were also quite influenced by the ethos of the school. I'm quite supportive of that ethos. It is a Catholic ethos, but also very self-conscious in terms of its educational philosophy – on what a person's development is. All those things combined – we thought it was good for him. (Lee SSB F)

Finding the right balance in terms of academic and personal development was mentioned by a number of parents.

> *Interviewer:* What would be your overall expectations from the school for Melanie?
> *Mr Keogh:* Somebody who has mixed ability, social qualities, ability and confidence to converse properly, leadership skills, generally to get a rounded education because nowadays a lot depends on how well put together somebody is, as how the package presents itself. (Barrow SSG F)

In choosing a school therefore Insider parents had undertaken extensive research on different schools. Their overriding concern was with the capacity of the school to deliver a good 'package' for their child academically and personally. The gender composition of the school (single sex or coeducational) was not a major issue among Insiders for two reasons. First, because there are few socially and academically elite schools that are coeducational in Ireland, and secondly, because parents did not think that gender balance, per se, was the most important factor in facilitating educational advantage for their children.

Educational level and intervention

All but one of the twelve parents in the Insider group had university degrees, and all of the parents reported that they 'loved' or 'really liked' mathematics and found it 'very interesting'.

Their own educational backgrounds enabled these parents to engage in high levels of intervention in their children's schooling. They were also very knowledgeable with regard to streaming policies in schools, and their own children's general progress and performance.

Intervention

Parents' intervention practices revealed the wealth of cultural and financial resources available to them. Different forms of intervention included approaching their child's school, helping at home or paying for extra tutoring.

1. Approaching the school

It was the norm for the Insider parents to approach the school and consult with, or even confront, staff in relation to different aspects of their child's schooling, both at primary and secondary level. There were different reasons for approaching the school including general problems a child had with a teacher, or more specific problems related to particular subjects. It was clear that the parents possessed both the confidence and skills necessary to deal with the school. In the following extract, a parent of a child attending a boys' school explains how he dealt with a problem encountered when the child was in primary school.

Mr Barrett: Mark wasn't happy – didn't like his teacher. He was eight or nine at the time. They had a yellow card system for misdemeanours and we'd check it out and it would be trivial and he would take a great sense of injustice at this. Most telling event – parent teacher meeting – we didn't have confidence in the teacher after the meeting – I actually asked him: 'Do you see anything positive in Mark?' and he said: 'Well, actually, no'. This is a bit much. I lost confidence. Brought it up with [the] Principal. He brought us all together – three parties – and he said if we assure Mark that the teacher wasn't against him and that – we just kept going until next year he got a great teacher, for him. So how did we deal with it? Well we went to see the teacher, see what he had to say and when we were not satisfied with it we went to the Principal to tell him what was going on. (Lee SSB F)

In the next excerpt a mother explains how she dealt with a difficulty her son was having in mathematics.

Interviewer: Did you think about talking to the teacher in the school about the problem?

Mrs Connelly: Yes, I had done but it was just a particular problem with a particular teacher and then once he moved into sixth class but I have spoken with all his teachers about him and maths and I have spoken with his first year teacher last year.

Interviewer: Did he have a different teacher last year?

Mrs Connelly: No, I think it was the same, Ms Lincoln, she had second year but I mean it is something I will keep an eye on. Most of [the] subjects have moved on so much it's only maths that I would actually be keeping an eye on. His maths book looks huge but whether it's a combination of the approach, but he certainly seems to be having less difficulties with it in secondary school than in primary school. Her approach is certainly working, whatever approach she has. (Lee SSB F)

In the next excerpt a father of a child in a fee paying boys' school explains the approach he took to ensure that an older sibling stayed in Higher level French and mathematics.

Mr Lynch: Well Richard at the time did honours French for his Junior Cert and… the politics in the school [School Z] … I was on the parents' committee – there were a certain number of students who were only allowed to do the honours. At the time the French teacher suggested that Richard do the pass for the Leaving – I said absolutely not, if he got an honour in his Junior Cert – it didn't seem to make sense. Well, he said, I just think in my opinion, and the same went for the maths. I said absolutely not – I'll dig the heels in here and fought them tooth and nail and in the end anyway in fifth year, I said if you are not going to budge on this, I am going to pull him out. [The Principal] didn't want him to be pulled out – I said well, he is going out – but the end result was that he did get an honour in both subjects in School Z. But that was my own pressure that I put him under. (Lee SSB F)

Apart from having the skills and confidence to deal with schools, being in possession of inside knowledge is also an important factor in intervention. In the following extract a father explains the action taken when his son was at primary level.

Mr O'Hanlon: He didn't like leaving School A, but he is kind of middle of the road. He is a bit above average we guess. He is the kind of guy who has ability but he has a lot to do to get those extra points, he is going to have to be pushed. So, while we didn't particularly want to do it, we took him out of School A and put him in School B – smaller classes, and he'd get a better education … We think [School B] is a fabulous school, very well rounded…One [friend] said to me that he took his son out of School C and put him into School B and it was worth 150 points. (Barrow SSG F)

While all parents attended parent teacher meetings, two parents reported experiences in which they had felt they were not getting enough feedback on their child's progress. In the following excerpts, however, it is clear that these parents would make sure that they get the information they sought. This extract is taken from an interview with the mother of a child attending an all girls' school.

Interviewer: So, in terms of the primary school – would you and your husband have got a lot of information about how Angela was getting on in school?

Mrs Feeney: You had parent/teacher meetings every year, but I don't think you got a huge amount of information unless you went looking for it. And when you went looking for it there was no problem whatsoever. You had access to the teachers. No difficulty of any kind whatsoever. So you got information but you had to go get it. No way that you were updated on a regular basis as to how they were getting on and – you have to look for it yourself. (Barrow SSG F)

2. Helping at home

Insider parents had the capacity to promote their children's educational success helping them with school related work at home. All the parents reported that they had helped at primary level:

Interviewer: Would you ever have taken that up with the teacher about the homework not being corrected?

Mrs Feeney: It just seemed to be the standard thing …Well, I suppose, I corrected the homework always, always, always. For all of them.

Interviewer: So that's quite a role for a parent. A lot of time devoted to it?

Mrs Feeney: There just wasn't enough attention. I suppose with Angela that I didn't go into her maths as much because she was very good at them. Whereas with Celia her maths weren't so good, but her English was brilliant, so I didn't need to concentrate on that, but with Angela you had to concentrate on English and Celia on maths. And it is not only relating to maths, I do firmly believe that there is far too little – the teachers do not check on their homework often enough, and unless a parent is there supervising or you know, checking up on things or correcting things. I mean if a child misses the day on which such and such a subject is introduced, that's it – they are lost. (Barrow SSG F)

Mrs Connelly: He had a lot of problems settling in with maths when he did move, particularly maths which was his weaker point and we had to spend a lot of extra time on it. He found the sixth class maths programme very difficult, long division, fractions, there just seemed to be a huge amount because I know he had a particular problem in that, the maths course, and it wasn't really covered in the year and we were trying to catch up at home. (Lee SSB F)

This mother went on to explain how she had the capacity to draw on family resources to help her son with mathematics.

Mrs Connelly: My mother is a primary school teacher and she did remedial teaching for a long time, so I sent him down to her for a week or two because I found the books difficult to follow myself … Now as I say he hasn't had a problem but my mother spent time on it and once it was explained it was OK, it just needed a bit more explaining and certainly from the maths books I couldn't help him. (Lee SSB F)

While many of these parents stated that their children needed a lot less help in secondary school, most of them said that they would be able to provide help if it was needed. This is illustrated in the following extract:

> *Mr Barrett:* I don't get involved in his maths homework…I'd say I would be able to help him though – I did a refresher course a few years ago in maths…I don't think we would send him to grinds… maybe we are very lucky in that way – my wife can speak French – trained as a teacher – I have maths – she has Irish – she has some other language – we have both history and geography. It would only be questions of time, whether we could fit in the time. (Lee SSB F)

Most of the insider parents also stated that their children had to follow strict routines in relation to doing their homework.

> *Mrs Connelly:* He comes in, has a snack and starts his homework … that's a house rule, it's something I always did myself. It's the training we would have given them, they come in, have something to eat and do their homework while they're fresh.
> *Interviewer:* What would he do on those non-sporting evenings, say, after the homework and dinner?
> *Mrs Connelly:* Probably watch football on television.
> *Interviewer:* Otherwise would he watch much television, do you have rules on that?
> *Mrs Connelly:* Yes, there are restrictions on TV viewing. It really doesn't go on much during the week, during school, and he would watch it on Saturday morning before he goes out to rugby provided his homework was finished on Friday evening, if not it is finished on Saturday morning. (Lee SSB F)

All but one of the Insider parents interviewed said they would have no hesitation in getting grinds for their children if they were required. A number of them reported paying for grinds for older siblings in mathematics. Expense was not cited as an issue.

Working at the Higher level

In the schools chosen by Insider parents, most of the students were expected to take the Higher level course in the core subjects of English, Irish and mathematics. Although accessibility to Higher level courses was not explicitly stated as a factor in school choice, it is clear that, in their decision to send their children to particular schools, Insider parents were ensuring that their children would be assigned to the advanced courses. Thus, although three of the six Insider parents were in favour of streaming, their support for this grouping system was contingent on the assumption that their own child would be taking the Higher level papers even if not in the highest stream.

> *Interviewer:* What do you think about the way the school is organised in terms of the streaming and so on?

Mrs Feeney: I think it is good that as many people as possible should get to aim for doing Higher papers. Equally, I think even by then you will have a fair idea of the people who are capable of doing the Higher papers and it has been my understanding that it is only the very, very weak students who are asked to do pass. People are actually encouraged to do the Higher papers even when it might be a struggle for them, and OK, they could drop back maybe next year. But they are encouraged to try for the Higher papers. And I would approve of that. (Barrow SSG F)

Another expressed concern about mixed ability grouping.

Interviewer: As far as you would be concerned the streaming would be related to levels, that's where your concern would be?
Mrs Connelly: Yes, if they're all at a level they are capable of doing Higher level. Now I would have a problem if there were people mixed in there who weren't able, and they were dragging.
Interviewer: That's a disadvantage if you have a greater range of ability and then you've got people in there who are less able?
Mrs Connelly: Yes, if they had a huge range of ability then I could see there would be a problem but we haven't had a problem. (Lee SSB F)

All of the parents seemed happy with their child's place in the grouping system in their schools, most stating that it 'suited' their child.

Knowledge of children's progress at mathematics

All of the Insider parents followed their children's progress in mathematics attentively. Most felt that their children were doing well and were generally 'good' or 'very good' at mathematics. However, it is important to note that for the parents 'doing well' meant that they were 'keeping up' with the class. Therefore their knowledge of their child's performance and progress at mathematics was very much set in a peer context or, as was often the case, in relation to older siblings.

Interviewer: How do you think that she is doing at maths particularly? How does she feel she is doing herself?
Mr O'Brien: I looked in on her about a week or so ago. I said one evening: 'How are you getting on at mathematics, Louise?' She said: 'It is getting very tough.' And I said: 'Are you all finding it tough, Louise?' She said: 'Yes we are'. So I would say the pace is quick. It steps up very quickly. (Barrow SSG F)

The parents were also able to identify particular problems that their children had in relation to mathematics. Parents tended to view performance in a comparative context: success was defined in terms of being at least as good as others in your class.

Mrs Connelly: I was quite concerned [about his maths], that would have been my one concern about his academic schooling, but he has been scoring well and keeping up. (Lee SSB F)

Mr Barrett: I think I would react badly if Shane expressed an interest [in maths grinds] – I think I would say to him: 'Cop on to yourself' and 'What are you doing in your class?' If he said: 'The teacher is no use' or 'I can't follow what she is saying' and I would say: 'Well hold on, is it Shane or is it everyone?' (Lee SSB F)

Views on teaching and learning of mathematics

Despite their strong views on the importance of good teaching and students' own hard work, four of the six parents seemed to believe that innate ability played a key role in succeeding at mathematics. Such beliefs were either stated explicitly or implicitly. This can be seen in the following excerpts. The first one concerns a mother who is discussing her three children and their performance at mathematics.

Mrs Feeney: I do believe an awful lot of it is instinctive. Some kids are good at maths and some kids just not … Well, I have got three of them. Angela, her instinct is mathematical, the other two, their instinct is not. Their instinct is, I mean, they automatically knew how to spell words. They didn't have to learn to spell them. Angela didn't have to necessarily learn how to add and subtract and multiply, it kind of just happened. So, I do believe an awful lot is ability based. (Barrow SSG F)

In this next quotation a mother is comparing her two sons' progress in mathematics.

Mrs Connelly: Yeah, my second son is sailing through but then he might be just more mathematical than Martin, so we haven't had to go in and try to explain them. (Lee SSB F)

Comments from three of the parents however, showed that they felt that there was a problem in the teaching of mathematics. They claimed that concepts were not explained properly and that this led to a lack of understanding among students. One father felt that this was the reason why he had struggled with maths when he was at school.

Mr O'Brien: On mathematics, maybe I am completely wrong. But anyone I have ever discussed mathematics with, we tend to come to the view that mathematics is a peculiar subject, you were either good at it or you weren't and if you don't have a mathematical attitude it is very, very hard … But maybe there is a better way of teaching it … I certainly believe I was taught maths by secondary teachers, [who] quite frankly … did not understand themselves … And you could tell that, they had

learned it off almost by rote …When I sat down as an adult to do it the stuff again, it began to dawn on me. I got really interested in it then and then I began to wonder why the hell I wasn't interested in it when I was in school. Did nobody stop to explain some of this? … I remember looking at differential calculus, you know the maximum and minimum turning points and … at that age, years later, I could actually understand. (Barrow SSG F)

This parent claimed that the problem still exists.

Mr O'Brien: Lecturers and teachers just rattle off their subject and they don't stand back and say, hang on, let us put this [into] some sort of a context so that at least you understand just the generalities rather than the specifics. (Barrow SSG F)

Parents' views on the advantage of grinds and on the school's role in providing extra help for students displayed an explicit acceptance in many cases that mathematics would not be explained fully in school.

Mr Lynch: I am all for [grinds]. Absolutely. If anything helps a student. If you have a class situation and you have an individual who does not want to continue to put his or her hands up – for whatever reason, maybe the teacher would say: 'Look I am tired of you – I am tired answering the same thing – why don't you go and study?' … If you can get a good grind from a teacher who can show you the short cuts and show you how to do the problems and explain them – what may be a problem in one area may solve several other problems in another area, and grind teachers tend to find that. I would be very much for it. (Lee SSB F)

Interviewer: And you don't feel it is the role of the school to pick up on that extra?
Mr O'Brien: Well no, it's funny, I think that somebody else can give you an angle or a dimension or a perspective on something. I think if you can talk to the one person, be it your teacher, I just think another person can give you a perspective that can actually just make the concept click. It is nice to have an additional angle on the thing. You can argue that why the hell do you pay school fees etc., etc., but I think it is nice just to have another person. I think it can be very refreshing just to see how somebody else sees the world … Also in his case, particularly in second and third year, I think if there were things that he couldn't understand he felt that maybe he was holding the class up or something … The first [grind teacher] was a university undergraduate who just explained, went over and followed the homework and explained again the concepts and then the teacher just really helped him face the exam and explained again and helped him. (Barrow SSG F)

The Insider parents had extensive experience of the education system, with most possessing university degrees. They had the cultural and financial capital to choose between schools and to intervene in schools at key stages, if necessary. All of the Insider parents held positive views of mathematics and monitored their children's progress in the subject by

comparing it with that of their peers. While most parents did believe that good teaching (especially good explanation) and hard work by the students was essential for success in mathematics, most also thought that success in mathematics was dependant on having 'natural ability' in the first instance.

Outsiders

School choice

Outsider parents did not choose schools for their children's primary or secondary education in the way that Insiders did. Their choice pattern reflected differences in both the economic and cultural capital between the two groups. Most of the Outsider parents had sent all of their children to the same schools, and these were mostly in close physical proximity to their homes. Some of the parents were inclined to let the child choose the school herself/himself.

> *Interviewer:* Choosing the school, you mentioned that you had another school in mind other than Nephin?
> *Mrs Sheridan:* I hadn't really another school in mind for Pauline. Her other friend Roisin she goes to School D at the moment and she was with her all through and then I said I hadn't problems with the others going along so I said I'll keep her. I gave her the choice in the end and she said she wanted to go to Nephin.
> *Interviewer:* Why Nephin?
> *Mrs Sheridan:* The whole lot of them went there. (Nephin VCC Fr)

Others chose the school they had gone to themselves.

> *Interviewer:* How did you choose the school for Jenny?
> *Mrs Timmons:* I went there and he [husband] went there and we were both happy – never had a complaint.
> *Interviewer:* Will it be the same choice for your sons?
> *Mr Timmons:* Yeah. (Errigal CS Fr)

The fact that these parents do not look into the possibilities of different schools suggests that they do not see their children's success in education as being greatly facilitated by school choice.

> *Mrs Evans:* It wasn't that it wasn't coed that I actually sent my eldest daughter there, I just sent her there because when I was growing up, it was called the Mercy, and it was actually supposed to be the best school. Now really in my opinion I think if the kids want to learn, they will, regardless of what school they're in. (Suir SSG Fr D)

Unlike the Insider parents, their views of schools were not grounded to the same degree in discourses of education. This is evident in one mother's account of why she chose a single sex school for her daughter.

Mrs Broderick: I wanted an all girls' school for them. I didn't want boys there, I heard that they're not as bright, and Michelle was always very bright and that boys don't study as much and they would hold the girls back. And she has done very well there.
Interviewer: Do you think they miss out on other things going to an all girls'?
Mrs Broderick: I think they're better off going to an all girls' school. (Suir SSG Fr D)

Educational level and intervention

Eight of the fathers in the nine Outsider families had completed their Leaving Certificate, while just three of the mothers had. The remainder of the mothers had either just completed their primary schooling, or had left school after their Group or Intermediate Certificate. Only one Outsider mother had Higher level mathematics in her Leaving Certificate. The remainder described their experience of mathematics in mostly negative terms, saying that they were 'not great at maths' or that they generally 'hated them' or 'didn't like them'. Unlike the Insider parents, many were vague about their own experiences:

Mrs Evans: I never really thought about whether I found it hard or not. It's a long, long time ago. In the vocational school there was an average amount of time spent on maths, what you'd normally spend on any subject. I done Junior Cert and a Secretarial Course and then I got out. I regretted it years later.
Interviewer: Would you have done pass maths yourself?
Mrs Evans: I actually can't remember, probably I would have done pass maths. (Suir SSG Fr D)

Intervention

1. Approaching the School
While parents with an inside knowledge of education and schooling were willing and able to approach the school about their children's progress, Outsider parents either did not think they had a right to do this, or did not feel comfortable doing it.

Mrs Roberts: All the girls last year who had that teacher ended up having to get maths grinds, that's not right, is it?
Interviewer: Did you approach the teacher?
Mrs Roberts:... I couldn't as a parent go in and tell her she wasn't teaching my child right. (Liffey SSB Fr D)

Another woman, who reported concern over her son's general progress when he was at primary level, told how she decided to 'stick it out' rather than challenge the school. Parents' lack of action in approaching schools was also seen in other parents' comments. One father stated that they 'waited for the school to call us if there's a problem'. Another waited until parent/teacher meetings to raise problems with her child's mathematics teacher:

> *Interviewer:* How did she do in her summer test in maths?
> *Mrs Evans:* She failed maths in her summer test and she done very well in everything else. She only got something like 37 per cent, it was very bad. But she had said all along she was going to fail her maths and she kept saying that she would have to get grinds.
> *Interviewer:* Have you spoken to her teacher?
> *Mrs Evans:* Well I only spoke to her maths teacher just when we would have parent teacher meetings. Actually the last meeting that I went to with her, she said she was getting on OK. Three or four of her friends failed. She was great in first year. (Suir SSG Fr D)

Two of the nine sets of parents stated that they did not know which teacher their child had for mathematics. This seemed to stem from a general problem with regard to the way that parent teacher meetings were organised in certain schools: in some situations the parent only met with a head teacher for the year group. Because of this, these Outsider parents did not feel they had the opportunity to express their concerns.

Parents' lack of knowledge about negotiating with schools, and the unsatisfactory response they got when they did approach a teacher, was very evident from the interviews. Parents also felt that the schools were placating them, telling them the child was fine or 'very good' when in fact they had problems and were not performing well.

> *Interviewer:* Did you approach the school when you realised she was having difficulty at maths?
> *Mrs Broderick:* Oh yeah, and even now at the end of first year when she got her report, I rang the teacher and she told me I have to get grinds at the end of this year.
> *Interviewer:* How did you feel about that – what did you do?
> *Mrs Broderick:* I think maybe up to now the school could have helped Joan along a bit. When they seen her going down – even by Christmas of the first year. Their comment was: 'Could be better if she tried'. This year her report is there, it's 30 per cent and very good is on it, which is not very good, you know that. There was nothing else said and I just was put off when they said about the grinds for her. (Suir SSG Fr D)

> *Mrs Allen:* I went in – told them I was having a nervous breakdown. It was really obvious that my Frank had a problem and there was nothing ever said. My Frank when he was about nine he couldn't spell 'it'. 'It' would be like f and g and that's it. And I went over to Mr Martin and I said: 'Look that child must be dyslexic or

something. Whatever was in front of him even taking it from there and putting it on a copy, it never would be the same.' And Mr Martin said: 'He hasn't got a problem. He can read, he's alright.' He said you just leave him alone. And I was having a nervous breakdown. And he says just leave him alone. So they just did nothing. (Liffey SSB Fr D)

2. Help at home

The majority of parents stated that they were not able to help with mathematics homework because they did not understand the mathematics themselves. One parent explained how her husband had been able to provide some help, but only at primary level:

Interviewer: Would you help the kids with their homework?
Mrs Evans: Helping my own kids with their homework, I was actually working at the time and I was on shift work but my husband was here and he was great with the kids. He was able to help them to a certain point but even they got too complicated for us. That would have been by the time they went to the secondary school. My husband had just done Inter Cert. (Suir SSG Fr D)

Another mother explained her lack of ability to help.

Interviewer: Do you help him with his mathematics?
Mrs Mallon: I think the maths are harder now. I can't really help him with what he's doing at the moment – even though I might have done some of this before, but I'm looking at what he does be doing in his homework I think they're very difficult.
Interviewer: Does he mention the fact that they're hard?
Mrs Mallon: Occasionally he would mention that they're hard if he can't finish something. I think he knows at this stage that there's not much point asking me for help …
Interviewer: Does he ask anyone else for help with his homework?
Mrs Mallon: He doesn't generally ask anyone else to help with his homework. He just generally will plough through whatever he has to do. If he can finish it he will, if he doesn't, he won't. (Mourne VCC Fr D)

Many of the parents felt that they could not help because the mathematics had changed since they were at school.

Mrs Roberts: I remember one day taking out a bag of potatoes when Natasha was in second or third class and she was talking about this regrouping and I said look if you've seven potatoes and you take away two and you've five left. And it was really driving me mad that I couldn't help her because the way I was helping her was wrong. (Liffey SSB Fr D)

Unlike the Insider parents, the parents who were Outsiders were unable to intervene to support their children in their education.

Mrs Allen: I found in primary now, if Frank came home saying there was a certain sum and he didn't know how to do it and you'd say: 'Why didn't you ask?' And he'd say: 'Well I put up my hand and they were told we went over that yesterday, were you not listening?' ... It isn't right because I wouldn't know how to show him. (Liffey SSB Fr D)

While a number of the parents said they would get grinds if their children needed them, expense was an issue. A number also said that they had never known of anyone in their area whose children had grinds and would not know where to go to avail of them.

Mrs Mallon: I don't think an awful lot of people could afford grinds in this area anyway. It's just part of the situation, there's an awful lot of unemployment. I don't think it would come into it an awful lot in this school – but there would be some probably. (Mourne VCC Fr D)

Mr O'Donnell: It's expensive, first off. If you've got three kids going to school, I think the programme with the school should cover all necessities. It shouldn't be a necessity for us to go and get another teacher. (Liffey SSB Fr D)

One mother did not know what a grind was.

Interviewer: What are your feelings about grinds?
Mrs Allen: I don't even know what a grind is. (Liffey SSB Fr D)

Working at the Ordinary or Foundation level

Most of the children of the Outsider parents were assigned to classes where they were being prepared for Foundation or Ordinary level in mathematics in their Junior Certificate. The parents did not comment on school policies with regard to either streaming or the level at which subjects were taught. A number of the parents said they did not know what level of mathematics their child would eventually take at the Junior Certificate. There was a general feeling among them that their children would 'not be able for honours' or that they were happy to leave it up to the child to decide. Three of the parents' children were in the top stream in mathematics. The other parents presumed their children would eventually take the pass level. One of these said that he would not push him to do Higher level if his son did not himself feel capable of doing it.

Interviewer: Can I just ask you, what do you feel about your own son and the level of mathematics – do you think it is important for Leonard to do honours?
Mr O'Donnell: No. I feel it is important for him to do what he wants to do. More important for him to make his choice. I can't tell him to do honours maths if he's

not capable of it and he'll actually do worse as a result of that – because he's under pressure from me, he's under pressure from the teacher.

Interviewer: But if he is capable?

Mr O'Donnell: If he's capable – I think though the main thing is, if a child has to ask, then he shouldn't be doing it, do you know what I mean? If he has to ask himself that question 'Can I do it?', well then he's in doubt … But I think there is enough pressure on the kids in school and I honestly don't believe that a child should be pressurised into doing an honours subject if he's not totally capable. (Liffey SSB Fr D)

Knowledge of children's progress at mathematics

Outsider parents spoke in very vague terms about their child's progress at mathematics. Two said that they 'didn't know' how their child was performing.

> *Mr O'Donnell:* Being honest I can't really say whether Leonard does or doesn't [find maths hard]. He hasn't said anything. Leonard, when you eventually get him to do his homework, he'll do it and he'll do it all, he'll stay there until he's finished. He doesn't mention the particular subjects or if he has a problem. (Liffey SSB Fr D)

Other parents reported that their children 'found the maths hard' but none were able to identify specific problems. Like the Insider parents, the child's progress was assessed in terms of his or her peers.

> *Mrs Allen:* He was even disappointed in the result of the maths test – he didn't do well. I asked a couple of his friends and most of them did say they found it hard. So they are all finding it tough. (Liffey SSB Fr D)

Views on teaching and learning of mathematics

Not all of the parents commented on mathematics teaching and learning. This appeared to be partly due to their lack of experience in discussing issues of this nature. There were exceptions however. One issue to emerge concerned the lack of explanation in mathematics teaching. One father, who had recently returned to education to complete his Leaving Certificate, believed there was an inherent problem in the way mathematics was being taught.

> *Mr O'Donnell:* If you are doing something, particularly in maths, you're taught this particular way of doing it – whatever you're doing at that particular time and you could do ten questions on that and get them all perfect, it doesn't mean you fully understand it, you come back a month later and it's out the window, a lot of it will

be out the window… But I find that when you are doing a particular part of maths, it's all repetition and you get good at that and then it's discarded – forgotten about. If I'm in class and I don't understand I'll say it to the teacher, I don't understand it, and I'm not embarrassed to do it but I've seen kids that won't open their mouth, so they'll never get to really understand. (Liffey SSB Fr D)

This parent also referred to the lack of revision and lack of connections in mathematics teaching.

Mr O'Donnell: …particularly I found with maths now that you start off and you do a certain part of maths and then you progress on to a different part and there's so many different things but during the course you never recap … [T]here should be an allotted time to recap on what needs to be done, and that should be carried right through the year so at no stage should you go six or eight or ten months without [revising]. When they come to an exam then they can't remember where they've seen [a particular part of maths] before because it has been a long time since they've seen it. (Liffey SSB Fr D)

Two other parents also hinted at the lack of explanation when discussing grinds.

Interviewer: What do you think grinds would do?
Mrs Broderick: I got grinds myself. Some of the chapters in the book she can't follow and [the grind tutor is] brilliant on some of the chapters in the grinds.
Interviewer: What do grinds actually do, do you think?
Mrs Broderick: The grinds just explain it fully. I found that myself. You wouldn't get that level of attention in school. (Suir SSG Fr D)

Mrs Mallon: If you were going on and needed high marks for something and it was important to get good points I'd say yes it is [important to get grinds]. I know they learn the basics in school and there should be enough to carry them through exams, but I think you would find some children who would need more help to understand the maths more. (Mourne VCC Fr D)

Another mother's comments revealed the same essentialist view of mathematical ability expressed by Insider parents generally.

Interviewer: I get the impression that you think how you do is something to do with ability, not with how you are taught. You were saying your eldest daughter is naturally good, do you think that is something within you or the way it is taught?
Mrs Broderick: I think how you get on at maths is something within you, that you can be brilliant at other things, she got A in home economics during the summer and in maths she only got 30 per cent. I think she has just turned against maths, she figures I'm no good at them. Anything else she can do it. (Suir SSG Fr D)

It also emerged that a number of parents tended to attribute failures (or successes) to the child rather than the school. In this regard, the child's willingness and ability to learn was seen as having little to do with the learning environment.

> *Interviewer:* Do you think the school makes a difference [to how they get on]?
> *Mrs Evans:* No, I actually think it depends on the person themselves. As I've just said, classes upon classes, it's been like that since I've been growing up, there are kids who want to learn and there are kids who don't want to learn … (Suir SSG Fr D)

> *Interviewer:* Are you happy with the way he's getting on in school?
> *Mr Mallon:* I'm happy with the way he's getting on in the school. The only problem, and it's not with the school it's with himself, that he won't knuckle down a bit more – he has potential and has the brains, I know he can do it and the teachers keep telling him that he can do it, he gets a bit distracted, boys that age – fourteen, football and everything, it's very hard to get them to … it's frustrating, you know that he can do it. He doesn't get bad marks, he gets average marks. (Mourne VCC Fr D)

While the Outsider parents did not have third level education, they had reasonably good levels of education, with six of the nine fathers having completed the Leaving Certificate. Like the Insiders, they wanted the best for their children. However, their cultural and financial resources limited their choice about what was best. One way in which Outsiders differed from the Insiders was in their depth of knowledge about education. They had less knowledge regarding the implications of tracking (streaming), and the level at which subjects were studied (Higher, Ordinary and Foundation levels) in particular. Some also lacked the economic and social capital (networks) for organising extra help for their children in circumstances where they were unable to help them themselves. They chose less as they had less resources (cultural, social and economic) with which to choose. Like Insider parents, there was a strong belief among a number of the Outsiders that innate ability was crucial to success in mathematics. Unlike Insiders, many Outsiders lacked the confidence to challenge teachers when their children got low grades. The option of moving school did not seem to arise.

Intermediaries

The third group of parents occupied an Intermediary position between the other two groups. They seemed to be more Outsiders than Insiders in terms of their knowledge of the education system, although what distinguished them from the other two groups was their interim position between the

Insiders and Outsiders. They were aware of the privileged schools, classes etc., but did not always find these within their reach. Like all parents, they wanted the best for their children, and had some knowledge of what they were 'supposed' to do in relation to ensuring their children's educational success. However, they were aware they were working with imperfect knowledge, and worried about this.

School choice

While seven of the thirteen sets of parents engaged in research about schools prior to choosing, there was little evidence that they had 'inside knowledge' to maximise their choices. Two of the parents indicated that they were interested in schools that were more socially selective than the school eventually chosen. They regarded themselves as Outsiders, however, with no opportunity to gather the information they needed about such schools.

> *Interviewer:* So when it came to making a decision about the school?
> *Mrs Kelly:* I had a lot of queries as to whether I was choosing the right school or not, but she had been so happy in the national school and also naively or otherwise, I didn't – by choice I would rather stay with the state system. I felt it was a betrayal of the national school – if there was a huge difference I would have gone for fee paying, but I wasn't convinced that what I would … necessarily get, any different or any better and it is very hard to judge being on the outside. I feel unless you actually know somebody personally on the staff who will tell you, that you never really know.
> *Interviewer:* What about word of mouth? Would there be a good level of information?
> *Mrs Kelly:* Well you see, again, I don't know whether it is a snobbish thing or not, but most people wouldn't send their daughter to the secondary school there – no. School E or School F or maybe School G. But then I went up and I was listening to Mark Niland [principal] – and I was really impressed. I know that it can always be just words, but I liked what he said and there were one or two things that I had heard about the school that turned out to be correct. But I feel that that could be in every other school as well. There will always be one problem area, I imagine – just being on the outside. (Nore SSG Fr)

> *Mrs Boland:* It's a chance you have to take with your children really sending them out to school and I've been talking for years about different schools and they all have the same attitude. You could spend a fortune sending your child to an outside school and it's very hard to see what's inside in them. (Nephin VCC Fr)

The Intermediary parents tended to describe their final choice of school in very general terms saying the school had a 'good reputation' or they had not chosen a certain school because they had 'got bad reports about it'.

They relied more on local information, particularly from friends and family, rather than undertaking the school visits and interviews with school personnel that the Insiders engaged in. The proximity of the school to home also emerged as an important consideration when choosing a school.

> *Mr McCaslin:* We went to the schools ourselves … The principal of the primary, being honest, he advised us to send him to School H, and we looked into it. He thought it would be a better school, but we sent him to Blackstairs. I've nephews and nieces going there and they did OK in it as well. It had a good reputation. (Blackstairs VCC Fr D)

> *Mrs Byrne:* My first preference was School I, I had done a bit of checking out and I had rang a number of schools, the principal of School I had actually spent a half-hour talking to me on the phone, and he seemed very interested in individual children and each child's potential, and he seemed to put as much value on apprenticeship and meeting the child's needs and I was very impressed and I went to their open day. But all James' friends were going to Lagan, so I actually felt there was much more chance that he would settle in Lagan… So it was the fact that all his friends were going that I chose Lagan – I didn't want to move him away from his friends. (Lagan SC Fr)

Wait and see

Interviews with the Intermediary parents revealed that, while a number of them anticipated problems with regard to their children's education, they were not proactive in preventing these. They tended to adopt a wait and see approach unlike the child-matching and regular monitoring policies of the Insider parents. In the following extract a mother explains the concern she had regarding the class her son would be put into in his first year of secondary school.

> *Mrs Fogarty:* I was dreading my son getting into one of these lower classes because I felt he would have no, absolutely no interest in schooling [if he was in a lower class] and he'd cousins [who] were all in these lower grade classes and had absolutely no interest in school. I thought if he starts off that way I would be afraid he wouldn't have the interest because he would be with the lads that wouldn't have the interest but, thank God, he did alright and he got into class B which was a middle average class and I was delighted with that. But he seems to be doing alright. He does his homework; I make sure his homework is done. It's completely different to when we were growing up. I want him to learn and I want him to get on, so the homework is done and encouraged at home. (Errigal CS Fr)

In the next excerpt, we see how a father adopted a wait and see approach with regard to his daughter's transition from primary to second level. From his comments it is clear that he felt he had no other option:

Interviewer: So then, say in sixth class when she was going into secondary – did the teachers give you any advice on where to send her?

Mr Kelly: Yes, the school teacher who is actually the teacher that she didn't particularly like – felt that Frances wasn't actually mature enough – she didn't know if she would actually handle the transition into secondary school because she would be quite distracted in sixth class. So, nobody would say what I was walking into and I couldn't find out what I was walking into or would it be better anywhere else, but it has worked out well. (Nore SSG Fr)

In the next extract a mother expresses her worries about her daughter's general progress at second level.

Interviewer: You feel she is working OK?

Mrs Bowen: I would hope she is, I think she is, she's young I think maybe she could do with another year, I feel that another year would certainly settle her, she won't be fourteen until March but she's kind of no younger than a lot of … her class either, but I feel that another year would make a big difference to her. I suppose I'm giving her the benefit of the doubt until Junior Cert but after that, it could unsettle and it could settle, you don't know, again I haven't decided which way, I'll meet that at the time to see how she is going. (Blackstairs VCC Fr D)

Taking interest but not challenging the school

Interviews with Insider parents show that they challenged or confronted the school if their child had a difficulty. Parents from the Intermediary group were also active on their children's behalf but appeared to have fewer options open to them. In this next excerpt, a mother and father explain their actions with regard to a problem of disruption in their daughter's classroom.

Interviewer: What have you done about the situation?

Mrs Kelly: There is one particular subject where there is a huge problem and again we got an extra grind to help her – we got a CD ROM so that she could follow the subject on the computer herself … Now, she hasn't used it very often, but I would definitely – come next September – we will have to get a grind for her every week. It is chaos.

Interviewer: Do you think any of the other parents have the same problem?

Mr Kelly: I do know that another parent has, yes.

Interviewer: What is being done?

Mr Kelly: Well, you see again, there is no back up for the principal. He has this problem of a teacher not being able to control the class – it is very difficult – there isn't an awful lot he can do.

Interviewer: Would there be any opportunity to change her to another class?

Mrs Kelly: There isn't another science teacher there to the best of my knowledge.

Interviewer: And would that teacher be teaching her next year?

Mr Kelly: Yes, to the best of my knowledge. That is why we will have to take control of it ourselves. But I don't think it is a problem that is peculiar to Nore. It is a hugely important subject and that is where my concern is. But, I think we will just have to take control of that situation – and take care of it yourself.

Interviewer: Would you think about bringing it up at the parent/teacher meeting or consider taking her out of the school?

Mr Kelly: Well, again because she is so socially accepted there that it would be hugely important – we were only talking about it the other evening. At the moment I don't think that is what he would do – we hope he [the principal] will come across a good science teacher and the science teacher come here and Frances will go to another class and take control of it that way ... You know making the decision in the first place about where to send them – you don't know these things...And you are depending more so on gossip – that is all. And you can't go to a secondary school and expect them to say that 'if it was my daughter I wouldn't send her to here' and yet there are people on that staff who will know what you should do, but as an outsider there is no way I can find out – it is a lottery to a huge extent. (Nore SSG Fr)

Another parent reported a similar sense of uncertainty about what to do when her son was having difficulties.

Interviewer: Would you ever consider taking him out of the school?

Mrs Byrne: I would find that difficult – things would have to be very bad, but having said that, all his friends are there and that would be hard. But one thing you have to do is nip it in the bud and if it seems like this problem is getting worse and the teachers are certainly not holding back in giving out when I come in – I would find it hard to judge. But hopefully it will improve. (Lagan SC Fr)

Personalising problems with mathematics

While the parents had concerns regarding their children's performance and attitudes to mathematics, they did not hold the school accountable for this. They had personalised the difficulties, regarding them as being linked in some way to their own negative experiences of mathematics.

Interviewer: How did you find school/maths yourself?

Mrs Stevens: ... where maths are concerned, specifically maths, the curtain just came down. It was just beyond me. So I understand how Catherine feels ... You get to the stage where you're not even in the running, so you don't even try. I feel so sorry for her because I know that's how she feels. It's like the basics, the foundation is not there, and that's not for the want of trying. I have paid for maths grinds for her when she was in primary school and I was very aware of not wanting her to miss out on that basic building block of learning the maths. I really didn't want that to happen and of course it did happen. I can't help her. It's so frustrating. You see her at night time and I say: 'Did you ask the teacher today?' and she says: 'He did explain and I understood it at the time'. If only I could help but I can't. With English or anything else I just have to figure it out with her but with the maths I just have to look at her. There's nothing I can do … It's just that I know how she feels because I have the same problem – it's awful, just a curtain comes down. [I know] … I'm not helping either by agreeing with her … I think my attitude seeps through as well. (Nore SSG Fr)

Interviewer: So Brendan… doesn't like maths at all?
Mrs O'Dowd: Well – the teacher says that he has a definite flair for it – but he is very pigheaded – if he doesn't like something he won't work at it, or have anything to do with it. I can understand it because I never got this in my head either. He doesn't understand what he can do with it. I would say Jimmy is the same [older brother] – all through school they said he was very good but he is only doing pass maths and even at that he seems to be struggling… Even the other day he said I might have to get a grind … Neither seem to know what maths is used for, and I don't even know what it is used for either – I know that it is used for engineering – I mean I know in theory – but I don't actually know in practice … I mentioned that to Mrs Boyle, the teacher, at the parent teacher meeting and she says: 'Well it is just almost like the way we did Latin as an academic exercise'. But she still didn't seem to be able to explain to me, and therefore to David, as to how it would be useful. But I suppose kids feel like that about a lot of subjects – certainly Irish. (Lagan SC Fr)

Mrs Fogarty: I used to say he was going to be very bad at maths, thinking of myself and you need maths,… I was always dreading maths for him because I was so bad myself. (Errigal CS Fr)

These anxieties were also shown with regard to more general aspects of their children's schooling.

Interviewer: Is it daunting to go from a very small school to the town school and into secondary as well?
Mrs Bowen: To tell the truth, it frightened the living daylights out of myself at the time, it was an awful daunting step and I worried so much about Helen coming into a big school and how she would cope and everything but she made the transition a lot easier than I did, an awful lot easier but then that said, she had her cousin next door and I think she kind of showed her the ropes whereas, personally, I had nobody and I think that made a difference as well. (Blackstairs VCC Fr D)

The parents whom we defined as Intermediaries occupied an interim place between the Insider and Outsider groups. While all but one of the twelve parents (six sets) who were Insiders held a university degree, only four of the twenty six (thirteen sets) of parents in the Intermediary group had degrees. In addition, all the Insiders were in middle-class occupations compared with 63 per cent of the Intermediaries. What differentiated Intermediaries most from the Insiders however, was not so much their lack of knowledge of the education system, as their lack of control over their child's schooling. Unlike the Outsiders, they knew how schooling worked and how it selected children out occupationally for the future. However, they seemed to lack the resources to act on this knowledge. They worried about their children's schooling without controlling it.

Conclusion

The inclusion of parents' views provides us with a more complete understanding of students' mathematical experience (Useem, 1992, West et al., 1998). The parents' perspective offers a unique insight into the connections between school and home and how this impacts on learning.

The data suggest that parents are key players in the education 'game'. Their capacity, or lack of it, to choose different schools or to intervene in educational matters on behalf of their children, can and does radically alter the nature of their children's education (Lareau, 1989). Parents' own educational experience, including their experience of mathematics, influenced their actions. Those with positive experiences of mathematics, and especially of schooling generally, were the most likely to be proactive on behalf of their children. Having the cultural, social and financial capital to act was also crucial (Bourdieu et al., 1977). It was upper middle-class parents who were most advantaged in this regard (Gewirtz et al., 1995; Reay and Ball, 1998).

A parent typology was drawn up in terms of parental knowledge of the education system and ability to intervene in their children's education. Broadly our classification defines the parents in our study as Insiders, Outsiders and Intermediaries. The Insider parents were shown to have an in-depth knowledge of the education system. They generally held very positive attitudes to education and described their own experience of learning mathematics in positive terms. Most of all they exercised control over the necessary cultural and financial capital, and were part of resourced social networks that enabled them to give considerable support to their children. The Insider parents were integrated into school affairs, engaging in different forms of intervention in their children's schooling as the need arose. In contrast, the Outsiders had much lower levels of education and had more negative attitudes to schooling and mathematics based on their own experiences. This group of parents did not have the capacity to intervene in their children's education to the same degree as the Insiders. Their Outsider status was manifested in a lack of knowledge about how the education system worked, and what was required to succeed in formal education. They also do not have access to the informed and resources education networks available to the Insider group.

The Intermediary parents resembled Outsiders to a much greater degree than Insiders; this applied both in terms of their capacity to intervene and their knowledge of the education system. While they possessed some knowledge of education, their knowledge was limited. Most of all they lacked the package of cultural, social and economic capital that would enable them to assume control over their children's learning environment.

While the Insider parents reported more positive experiences of learning mathematics, and were much more positive about mathematics as a subject than the other parents, they were similar to other parents in their allegiance to an essentialist view of mathematical skills. They attached considerable importance to children's 'innate ability' for successful learning in mathematics. However, they attributed more importance to the quality of schooling than other parents, a view that was not unrelated to their ability to regulate schooling by intervening with teachers and, if necessary, moving children between schools.

What was notable in parents' accounts on schooling was the strong focus on the school's general reputation when choosing a school, rather than its gender composition. While some parents did say they chose single-sex girls' schools because they were single sex, a 'good' reputation was measured in terms of academic success rather than gender balance. The same applied in boys' schools. Very few parents said they actively avoided coeducational schools because they were coeducational. Rather, they actively chose single sex schools as these were reported to be strong academically and/or were prestigious because of their socially selective intake.

Notes

[1]Gewirtz et al. (1995) claimed there were three types of parent in terms of school choice: privileged or skilled choosers, semi-skilled choosers and the disconnected.
[2] For a full discussion on the forms of capital see Bourdieu (1986).

12

The Social Context of Mathematics Education: Issues to be Addressed

Introduction

Both national and international research developments, and national policy considerations, provided the stimulus for this study. At the national level, research regarding the implications of coeducation stimulated a debate about the possible negative implications for girls attending coeducational schools, particularly in terms of mathematics (Hannan et al. 1996). While the authors found that girls in coeducational schools had lower grades than their single sex counterparts, what was not clear from the study was the extent to which the lower attainment of girls in coeducational schools was a function of the differences in the levels of mathematics (Higher, Ordinary and Foundation) being taken in single sex and coeducational schools. Neither was it possible to determine from a national study of the kind undertaken by Hannan and his colleagues what impact the culture of mathematics classrooms had on learning of mathematics, nor how the practices of individual teachers impacted on learning. The authors suggested that further more in-depth research was necessary to explore these issues.

What the national research suggested therefore was that if we were to understand gender differences in the experience of mathematics education, we needed to study life in classrooms in depth. We needed to see what was happening in educational settings rather than what students and teachers reported was happening. The culture of mathematics classrooms could only be understood by observing and recording these classes, by exploring with teachers and students how they interpreted the lessons, and checking our interpretations with those of the classroom participants.

In the international arena, mathematics education constitutes a major research subject in its own right (Grouws, 1992; Boaler, 2000). Within this context, students are increasingly recognised in their diversity, and gender is one of the defining features of that diversity (Burton, 1995; Fennema and Leder, 1990; Secada, 1995). However, the debate about gender has become more complex as scholars recognise the limitations of unidimensional research focused solely on gender (or race, class or ethnicity) (Secada, 1992). There is a growing recognition that statuses and identities are complex and overlapping and that any research on gender needs to take cognisance of how social class, race, ethnicity, language and other differences impact on learning (ibid).

In addition, there is what Lerman (2000) terms 'a social turn' in mathematics education research. While research on mathematics education had previously been dominated by the disciplines of psychology and mathematics (Kilpatrick, 1992), over the last fifteen years there has been a change in this trend. The growing influence of the work of Vygotsky in particular, has generated an interest in the social context of learning. It has opened mathematics education research to the influences of anthropology, sociology and cultural psychology (Lerman, 2000, p. 25). It is increasingly accepted that learning is not solely a private individual matter; it is a situated and socio-cultural experience. Knowledge has to be understood relationally, between people and settings. Learning is about becoming competent in life settings (Lave and Wenger, 1991). Understanding how students learn therefore is about understanding not only how they experience mathematics but also how the other major players in their educational world, especially teachers and parents, define their learning experience. It is about how individual learners are created in the social and cultural practices of education, and how individuals are agents in the shaping of these practices.

What was clear from international research therefore was that if we were to understand gender differences in the experience of learning mathematics, we could not focus on gender alone. We needed to examine differences that interfaced with gender, including social class, racial, ethnic or other differences.

> Even though gender is often a significant determinant of aspirations, expectations and behaviour, there are many other variables, including race and class for example, which have an important and interactive impact. For future research to incorporate such within-group differences is consistent with the plea already made for a more explicit recognition of individual differences. (Leder, 1992b, p. 617)

Because the experience of learning mathematics is not a private affair, but one that is situated in particular socio-cultural and historical contexts, we also needed to examine how teachers and parents in particular defined the learning process for students in school.

The cumulative outcome of these research considerations led us to design a two phase study. First, we needed to establish whether the differences in attainment for girls attending single sex and coeducational schools, identified by Hannan et al. (1996), held true over time. We also needed to establish whether or not the differences were a function of the type of school attended, or the level at which subjects were being offered across school types. Using Junior Certificate Examination data, gender differences in attainment in the Junior Certificate Examinations were examined over a five-year period. The research focused in particular on the differences in both take-up rates of different levels of mathematics (Foundation, Ordinary and Higher) across schools, and on the differences in attainment rates *within* each level for different types of schools. The period chosen for investigation was 1992 to 1996, as the examination data from these years was the most recent available when the study was planned in 1997/8. The analysis of the national examination data took place prior to the case studies in the schools, as it was believed that the findings from the national data would give a good indication as to what were the most significant factors that needed to be explored in the case studies.

In the light of the findings from the National Junior Certificate study, it became clear that while there were differences between single sex and coeducational schools, these differences appeared to be related to differences across school type, differences in the level of subject offered and differences in school intake. Gender appeared to be a less salient factor in explaining differences in take-up and attainment than social class background. In the light of this, it was decided to undertake an intensive study of the teaching and learning of mathematics in schools that were relatively polarised in terms of social class intake (feepaying and designated disadvantaged schools) as well as schools that varied in terms of their single sex/coeducational status and their management structure. Given that prior research on schools had indicated that track or stream position also impacts on classroom experience, classes were chosen for observation that were either top streams (and taking Higher level mathematics) bottom streams or bands (taking Ordinary and sometimes Foundation level) or mixed (with students taking different level courses within the one class).

The case studies undertaken to analyse the teaching and learning of mathematics were intensive and wide ranging. Ten schools were chosen and one teacher and class was videotaped on two separate lessons in each. The students observed in these classes were also given a detailed questionnaire about their learning experience of mathematics and were interviewed subsequently about their experience. The teachers were also interviewed about their teaching and given the opportunity to comment and suggest changes in our interpretations of their teaching style. A sub-sample of parents of the students surveyed was also interviewed about their children's experiences of schooling and of mathematics in particular.

A triangulated view of the research problem was obtained by dialoguing with all the main parties to the learning process – students, teachers, school principals and parents – by comparing their interpretations of the learning process.

The study employed a co-operative mode of research inquiry with teachers in particular, and to a lesser degree with students. In so far as time and resources permitted, we operated a dialogue with the case study teachers as to the authenticity of our interpretations of their classroom teaching. Two of the ten case study teachers expressed a keen interest in the study; one of these read and commented on drafts of the final text.

What was involved in the research therefore was really a series of studies, designed to understand the complex phenomenon of mathematics teaching and learning. The question was not whether we should use quantitative or qualitative methods but rather how could we better understand the research problem. It involved 'the intelligent use of multiple methods' (McLeod, 1992, p. 591).

The Study of Junior Certificate Examination results

The study of the Junior Certificate Examination over a five-year period revealed a number of important trends in mathematics take-up and performance. First, it was clear that the pattern of take-up in mathematics was quite different to that in other comparable subjects, most especially to that of English and science. While the majority of students taking English and science took these subjects at the Higher level (61 per cent and 69 per cent respectively) only 36 per cent of students took Higher mathematics at the Junior Certificate level. The pattern identified between 1992 and 1996 has persisted up to the present time. In 2000, there were still only 36 per cent of students taking Higher level mathematics nationally, compared with 61 per cent taking Higher English (Department of Education and Science, 2001). The relatively low take-up rates in Higher mathematics is undoubtedly related to the fact that, in 64 per cent of Irish schools, 40 per cent or fewer students were taking the Higher level examinations in 1996. There were a small number of schools (7 per cent) that did not examine mathematics at the Higher level at all, while in 1 per cent of schools students were only examined in Foundation mathematics. The schools with the most disadvantaged students are the ones in which there is the highest take up of Foundation and Ordinary mathematics, and these also tend to be disproportionately vocational schools and community colleges.

Take-up rates do not vary much by gender, although slightly more girls were taking Higher mathematics in 1996 and in 2000. While there were differences between girls and boys in take-up rates, these differences were more a function of the type of schools the students were attending (and by implication their social class background and attainment levels at entry) rather than their gender per se. Both girls and boys in secondary schools were much more likely to be taking Higher mathematics than girls or boys in vocational schools or community colleges. Conversely, the take-up of Foundation level mathematics was especially high in vocational schools and community colleges.

Such differences must be interpreted with caution however, as the profile of students in these schools is quite different, with secondary schools being generally more middle class and more academically selective in intake than all other school types (Hannan et al., 1996). The fact that 43 per cent of vocational schools and community colleges are designated disadvantaged compared with 22 per cent of single sex secondary schools is itself proof of the differences in intake between the two school types.

Within given school types, it was boys in single-sex secondary schools who were most likely to take Higher level mathematics, either compared with girls in this sector, or students of either gender in the other school types. While take-up differences between males and females within the secondary sector were moderate, those between males in single-sex schools and *both* males and females in vocational schools and community colleges, were considerable.

Differences in performance that were identified across school types also need to be interpreted in the light of both intake differences between schools, and the widespread use of grinds (private tutoring) to boost grades. Thus, while students (girls and boys) in single sex schools had higher rates of attainment in mathematics across the years than students in vocational schools and community colleges in particular, these higher rates must be understood in context of the fact that single sex schools are more middle class and less disadvantaged in intake, and also traditionally more directly and indirectly selective (Hannan and Boyle, 1987, 1996; Lynch, 1989). We do not know to what extent Junior Certificate students in different school types receive 'grinds', but the evidence available suggests that they do. It also suggests that it is the relatively economically advantaged who are best positioned to avail of such privately funded tutoring (Lynch and Lodge, 2002).

In terms of gender, while girls, on average, achieved higher scores than boys at each level of mathematics, boys consistently achieved a higher proportion of A grades in Higher level examinations, and this was true across all types of schools with the differences being greatest between girls and boys in comprehensive schools.

An examination of gender differences *within* these school sectors showed that female and male grades were very similar across all three levels, especially when compared with differences across types of schools. The greatest disparities in both take-up and attainment in mathematics were between students in disadvantaged schools, and students in fee-paying schools, not between boys and girls per se. This confirms the findings of Gorard et al. (2001) in Wales and Arnot et al in England and Wales (1998), that gender differences in performance generally are not as great as they have been portrayed to be in the popular media. While recognising the importance of gender difference 'it is inappropriate to ignore or minimise the substantial variations that exist within groups of males and females' (Leder, 1992b, p. 616)

Not only did students in disadvantaged schools not achieve as highly as students in non-disadvantaged schools, but the differences identified generally across school types (that is between secondary and other school types) also obtained between schools in the disadvantaged sector, especially for girls. While both girls and boys in disadvantaged community and comprehensive, and in vocational schools and community colleges, had lower rates of attainment generally than their peers in disadvantaged secondary schools (both coeducational and single sex), the disparity between the girls was slightly higher than that between boys. In Higher mathematics, girls in disadvantaged single sex schools achieved the equivalent of a half a grade higher score than girls in disadvantaged vocational schools and community colleges. Girls in disadvantaged coeducational secondary schools also had higher scores than girls in vocational schools and colleges, and than girls in disadvantaged comprehensive and community schools, although the differences were not as pronounced.

In terms of the A grades awarded at Higher level, girls in disadvantaged comprehensive schools, and in vocational schools and community colleges, had lower aggregate grades compared with boys *within* their schools. While the boys in disadvantaged single sex secondary schools also had higher grades than girls in disadvantaged single sex schools, the differences were not as pronounced. At Ordinary level, girls got more A grades in disadvantaged schools in the secondary sector, while the reverse was true in vocational schools and community colleges and in community schools. In addition, while girls in secondary schools got fewer very low grades in Higher and Ordinary mathematics, girls in other schools had a proportion of low grades that were relatively equal to that of boys (Table A2.8, A2.9). The findings suggest that while the performance of both girls and boys are lower in disadvantaged schools outside the secondary sector, the performance of girls within these is somewhat lower than that of boys.

Discussion

The findings from the Junior Certificate study raise a number of important issues both about education generally and mathematics in particular. First, it is evident that the take-up of Higher level mathematics is low by comparison with other Junior Certificate subjects, except for English. There is a need to examine why this is the case. Is it related to the fact that Ireland remains unique in Europe in teaching mathematics (and English and Irish) at three levels for the junior phase of second-level education? (While the UK has two levels, a number of EU countries only teach the subject at one level). It cannot be solely related to this, however, as the three-tier system does not seem to have affected the take-up of Higher English, although the take-up of Higher-level Irish is also low (40 per cent in 1996 and 37 per cent in 2000).

Another hypothesis is that it is related to the culture of teaching and learning that has developed in mathematics, which presents the subject to students as static rather than dynamic, abstract, formal and remote rather than relevant and accessible (Dossey, 1992; Nickson, 1992). Burton suggests that it is not mathematics *per se* that students may be rejecting but the form in which mathematics is presented in schools. School mathematics is often presented didactically and procedurally. As such it does not relate either to the discipline as it is lived in practice, or as it is taught in the university (Burton, 1999a). Rather, in traditional classes, mathematics is perceived as a subject in which 'obedience, compliance, perseverance and frustration' play a central role (Boaler and Greeno, 2000, p. 184). Mathematics can appear to the learner therefore to be alien, lacking conceptual depth and without imagination and creativity (Burton, 1999a). As such, it may not be attracting educationally ambitious students who expect a subject to offer them the opportunities for agency and creativity that is available in other fields (Boaler and Greeno, 2000). School mathematics may not be attractive to students therefore both because of its substantive content, and because of the way it is taught and examined in schools.

A further hypothesis that needs to be explored is the claim that mathematics teachers present Higher mathematics to students as being difficult and only accessible to a select cohort. There may be a perception that only certain types of girls and boys can take Higher mathematics. Research on the images students hold of mathematicians reinforce the view that students regard the subject of mathematics in quite problematic ways, and the images they hold of the subject relate to the way they are treated within it. Research across a number of European countries (UK, Finland, Sweden and Romania) and the US on the images twelve to thirteen year olds hold of mathematics teachers suggests that they are often intimidated in mathematics classes. Students reported being fearful of being criticised for making mistakes in their work, while feeling overpowered by the teachers' knowledge to the point that some students depicted their mathematics teachers as wizards with magic potions! (Picker and Berry, 2001). 'The dominant image of a mathematician that emerged from this study is that of a white, middle-aged, balding or white-haired man' (ibid, p. 55) This points to a gender, racial and age gap in students' images of mathematicians, a finding that concurs with earlier research in school children's image of scientists (Barman, 1999; Chambers, 1983).

A related issue for mathematics educators is the question of the relationship between mathematics and personal identity. Students choose subjects and fields of study, not only because of their intrinsic interest in the field and the perceived utility of the subject, but also because of the profile of the teacher who teaches it. They also choose a subject in terms of how the subject offers them an opportunity to develop a particular educational and social identity. As mathematics is currently taught in many schools across the world, it is presented as a relatively fixed body of knowledge that has to be acquired in a relatively passive manner (Nickson, 1992). The image of the mathematician is that of a received (generally male) knower rather than active agent creating and developing the subject. As Boaler and Greeno observe:

A large proportion of the students interviewed appeared to reject mathematics because the pedagogical practices with which they had to engage were incompatible with their conceptions of self ... these students considered themselves as *constructive** knowers in other schools subjects. They understood themselves as *received** knowers in the limited circumstances of the mathematics classes in which the learning practices available to them required that they acquire specified procedures with no opportunity that they perceived to be thoughtful or creative about what they needed to learn to do (Boaler and Greeno, 2000, p. 186). (*emphasis is ours)

What seems to be happening in many mathematics classes is that students are being turned away from the subject not by their inability to do mathematics, but rather because the substantive content of what is taught in schools, and the pedagogical and examination practices employed, all of which alienate them from the subject (Burton, 1999a, 1999b; Boaler and Greeno, 2000).

Why girls in certain types of disadvantaged schools are not performing as well as girls in other disadvantaged schools, and boys in their own schools, is not easily explained however from within the existing literature. Much more would need to be known about the gender profile of staffing and leadership in these schools, as well as that of mathematics teachers within them. How gender sensitive teachers of mathematics are in their classroom practice would also need to be explored, as would the way in which students construct their personal identities in relation to mathematics. When students reject mathematics their reasons go 'beyond cognitive likes and dislikes to the establishment of their identities' (Boaler and Greeno, 2000, p. 187). Boaler and Greeno found that even high achieving girls rejected mathematics, because it did not give them opportunities to be creative, verbal and humane. There is also a growing body of evidence that suggests that certain classes of girls[1] may become alienated from achieving in school (and by implication in mathematics) because it does not accord with their preconceived, structurally generated, classed and gendered identities (McRobbie, 1978; Skeggs, 1997). As Skeggs (1994, 1997) has observed, many working class girls (and these are the girls who predominate in the disadvantaged non-secondary schools where girls were performing lowly relative to boys, and to girls in other schools) do not identify with the middle class 'civilising' (colonising) project of the school. Their identities are constructed around roles and relationships of caring and earning that are very removed from school mathematics (Mahony and Zmroczek, 1997; Walkerdine and Lucey, 1989). Their poorer performance cannot simply be explained in terms of teaching or school-specific variables, crucial as these may be. It must also be understood in the wider socio-cultural context in which gender identities are created and reinforced.

General research on women's experience of, and attitudes to, mathematics reinforces the importance of pedagogy and identity as key factors in determining their response to the subject. A number of studies have shown that women and girls tend to reject subjects that do not offer opportunities for deep and connected understanding, even though many may view mathematics as a deep subject (Becker, 1995; Burton, 1995). Women opt for subjects that are seen to give opportunities for caring, creativity and expression. Mathematics is frequently not perceived to offer these kinds of opportunities so it is not the kind of subject with which women want to identify (Boaler and Greeno, 2000). In addition, mathematics is a subject in which teachers are seen to be masculine (Picker and Berry, 2001), while the learning environment in mathematics classes has been shown to be experienced by girls more than boys as exposing them to public shame (when shouting out answers is encouraged and students are named as either right or wrong) (Boylan, Lawton and Povey, 2001). The lack of interest that girls and women display in mathematics-related careers therefore needs to be understood in the context of personal and career identities that are prescribed culturally for women and men, and with which women and men identify. How the culture of schooling reinforces or challenges stereotypical gender expectations around mathematics, in terms of pedagogy, assessment and process also needs to be explored.

The reasons why students may not be opting for Higher mathematics therefore are not simple; neither is it clear from the research literature why certain types of girls are not achieving as highly as others. The national and international literature suggests that it may relate to a combination of forces: these include the structure of opportunities in schools; the attitudes of teachers to the subjects; the pedagogical styles in mathematics classrooms (which in turn is related to modes of assessment); and the way in which students comprehend their own identity in terms of mathematics.

The case studies

Traditions die hard: drill and practice in the classroom

The mathematics teachers we observed were respected and experienced teachers in their schools, people who were deeply committed to their work. While most of them believed that varying teaching methodologies, and having practice at the subject, improved learning, learning itself was most often equated with the memorisation of formulae and procedures. It was not equated with thinking creatively, being able to provide reasons for solutions, or understanding how mathematics is used in the real world. The views of our case-study teachers were found to be broadly in line with those of mathematics teachers in the national TIMSS research (Beaton et al., 1996).

Teachers did not only hold a formal approach to the subject in theory, they also implemented a formal approach in class; their views of teaching influenced their pedagogical practices. We found a high degree of consistency between teacher reports of their pedagogical style and their actual pedagogical styles (Clark and Peterson, 1986; Shavelson and Stern, 1981; She 2000). Teachers reported that much of their time in mathematics lessons involved demonstration of procedures and monitoring of students' progress and the video analysis bore this out. Overall, the data from the teachers interviews confirmed that the didactic approach to teaching mathematics was the norm for the ten teachers in this study, both in theory and in practice.

All twenty mathematics lessons that we videotaped were taught in a traditional manner. While a very small amount of time was devoted to outlining lesson aims and homework in class, most time was spent on exposition by the teacher, followed by a programme of drill and practice. Overall teacher-initiated interaction comprised 96 per cent of all public interactions in the classes, and within this context a procedural rather than a conceptual and/or problem-solving approach to the subject prevailed. Little time or attention was devoted to the problem-solving nature of mathematics, to the practical application of mathematics in the physical world, or to alternative methods of solving mathematical problems, other than those prescribed by the text or the teacher. Teachers were far more likely to use lower order than higher order questioning, and to use drill and repetition rather than discussion-type questions, to teach mathematical concepts. The work programme of the class therefore was strongly teacher-determined, with a resultant lack of student participation in the organisation of their own learning. Learning for the examination was the central task. Mathematics was presented as a subject that was characterised by systems of strong classification and strong framing (Bernstein, 1977) That is to say, mathematics was generally presented as a fixed body of knowledge with a definitive content (framing), separate from other subjects (classification).

While there is evidence both from other recent research on Irish classrooms (Lynch and Lodge, 2002) and from our own study of English classes, that teaching in Irish second-level schools is strongly didactic, the evidence from this study is that mathematics classes are especially didactic. This finding confirms the findings from international studies regarding the strong adherence to traditional methods of teaching mathematics up to recent times (Nickson, 1992). While some countries have encouraged a more constructivist approach towards the teaching of mathematics, this is by no means a uniform trend even in countries like the United States where there has been much discussion of change (Romberg, 2001).

We found many similarities between the teaching of English and the teaching of mathematics, not least of which was the fact that classroom work was generally teacher led and teacher controlled in both subjects: 92 per cent of public interactions in class were teacher led in English compared with 96 per cent in mathematics (Chapter 8); however, we also identified several differences.

One of the most visible differences between the subjects was the manner in which the subject matter was presented to students. While mathematics was taught as a fixed body of knowledge English was not (Burton, 1994a). The pedagogical styles employed by the English teachers fostered investigation and discussion of alternative interpretations most of the time. They displayed a willingness to take different ideas and opinions on board in interpreting the text. In contrast, mathematics was not taught in an exploratory mode; it was generally presented as a given or received set of procedures to be learned, not as a problem-solving experience or as a subject to be constructed by the learner.

English was also characterised by greater relativity and openness to interpretation; an exploratory, interpretative rather than a positivist paradigm seemed to prevail. Whether these differences are a by-product of deep epistemological differences between the subjects, or merely differences in pedagogical styles that have developed in the cultures of teaching, is a matter of debate (Thomas, 1990; Burton, 1994a; White 1996). Whatever their origins, however, they led to very visible differences in the ethos of mathematics and English classrooms.

English classes also differed from mathematics in the way that learning occurred through conversation. Dialogue was a medium of learning in English in a way that it was not in mathematics. In addition, English teachers made connections between what had been learned in the past and what is currently being taught. They explained relationships between topics and provided the students with reasons as to why they were covering particular material in a lesson, or why they were being told to complete a certain exercise. There were also many incidences in which connections were being made between the subject of the text, real life situations and moral dilemmas, thereby indicating to students that English was a lens through which one could arrive at understanding of events in every day life. In contrast to this, mathematics was presented in a more formal way with much emphasis being placed on preparation for the examination. There was no such reference in the sample of English classes.

Fear and anxiety

'You can feel a bit weird asking a question.'
(a quote from an interview with a girl about her learning experiences in her mathematics classes)

There is a growing literature in mathematics education on the role of emotions and affective considerations in the learning of mathematics (Hazin et al., 2001; McLeod, 1992). While there are important differences within this literature between research on attitudes, values, beliefs and emotional responses generally, (with much research being done on attitudes and less on emotional responses) what is clear from the work is that mathematics is a subject that evoked strong feelings in people who have studied it. While those who have been successful in finding solutions or in making conjectures have experienced mathematics with pleasure and joy, one major study found that the prevailing emotional reaction of adults generally to mathematical tasks was that of panic (Buxton, 1981, cited in McLeod, 1992). Being asked to complete mathematical tasks evoked feelings of anxiety, fear and embarrassment as well as panic. Work by Boylan and Lawton (2000) and Boylan, Lawton and Povey (2001) suggests that feelings of anxiety, vulnerability and insecurity are still prevalent among second-level mathematics students.

Our own findings from interviews with students about their experience of their mathematics classrooms, and our analysis of video observations of these same classes, lend strong support to the contention that mathematics is a subject that evokes feelings of vulnerability among students. Students spoke about finding it 'unnerving' when questioned in class, feeling that 'everyone is watching you' when you are asked to do a problem on the board. They spoke about hoping 'you got it right' and feeling 'Oh no!' if you got it wrong.

Mathematics classrooms were remarkably uniform in terms of the prevailing discourse. There were regular references to 'the exam', with the subject matter being defined in binary codes as either 'difficult' or 'easy', 'hard' or 'simple'. Answers were classified also along polarised lines as either 'right' or 'wrong'. The subject of mathematics was one therefore in which there was a clear judgement of the student's work, a judgement that was often made in public. This implicitly, and at times explicitly, judgmental atmosphere created anxieties and tensions for students in relation to the subject of mathematics itself.

The importance of student feelings about mathematics was evident from the comments they made about their teachers. Teachers tended to be negatively or positively evaluated to a considerable degree in terms of how they managed students' feelings of exposure and vulnerability in mathematics classes. Teachers whom students claimed made them feel 'fearful' or anxious in class, or who 'gave out' to them for 'getting things wrong' when solving mathematical problems, were especially negatively evaluated.

Not only did students define their mathematics teachers negatively or positively to a noticeable degree in terms of the extent to which they made them feel vulnerable in class, they also expressed strong views generally about the fear they had about asking questions in mathematics classes. Students spoke of their fear of being exposed (and publicly criticised by their teacher, and silently mocked by their peers). Our conversations with them revealed the sense of pressure (especially in top sets or bands) that one was expected to 'get it right'. Other students said they were 'afraid of being put on the spot if they asked a question'. Even in classes where the students were positive about the teacher and the classroom experience as a whole, fear and anxiety were prevalent. In such classes, students spoke about being 'embarrassed to ask' 'if everyone else understands'. Even though students were encouraged to ask questions in these classes, as one group of girls put it '... you can feel a bit weird asking'. Students took their cues from other students, and were fearful of being the only one who needed to ask. One top set student said she waited to the end of the class to ask in the hope that the teacher might explain the problem again. If the teacher did not, then she would ask the girl beside her 'Do you understand that?' and if she says 'Yes', then I wouldn't ask'. Not all classes were viewed positively and in those that were not the sense of fear and anxiety was heightened by the fear of teacher criticism (as opposed to peer ridicule). There were numerous references to the fact that students did not like to ask questions in class, because the teacher might 'give out to you if you get it wrong'.

The fear of asking and 'being wrong' was especially strong in the top sets or streams. The fear that students felt in these classes was that one would be seen as 'stupid' in a class where others were 'just amazing'. In these classes also the pace of the class was regarded as being 'too fast'. Students said the teachers 'explained things too quickly', that there was 'a lot of pressure to do well'. They claimed the class ' is more competitive because you feel like if you don't know it you shouldn't be there'. One girl explained how the teacher questioned her persistently when she got something wrong until 'I was nearly reduced to tears about it in the end. And I rarely ask questions since'.

In contrast to mathematics classes, English classes were characterised by the absence of evaluative language, in particular terms such as 'wrong' or 'incorrect'. Neither was the material coded in advance for students in terms of its intellectual demands: no English teacher referred to material as 'hard', 'difficult' or 'easy'. The binary codes of 'right and wrong', 'hard and easy' seemed to be an integral part of the mathematics teachers' framework for presenting their subject, while English teachers did not utilise such binary and evaluative codes.

Does the teacher make the subject?

While there was a general tendency for girls, top stream classes, and middle class students to hold the most positive views of mathematics overall, the profile of the classes with the most positive perspectives on mathematics shows that teacher practices also impact on attitudes to the subject (Chapter 10, Table 10.6).[2]

Thus, while the most 'positive' class was a top stream and the highest-performing group in the TIMSS-related test, the most 'negative' class was also a top stream and was ranked second highest in the TIMSS-related test. In addition, while two of the 'positive' classes were in the top-stream in their year group, this was also the case for two of the most 'negative' classes.

The focus group discussions highlighted the importance of the style of individual mathematics teachers in determining attitudes to, and experiences of, the subject. Students' views of mathematics generally were very much mediated by the character and style of the individual teacher. All students spoke about mathematics in terms of their *teacher* and rarely mentioned other issues like the curriculum, the examination system or resources for the subject. Three types of teachers were identified: those who were perceived as 'good' and supportive of students in their work; those who were experienced negatively and were variously defined as being too critical of students' work, pressurising, or 'going too fast' and those who were experienced more neutrally as falling between the two extremes. This finding concurs with international research suggesting that students' views of the subject are strongly influenced by their classroom experience of learning it (Dick and Rallis, 1991; Johnston, 1994; Ma, 1997).

There were three teacher practices that seemed to contribute to negative views on mathematics: when teachers taught at a very fast pace, when they were critical of students when they made errors or sought help, or when they pressurised students to achieve without giving positive support. Students' accounts of mathematics classes were also more negative when the teacher lacked good humour, or rarely praised or encouraged students in class. Students who were positive about their experience of learning mathematics described their teacher as a 'good' teacher with a strong knowledge of the subject, capable of explaining the material and interacting with them in a humorous, supportive and non-judgmental way. Even in these 'ideal' circumstances, however, students were often reluctant to look for help from the teacher, seeing family or friends as a less threatening source of help. A fear of being seen to be 'wrong' was an overriding concern of students in all types of mathematics classes, a finding that concurs with those of Boylan and Lawton (2000), Boylan, Lawton and Povey (2001) and Picker and Berry (2001).

The extent to which students identified the subject with the teacher was especially evident in Errigal (CS Fr) where all the students interviewed (both girls and boys) had a positive view of the teacher. One student even said that she would rather stay with Ms Ennis and do Ordinary level mathematics than move to another teacher (even though she could move to a Higher level mathematics class if she wished). In this school, parents and students put in special requests to have Ms Ennis as their mathematics teacher. As one student put it: ' A lot of students come begging to her door to be taken into her class'. Ms Ennis had all the attributes of the good mathematics teacher from the students' perspective: not only did she know her subject well, she was willing and able to explain the subject matter to the students; in addition she was non-judgmental, and did not make students 'feel bad' if they did not understand. She was respectful of the students, explaining material clearly, and was conscious of their vulnerability in class. The two other teachers (Mr Butler and Ms Brennan) who were defined as 'good teachers' by the students were also praised for their ability to explain topics clearly, with students in Mr Butler's class in Blackstairs (VCC Fr D) pointing out that he was especially helpful as he 'brings you out of yourself', showed students different ways of doing problems, and 'takes things [examples] out of his head'.

Good teachers, were not only those who were good communicators of mathematical knowledge, patient, good humoured, not sarcastic and fair, they were also people whom students were not afraid of. In defining her teacher as really good, one student pointed out that the reason for this was because 'she doesn't make you feel bad just because you made a mistake', while one of the boys in the same class said 'she wouldn't make fun of you [if you got something wrong]. She's nice like that – fair like'.

'If they don't have that innate mathematical ability... they are not going to improve'

(a quote from Mr Butler, one of the case study teachers)

All of the teachers in the case study, and more than nine in ten of the mathematics teachers surveyed nationally for the TIMSS, held strongly essentialist views about mathematical abilities: they believed that some students have a natural talent for the subject while others did not (Chapter 9, Figure 9.1). This finding concurs with previous findings by Fontes and Kellaghan (1983) regarding the strongly essentialist view of the Irish public generally and teachers in particular regarding the nature of human intelligence. What is surprising perhaps is that little appears to have changed in this respect in twenty years, at least with mathematics teachers. Implicitly, if not explicitly, a student's attainment in mathematics appears to be taken as a surrogate measure of human intelligence. This occurs in spite of the vast international research indicating that mathematical intelligence is but one of a multiplicity of intelligences, and that all intelligences are strongly developmental in character (Devlin et al., 1997; Gardner, 1985; 1999).

The views that teachers held about mathematical ability were openly expressed at our interviews with them after their classes were videotaped. The most commonly used adjective to describe students who were not successful at mathematics was to refer to them as 'weak'. All ten mathematics teachers believed that mathematical talent was an innate gift that could not really be improved on if the student 'did not have it' or were very 'weak'. Even a teacher like Ms Ennis, who was very highly regarded by students, believed that there were certain students who were too weak to improve beyond a certain level. In the context of stressing the importance of building up students' confidence in mathematics and encouraging them to succeed, she observed that she 'couldn't bring [up] someone who is very weak'. 'I could not bring them up to honours standard – ability of course comes into it'. The two other very positively regarded teachers in the study (Ms Brennan and Mr Butler) as well as those who were more neutrally or negatively regarded, held similar views. Mr Butler pointed out that it was clear to him that 'in first year, some of them just won't have it with maths – they're not going to change … If they don't have that something, that innate ability, they just won't acquire it, it just won't happen'. Other teachers classified students as 'very bright', 'quite intelligent' or 'weak' in their discussions of their teaching.

Teachers' perceptions of how mathematical capabilities were acquired and developed impacted on how they interpreted the progress, or lack of it, of their students. Teachers generally attributed students' improvements in mathematics to having an innate ability, and being encouraged and supported by the teacher. On the other hand, teachers did not hold themselves responsible for any observed deterioration in students' mathematical performance. Here students' own attitudes, behaviour or lack of ability were deemed to be the main causal factors. Students that teachers defined as 'weak' were largely seen to have limited opportunities for advancement, although some of the teachers believed that it was possible to give such students more confidence and encouragement in mathematics.

The essentialist view of mathematical ability was not confined to teachers. Parents from all types of social backgrounds attached considerable importance to children's 'innate ability' for successful learning in mathematics (Chapter 11). However, those parents who were most educated and who had detailed knowledge of how schooling worked as a selection mechanism for work and education (the Insiders), attributed more importance to the quality of schooling than others. They were also the parents who regulated their children's schooling by intervening with teachers and, if necessary, moving children between schools.

Only the students themselves rejected the essentialist view of mathematical skill and ability. Unlike teachers especially, but also many parents, they attributed success in mathematics to good teaching and systematic study (Chapter 11). What appears to be happening in education therefore is that students who enter second-level schools with low rates of attainment in mathematics, or who do not achieve in their first years in second-level school, come to be defined as 'weak students' (not weak-at-mathematics) by teachers in particular, but also even by parents. What is, in effect, a quality of attainment in a given field comes to be defined as a defining attribute of the person. The irony is that future achievements are explained in terms of this dubiously defined attribute. What is called mathematical 'ability' is merely mathematical attainment at a given time on a given (pen and paper) test for a given student. Using it to explain attainment at a later date is to explain mathematical attainment in terms of itself (Secada, 1992).

Using tests of attainment to define students' entire educational profile is a seriously problematic educational practice (Gardner, 1985, 1999). Yet it is by no means confined to mathematics. The labelling of students as 'weak' (especially) or 'bright' seems to be endemic in schooling in Ireland, with its attendant dangers of creating a self-fulfilling prophecy for students who are negatively defined (the so-called 'weak ones'). Given the strong interface between working class status and lower attainment generally, the problem is especially acute for working class students. Lower attainments, which are generally the by-product of major differences in resources and opportunities across classes and groups, comes to be defined as a personal attribute of the individual, something that cannot be changed. What is in effect a social product becomes a psychological construct (Secada, 1992). This is an educational practice that needs to be seriously deconstructed and challenged if schools are to be part of the solution rather than reproducers of the problem of inequality in education (Lynch and Lodge, 2002).

The gender code: gender balance and gender awareness

There were ten coeducational classes in the study and in four of these boys received significantly more teacher attention than girls; there was only one class in which girls received significantly more teacher attention. While the remaining five classes were more gender balanced, in all but one of them teachers interacted more often with boys than with girls (Table 6.1, Chapter 6).

Not only were girls less likely to get attention in coeducational classes, girls were, on average, less likely to ask questions and to be asked a question by the teacher than boys. Although there were few higher order questions asked in any of the classes, girls were slightly less likely to be asked these than boys in coeducational classes (although the girls in coeducational classes were asked more of these type of questions than girls in single sex schools). As almost all public interaction is work-related, the findings indicate that boys are effectively more involved in the business of the mathematics lesson than girls in coeducational schools. The only area in which girls in coeducational classes got more attention than boys was in terms of praise, although neither girls nor boys received much praise overall.

Aggregate scores for all classes conceal important variations *within* individual classes however. They also blind us to differences between the learning climates in single sex boys' and girls' classes. In all the coeducational classes in which boys dominated, it was a small minority of boys who were involved. These boys dominated the interaction compared with other boys as well as girls, a finding that concurs with that of Lynch and Lodge (2002) and Barnes (2000). The tendency for a small number of students to dominate classroom interaction occurred also in boys' single sex classes, but not in girls' classes.

Interestingly, the gender differences in interaction patterns across single sex classes were more noticeable than those within coeducational classes. In all, 57 per cent of boys in single sex classes were not asked any questions while this happened to only 9 per cent of girls in single sex classes. In coeducational classes 27 per cent of boys and 31 per cent of girls were not asked any questions in class. What is clear therefore is that the girls' mathematics classes were more inclusive in terms of teacher-student engagement than coeducational classes, and particularly more inclusive than boys' classes. Within coeducational classes however, more boys were more actively involved with the teacher in working on mathematical problems within the class than girls.

When the factors associated with different gender patterns of interaction were examined, the most important factor appeared to be teacher awareness of the need for gender balance. The classes that were most gender balanced were those in which the teachers were gender aware. Of the five teachers of coeducational classes, it was the three female teachers who displayed most awareness, with one teacher operating a systematic policy of gender balance in her class.

The analysis of the video material from classes that were most male-dominated suggested that having a disproportionately large number of boys in the class, having a teacher who focused on boys and their interests, and having a teacher who had low gender awareness, all contributed to lack of gender balance.

The boys who dominated exercised hegemonic learning styles (by shouting out answers, calling for attention, moving and shuffling at their desks, or interrupting other students and the teacher). They dominated the verbal, and sometimes the physical, space of the groups to which they belonged, although the styles they adopted varied with the culture of the school and indeed the stream or track they were in. Overall they had interactional styles that were competitive in attention-seeking terms, and exhibited traits of dominance commonly associated with hegemonic forms of masculinity (Mac An Ghaill, 1994; Connell, 1995).[3] Teachers seemed to co-operate with dominating students when their dominance involved work interactions; they were forced to engage with it when it involved disruptive behaviour.

The findings confirming the dominance of boys in coeducational classes is in accord with the general findings in other studies internationally (Drudy and Uí Catháin 1998; Howe 1997; Lee 1993; Sadker and Sadker 1985; Warrington et al., 2000). However, the findings also suggest that aggregate gender scores for classroom interaction conceal important differences between and within classes. Male dominance in classes is accounted for often by a minority of boys (and this happens to a greater degree in single sex boys' classes than in coeducational classes). Such boys control the learning environment not only for girls but also for other quieter boys in the class (Barnes, 2000; Lodge, 1998; Lynch and Lodge, 2002).

Although Howe (1997) has drawn attention to the fact that there is a lack of evidence linking male dominance in class with superior examination performance, nonetheless our findings do raise questions about the overall long term effects for girls and certain quieter boys of being subordinate in their classroom experiences. There is evidence that public disengagement may reinforce negative attitudes to traditionally 'non-female' subjects among girls (such as mathematics) even if it does not directly influence examination performance (Jovanovic and King 1998). The regular day-to-day experience of lacking control and influence in class is most certainly a form of socialisation. Certain young women and subordinate males are practising being relatively silent in the presence of other young men in coeducational classrooms. Given that our interviews with students about their experience of mathematics' classes showed that girls were more afraid of asking questions and seeking explanations than boys, it would seem that the competitive culture of mathematics classes (especially true in top streams) may be alienating girls from identifying with the subject (Chapter 10). However unintended, mathematics classes are often experienced by students, and particularly by girls, as threatening environments. They are places in which errors can result in naming and shaming in front of your peers, something all students want to avoid.

Most research in classrooms focuses on the actively engaged or the actively deviant. There is a real danger however that the majority of students, be these girls or boys, are ignored in the process. Because the quietly disengaged are not disruptive in class, this does not mean that their silence is unproblematic (Nardi and Steward, 2001). While students may be quietly engaged, there is a very real danger that their silence is indicative of a detachment from the subject and the learning process. Their non-participation may be a rational choice to opt out of the subject, as often as it is indicative of quiet contentment, or a symptom of pathology (Dorn, 1996).

On the more positive side, the data do indicate however, that not all coeducational classes are male-dominated. Those classes in which teachers were strongly gender aware, and those in which there were a relatively equal number of girls and boys, were the most egalitarian in terms of interaction. Such gender-balanced learning environments have been found to promote improved attitudes to learning among girls in non-traditional subject areas (Jovanovic and King, 1998).

Another positive finding from the study relates to teacher attitudes to gender. While earlier studies of teacher attitudes to gender differences in mathematics found that teachers held quite stereotypical views of female and male capabilities and approaches (Fennema et al., 1990), our inter-views suggest a more complex picture of gender perceptions among teachers. Teachers were quite hesitant and ambivalent in their interpretation of gender relations, with only one of the ten holding clear stereotypical views. Teachers were almost equally divided between those who thought that there were no gender differences in success rates in learning mathematics, those who did not know and those who said there were differences. Girls and boys were seen as having different approaches to the learning of the subject, not as being more or less capable at the subject. The findings concur with related research by Leder and Forgasz (2000) and Francis (2000), both of whom found evidence of a decline in gender stereotyped expectations among students, the former in relation to mathematics, and the latter in relation to students' subject preferences. Our findings also lend support to Arnot's (2002) and Connell's (1997) claims that concepts of femininity and masculinity are becoming increasingly fractured and diverse in contemporary society.

Class actions: the importance of grouping procedures and parental interventions

Traditionally much research on mathematics education has been 'unidimensional in scope'. Studies examined 'issues of social class, race, language background or gender in isolation from each other' (Secada,

1992, p. 635). In addition, social categories of student diversity have often been treated as unquestioned givens, being often transmuted into other issues in the research analysis. The lack of interest in student diversity in mainstream mathematics education was, according to (Secada, ibid, p. 654), 'both unconscionable and untenable'.

The diversity deficit has begun to be addressed in recent years as scholars recognise increasingly the interface between the psychological, the cultural, the political and the social in determining learning outcomes. It is increasingly accepted that gender is but one 'code' within schools and classrooms (Arnot, 2002); gender interacts with, and is influenced by other differences. The social turn in mathematics education has generated a growing recognition that social origins and atrributes play a crucial role in the learning process (Lerman, 2000; Wenger, 1998). It is accepted increasingly that learners are not simply of a particular gender, race or social class; they simultaneously embody and recreate the structurally situated particulars of their own social class, gender, race, ethnicity and sexuality. Therefore, binary oppositional categorisations based on gender (or race or class) alone are not adequate for analysing classrooms (Gordon 1996, p. 36).

What we undertook to do therefore was to examine the ways in which gender experiences interfaced with social class experiences. The findings from our own analysis of Junior Certificate data, and the results of a range of other studies, had indicated that learning experiences are mediated by social class in particular[4], and also by the track (stream, set or band) to which one is allocated (Hannan and Boyle, 1987; Lynch and Lodge, 2002; Oakes, 1985; Sorensen and Hallinan, 1986). As international research increasingly emphasised the important role parents played in determining students' relationships with school (Gewirtz et al., 1995; Lareau, 1989; Reay, 1996; Wells and Oakes, 1996), we also focused attention on how different types of parents related to schools and to the teaching of mathematics.

In common with a number of international studies, both nationally and internationally, we found that top tracks experience a more intense, work-focused and competitive learning environment than lower tracks (Boaler, 1997c; Burgess, 1983; Gamoran, 1986; Oakes, 1985; Lynch and Lodge, 2002). There were important qualitative differences in the *type* and *quality* of pedagogical practices deployed by teachers in different tracks. The most striking differences were found between the bottom and top streams. In the bottom stream, the teacher's pedagogical approach was characterised by slow pace, constant repetition and an emphasis on the practising of very basic, procedural skills (Chapter 7). The teacher's approach appeared to reflect the generally low expectations held of the bottom stream. The pedagogical approach of the teachers of the top streams was characterised by a fast pace and an air of urgency. The teachers had higher expectations of the higher streams or tracks.

A dialectical relationship appeared to develop between the teachers' pedagogical styles and the students' learning styles across tracks: the dependent and unconfident attitudes of the low track students to mathematics, combined with low proficiency of basic skills in the subject, seemed to evoke a response from teachers that reinforced dependency. The teachers focused on developing basic procedural skills, moving slowly and systematically through the material with very low-level questioning and answering. In high tracks, the opposite dynamic was in operation.

The analysis of mixed 'ability' classes gave a very clear indication of how social class and stream can interface with each other. While mixed classes did occupy an interim position between top and bottom tracks generally, in terms of learning and teaching climate, their social class composition seemed to impact on whether the ethos leans towards that found in top or bottom streams. The learning climate in the mixed 'ability' class in an upper middle class school was more similar to that in a top stream, while the mixed class in a more lower middle class and working class school was similar to that in lower streams or bands in other schools. The findings here concur with other research which suggests that grouping by so-called 'ability' is an important part of the process of social class reproduction (Lynch and Lodge, 2002).

The cultural deficit interpretation of class difference

The analysis of teacher expectations and perspectives on students indicated that these were influenced by the students' social class background (Sorenson and Hallinan, 1986; Taylor, 1993; Wang and Haertal, 1995; Hallam and Toutounji, 1996). In Suir (a designated disadvantaged girls' school) the teacher believed that the students' poor performance in school was directly related to their 'disadvantaged' family background rather than an outcome of the grouping system or teaching they had received. However, she did say that many of the bottom stream '*lacked the basic skills*' of mathematics when they came to second-level education. By contrast, in Barrow (a fee-paying girls' school) and Lee (a fee-paying boys' school) the teachers believed that the students' middle class backgrounds had a positive impact on their learning. Moreover, the teachers of these classes indicated that they had high educational expectations for their students. This contrasted with the relatively low expectations of the teacher in schools such as Liffey (a boys' disadvantaged school) although the class observed in Liffey was a top stream within that school.

While teachers held quite varied views on gender roles and relationships, they were more unanimous in their views on social class. Overall, teachers tended to adopt a cultural deficit interpretation of the lower rates of attainment of working class students; low achievement among working class students was primarily interpreted in terms of the perceived 'inadequacies' of their cultural background. It was not regarded as a by-product of prior teaching in particular, although teachers did also recognise that the greater resources (educational and material) available to upper middle class students were crucial to their educational success. Six of the ten teachers claimed that students from 'poor' backgrounds were disadvantaged in learning mathematics by their parents' lack of knowledge of, and especially interest in, education. Only one of the ten teachers claimed that schooling procedures (labelling students from particular backgrounds and placing them in low streams/tracks) contributed to their lower attainment. Our findings here concur with other Irish research on teacher attitudes to students from working class backgrounds (Lynch and O'Riordan, 1998).

Parent Power

Our data corroborates the findings from a number of other studies regarding the key role that parents can play in the education process. Their capacity, or lack of it, to choose different schools or to intervene on educational matters on behalf of their children, can and does radically alter the nature of their children's education (Lareau, 1989; Useem, 1992; Wells and Serna, 1996; West et al, 1998).

We found that parents' own educational experience, including their experience of mathematics, influenced their relationship with the school and the subject. Those with positive experiences of mathematics, and especially of schooling generally, were the most likely to be proactive on behalf of their children. From the interviews with parents, it was clear that upper middle class parents in particular were those who had the most informed and positive views on education generally. They also had the cultural, social and financial capital to act in their children's interests (Bourdieu and Passerson, 1977; Gewirtz et al, 1995, Reay and Ball, 1998). They were part of resourced social networks that enabled them to give considerable support to their children. The Insider parents were also integrated into school affairs, engaging in different forms of intervention in their children's schooling as the need arose.

In contrast, the Outsiders had much lower levels of education themselves and were mostly from working class backgrounds. They had more negative attitudes to schooling and mathematics based on their own experiences. They lacked the resources, skills and knowledge to intervene in their children's education to the same degree as the Insiders. The Outsiders did not have complete information when making choices with their children's schooling; they did not understand fully the implications of taking Ordinary or Foundation-level examinations for both the educational and occupational future of their children. The Insider parents, however, were keenly aware of the limitations of taking subjects at lower levels and made it clear that they resisted such placements. Some said they were willing and able to take their children out of particular schools if they were not taking subjects at Higher levels.

The third group of parents, the Intermediaries, occupied an interim position between the other two groups, although they were more similar to the Insiders in social class terms. What differentiated them most from the Insiders however, was not so much their lack of knowledge of the education system, as their lack of control over their children's schooling. Unlike the Outsiders, they knew how schooling worked and how it selected children out occupationally for the future. However, they seemed to lack the resources to act on this knowledge. They worried about their children's schooling without controlling it.

What seems remarkable from the interviews with teachers and parents is the lack of obligation on schools (and the lack of resources available to them) to make up the deficit in parents' knowledge of schooling. There is no procedure or mechanism for informing parents about how the school system works from the inside out. In particular, parents are not informed in any systematic way about the grouping of children in school, or indeed about the implications of grouping or taking subjects at different levels.

There is no doubt but that the different patterns of take-up for different levels of mathematics across school types (reported in Chapter 2) is related to the information differential and the resource differentials between parents across social classes and groups. The fact that the take-up of Higher mathematics is highest in fee-paying schools and lowest in vocational schools and community colleges (almost half of which are designated disadvantaged) indicates strongly that the most disadvantaged schools may be reinforcing class inequalities by the manner in which they provide subject options. There is no doubt that certain students are entering second level educationally disadvantaged in mathematics, as was observed by a number of the teachers we interviewed. However, this begs the question as to why this is the case and why the problems have not been addressed at primary level. It also forces us to ask why it is that second-level schools are not given the resources and supports to make up the deficit rather than being required to accept it as an annual given, simply because the students come from a particular social class background.

One of the problems in Irish schools seems to be that schools' accountability in terms of how they group students, or the level at which subjects are offered to different classes of students within school, is largely parent dependent. If parents do not demand or ask for information they are not offered it. If parents do not know what questions to ask, no one tells them what they need to know to make an informed judgement for their children's future. The injustice of ignorance is a major issue not being addressed in education.

Concluding remarks

While mathematics is, arguably, taught in a more didactical style than other subjects, the epistemological and pedagogical frames utilised in the teaching of mathematics is but a variation on a wider theme (see Chapter 4). A system of strong framing (strong rules governing what is to be known and how) and strong classification (strong boundaries between subjects) (Bernstein, 1977) characterises most subject teaching in schools. School subjects, with some minor exceptions, have clearly defined boundaries and content; they are not presented in an integrated manner. In addition, the syllabus is presented largely as a set of certainties or skills 'to be grasped' by students for 'the exam'. While there are variations in epistemological assumptions and pedagogical practices, and in the discourses employed across subjects (as can be seen in our analysis of English classes in Chapter 8), there are also several remarkable similarities between them (Lynch and Lodge, 2002).

To interpret the traditional approach to the teaching of mathematics as a matter of individual teacher choice and responsibility, therefore, would be to simplify a complex problem in teaching and learning. Mass public education has a long history in western European societies; it is a history that demonstrates a strong allegiance to 'drill and practice' for all subject teaching, not just for the teaching of mathematics (Bowles and Gintis, 1976; Coolahan, 1981; Foucault, 1977). Moreover, recent research on Irish schools reveals that they are deeply hierarchical in their organisation and practice, and this is not confined to any particular subject (Lynch and Lodge, 2002). While it is true that teachers are relatively autonomous in their own classrooms, in terms of the pedagogical approaches they employ, they are also subject to a range of internal as well as external controls, not least the control of public examinations. They experience their own role as both powerful and powerless and this, in turn, influences their capacity and motivation to be innovative or experimental (Davies, 1996).

If we are to achieve change in teaching practice, the focus cannot simply be on changing teaching practice itself, important though this may be. As Thompson (1992) has observed, changing dispositions and even the architecture of schools does not change the relations of power and domination in mathematics classrooms. To understand how education works and how change can be realised, one needs to marry psychological models of teacher and student beliefs with a structural analysis of how beliefs and attitudes are patterned and reproduced over time. 'As researchers, it requires us to go beyond the data of observable practices and into the realms of those patterns and generative principles of which the teachers themselves may not even be aware' (Gates, 2001, pp. 22-23). For policy makers it requires a shift in emphasis from the individual to the school organisation, and from the school itself to the wider socio-cultural and socio-political structures of which it is a part. It is not possible to change classroom practices by simply focusing on student or teacher attitudes and practices, important as these may be. Attitudes and values, and teaching practices, exist in the wider field of mathematics education and of education generally. They are situated and constrained by the wider social context of external examinations, parental expectations, the structures of paid and unpaid labour markets, the hierarchical ordering of educational relations, as well as the traditions and identities of particular schools. To understand and to change traditional approaches to the teaching of mathematics, therefore, we need to be mindful of the wider educational and socio-political contexts within which teaching takes place.

Notes

[1] This has already been well established to be true for working class boys (see Willis, 1977)

[2] Although students in the three bottom streams (Suir, SSG Fr D, Nephin, VCC Fr, Mourne, VCC Fr D) did not have positive attitudes to mathematics or positive self images, expectations or learning experiences, students in one of these, Nephin, had more positive attitudes to mathematics than the boys in the mixed class in Lee (a fee-paying boys' school) where all of the boys were planning to do Higher level mathematics. Even their mathematics self image was only marginally lower than that of the boys in Lee. The students in Nephin (VCC Fr) (a bottom stream) also had more positive attitudes and self images than the top stream in Liffey (SSB Fr D). The classes in which low levels of negative interactions with teachers were reported (Barrow SSG F) and Errigal (CS Fr)) were also those where attitudes and self image were most positive.

[3] Connell (1995) suggests that domination of women and subordinate men is one of the defining features of hegemonic masculinity.

[4] Race and ethnicity are of growing significance in determining one's educational

experience in Ireland, especially since 1997 (when this study was planned) (Fanning et al., 2001). In addition, there is a growing public recognition that differences arising from sexuality, religion and disability can and do result in exclusions within schooling generally (Lynch and Lodge, 2002). We did not focus on these differences in this study, however, not because we do not think they are important, but rather because our own study of Junior Certificate data, and previous Irish research, had indicated that social class and socio-economic origins had a major and prolonged impact on educational outcomes in Ireland (Clancy, 2001; Hannan et al., 1996). To explore the impact of disability, ethnicity or race on students' learning experience of mathematics in any depth would require a separate and more focused study.

Bibliography

Abrantes, P. (2001), 'Revisiting the goals and the nature of mathematics for all in the context of a National curriculum' in M. van den Heuvel-Panhhizen (ed.), *Proceedings of the 25th Conference of the International Group for the Psychology of Mathematics Education*, The Netherlands: Freudenthal Institute, vol. 1, pp. 25-40.

Allen, K. (2000), *The Celtic Tiger: The Myth of Social Partnership in Ireland*, Manchester: Manchester University Press.

Arbreton, A. (1993), *When Getting Help is Helpful: Developmental, Cognitive and Motivational Influences on Students' Academic Help-seeking*, unpublished PhD Thesis, University of Michigan.

Arnot, M.and Weiler, K. (eds.) (1993), *Feminism and Social Justice in Education,* London: Falmer Press.

Arnot, M., Gray, J., Rudduck, J. and Duveen, G. (1998), *Recent Research on Gender and Educational Performance,* London: The Stationery Office.

Arnot, M. (2002), *Reproducing Gender? Essays on Educational Theory and Feminist Politics*, London: Routledge Falmer.

Ball, S. J. (1981), *Beachside Comprehensive,* Cambridge: Cambridge University Press.

Ball, S. J. (1997), 'Good School / Bad School: paradox and fabrication', *British Journal of Sociology of Education,* vol. 18, no. 3, pp. 317-335.

Ball, S.J. and Gewirtz, S. (1996), 'Education Markets, School Competition and Parental Choice in the UK: A Report of Research Findings', *International Journal of Educational Reform*, vol. 5, no. 2, pp. 152-158.

Ballard, K. (ed.) (1999), *Inclusive Education: International Voices on Disability and Social Justice,* London: Falmer Press.

Barman, C.R. (1999), 'Pupils' views about scientists and school science: engaging K-8 teachers in a national study', *Journal of Science Teacher Education*, vol. 10, no. 1, pp. 43-54.

Barnes, M. (2000), 'Effects of dominant and subordinate masculinities on interactions in a collaborative learning classroom', in J. Boaler (ed.), *Multiple Perspectives on Mathematics Teaching and Learning,* Connecticut: Ablex Publishing.

Barrett, M., (1980), *Women's Oppression Today*, London: Verso.

Beaton, A.E., Mullis, V.S., Martin, M.O., Gonzalez, E.J., Kelly, D.L. and Smith, T.A. (1996), *Mathematics Achievement in the Middle-School Years: IEA's Third International Mathematics and Science Study*, Boston: TIMSS International Study Centre.

Becker, J. R. (1990), 'Graduate education in the mathematical sciences: factors influencing women and men', in L. Burton (ed.), *Gender and Mathematics: An International Perspective,* London: Cassell.

Becker, J. R. (1995), 'Women's Ways of Knowing in Mathematics', in P. Rogers and G. Kaiser (eds.), *Equity in Mathematics Education: Influences of Feminism and Culture,* London: The Falmer Press.

Beechey, V. (1987), *Unequal Work,* London: Verso.

Bernstein, R. (1976), *The Restructuring of Social and Political Theory,* New York: Harcourt, Brace Jovanovich.

Bernstein, B. (1977), 'On the classification and framing of educational knowledge' in *Class, Codes and Control,* vol. 3, 2nd edn, London: Routledge and Kegan Paul.

Bernstein, R. (1983), *Beyond Objectivism and Relativism: Science, Hermeneutics and Praxis,* Pennsylvania: University of Pennsylvania Press.

Bloor, D. (1976), *Knowledge and Social Imagery,* London: Routledge and Kegan Paul.

Bloor, D. (1983), *Wittgenstein: A Social Theory of Knowledge,* New York: Columbia University Press.

Boaler, J. (1997a), *Experiencing School Mathematics: Teaching Styles, Sex and Setting,* Buckingham: Open University Press.

Boaler, J. (1997b), 'Reclaiming school mathematics: the girls fight back', *Gender and Education,* vol. 9, no. 3, pp. 285-305.

Boaler, J. (1997c), 'Setting, social class and survival of the quickest', *British Educational Research Journal,* vol. 23, no. 5, pp. 575-595.

Boaler, J. (1997d), 'The effectiveness of open and closed teaching approaches', *The British Council Science Education Newsletter,* no. 132, URL: www.britcoun.org/education/sen/132forum.htm.

Boaler, J. (1997e), 'When even the winners are losers: evaluating the experiences of "top set" students', *Journal of Curriculum Studies,* vol. 29, no. 2, pp. 165-182.

Boaler, J. (ed.) (2000), *Multiple Perspectives on Mathematics Teaching and Learning,* Connecticut: Ablex Publishing.

Boaler, J. and Greeno, J.G. (2000), 'Identity, agency and knowing in mathematics worlds', in J. Boaler (ed.), *Multiple Perspectives on Mathematics Teaching and Learning,* Connecticut: Ablex Publishing.

Boaler, J., William, D. and Brown, M (eds.) (2000), 'Students' experiences of ability grouping – disaffection, polarisation and the construction of failure', *British Educational Research Journal,* vol. 26, no. 5, pp. 631-648.

Bornholt, L., Goodnow, J.J., and Cooney, G. (1994), 'Influences of gender stereotypes on adolescents' perceptions of achievement', *American Journal of Educational Research,* vol. 31, no. 3, pp.675-693.

Bourdieu, P. (1977), *An Outline of the Theory of Practice,* Cambridge: Cambridge University Press.

Bourdieu, P. (1986), 'The Forms of Capital', in J.E. Richardson (ed.) *Handbook of Theory of Research for the Sociology of Education,* New York and London: Greenwood Press.

Bourdieu, P. (1996), *The State Nobility: Elite Schools in the Field of Power,* Oxford: Polity Press.

Bourdieu, P. and Passerson, J.C. (1977), *Reproduction in Education, Society and Culture,* Beverly Hills: Sage.

Bowles, S. and Gintis, H. (1976), *Schooling in Capitalist America: Educational Reform and the Contradictions of Economic Life,* London: Routledge and Kegan Paul.

Boylan, M. and Lawton, P. (2000), '"I'd be more likely to talk in class if...": How some year eight students experience teacher questioning and discussion strategies', *British Society for Research into Learning Mathematics: Proceedings,* vol. 20, no. 3, pp. 7-12.

Boylan, M., Lawton, P. and Povey, H. (2001), '"I'd be more likely to talk in class if...": Some students' ideas about strategies to increase mathematical participation in whole class interactions', in M. van den Heuvel-Panhhizen (ed.) *Proceedings of the 25th Conference of the International Group for the Psychology of Mathematics Education,* The Netherlands: Freudenthal Institute, vol. 2, pp. 201-208.

Broadfoot, P. (1979), *Assessment, Schools and Society,* London: Methuen.

Broadfoot, P., Osborn, M., Planel, C. and Sharpe, K. (2000), *Promoting Quality in Learning: Does England Have the Answer?,* London: Cassell Publications.

Brown, J.S., Collins, A. and Duguid, P. (1989), 'Situated cognition and the culture of learning', *Educational Researcher,* vol. 18, no. 1, pp. 32-42.

Brown, S., Cooney, T. and Jones, D. (1990), 'Mathematics Teacher Education' in R. Houston, M. Haberman and J. Sikula (eds.), *Handbook of Research on Teacher Education,* New York: Macmillan.

Burgess, R. G. (1983), *Experiencing Comprehensive Education: A Study of Bishop McGregor School,* London: Methuen.

Burton, L. (1992), 'Evaluating an "entitlement curriculum": mathematics for all?', *The Curriculum Journal,* vol. 3 no. 2, pp. 161-169.

Burton, L. (1994a), 'Clashing Epistemologies of Mathematics Education: Can we see the 'wood' for the 'trees'?', *Curriculum Studies,* vol. 2, no. 2, pp. 203-219.

Burton, L. (1994b), 'Differential performance in assessment in mathematics at the end of compulsory schooling: A European comparison', in L. Burton, (ed.) *Who Counts? Assessing Mathematics in Europe,* UK: Trentham Books Ltd.

Burton, L. (1994c), 'Whose Culture Includes Mathematics?', in S. Lerman (ed.), *Cultural Perspectives on the Mathematics Classroom,* London: Kluwer Academic Publishers.

Burton, L. (1995), 'Moving Towards a Feminist Epistemology of Mathematics', in P. Rogers, and G. Kaiser (eds), *Equity in Mathematics Education: Influences of Feminism and Culture,* London: Falmer Press.

Burton, L. (1996a), 'A socially just pedagogy for the teaching of mathematics' in P.F. Murphy and C.V. Gipps (eds.), *Equity in the Classroom: Towards Effective Pedagogy for Girls and Boys,* London: Falmer Press.

Burton, L. (1996b), 'Equity and the Learning of Mathematics', *Curriculum Studies,* vol. 4, no. 2, pp. 289-295.

Burton, L. (1999a), 'Exploring and reporting upon the content and diversity of mathematicians' views and practices', *For the Learning of Mathematics,* vol. 19, no. 2, pp. 36-38.

Burton, L. (1999b), 'The practices of mathematicians: What do they tell us about coming to know mathematics?', *Educational Studies in Mathematics,* vol. 37, no. 2, pp. 121-143.

Buxton, L. (1981), *Do You Panic About Maths?*, London: Heinemann.

Chambers, D.W. (1983), 'Stereotypic images of the scientist: the draw-a-scientist test', *Science Education*, vol. 67, no. 2, pp. 255-265.

Clancy, P. (2001), *College Entry in Focus: A Fourth National Survey of Access to Higher Education*, Dublin: Higher Education Authority.

Clark, C.M. and Peterson, P.L. (1986), 'Teachers' thought processes', in M.C Wittrock (ed.), *Handbook of Research on Teaching*, 3rd edn, New York: Macmillan

Close, S., Kellaghan, T., Madaus, G.F. and Airasian, P. (1978), 'Growth in mathematical attainment of pupils', *The Irish Journal of Education*, vol. 12, no. 1/2, pp. 3-21.

Cobb, P. (1994), 'Where is the Mind? Constructivist and Sociocultural Perspectives on Mathematical Development', *Educational Researcher*, vol. 23, no. 7, pp.13-20.

Cobb, P., Wood, T., Yacke, E. and McNeal, B. (1992), 'Characteristics of Classroom Mathematics Traditions: An Interactional Analysis', *American Educational Research Journal*, vol. 29, no. 3, pp. 573-604.

Cohen, M. (1998), 'A Habit of Healthy Idleness: Boys' underachievement in historical perspective' in D. Epstein, J. Elwood, V. Hey and J. Maw (eds.), *Failing Boys? Issues in Gender and Achievement*, Buckingham: Open University Press.

Coleman, J. S., Campbell, E.Q., Hobson, C.J., McPartland, J., Mood, A.M., Weinfeld, F.D. and York, R.L. (1966), *Equality of Educational Opportunity*, Washington D.C.: Department of Health, Education and Welfare.

Connell, R.W. (1995), *Masculinities*, Cambridge: Polity Press.

Connell, R.W. (1997), 'The Big Picture: Masculinities in Recent World History', in A.H. Halsey, H. Lauder, P.Brown, and A. Stuart Wells (eds.), *Education: Culture, Economy, Society*, Oxford: Oxford University Press.

Connolly, P. (1998), *Racism, Gender Identities and Young Children: Social Relations in a Multiethnic, Inner City Primary School*, London: Routledge.

Coolahan, J. (1981), *Irish Education*, Dublin: IPA.

Cooper, B., Dunne, M. and Rodgers, N., (1997), 'Social Class, Gender, Item Type and Performance in National Tests of Primary School Mathematics: Some Research Evidence from England', paper presented at the *Annual Conference of the American Educational Research Association*, Chicago, March.

Cooper, B. and Dunne, M. (1998a), 'Anyone for tennis? Social class differences in children's responses to national curriculum mathematics testing', *The Sociological Review*, vol. 46, no. 1, pp. 115-148.

Cooper, B. and Dunne, M., (1998b), 'Social Class, Gender, Equity and National Curriculum Tests in Mathematics', paper presented at *Mathematics Education and Society: An International Conference*, University of Nottingham, September.

Cooper, B. and Dunne, M. (1999), *Social Class Differences in Children's Difficulties with Realistic Mathematics Testing*, Buckingham: Open University Press.

Crozier, G. (2000), *Parents and Schools: Partners or Protagonists?*, Stoke on Trent: Trentham Books.

Cuban, L. (1984), *How Teachers Taught: Constancy and Change in American Classrooms, 1890-1980*, New York: Longman.

Dale, R. (1997), 'The State and the Governance of Education: An Analysis of the restructuring of the State-Education relationship', in A.H. Halsey, H. Lauder, P.Brown, and A. Stuart Wells (eds.), *Education: Culture, Economy, Society*, Oxford: Oxford University Press.

Daly, P. and Shuttleworth, I. (1997), 'Determinants of public examination entry and attainment in mathematics: Evidence on gender and gender-type of school from the 1980s and 1990s in Northern Ireland', *Evaluation and Research in Education,* vol. 11, no. 2, pp. 91-101.

Daly, P. and Defty, N. (2000), 'Investigating variation across high schools in students' attitudes to school, in their attitudes to mathematics and in their achievement of mathematics' Paper presented at the *Annual Meeting of the American Educational Research Association*, New Orleans, April.

David, M. (1993), *Parents, Gender and Education Reform,* Oxford: Polity Press.

Davies, B. (1996), *Power/Knowledge/Desire: Changing School Organisation and Management Practices*, Canberra, Australia: Department of Employment, Education, Training and Youth Affairs.

Davis, P. and Hersh, R. (1983), *The Mathematical Experience*, Harmondsworth: Pelican (Penguin) Books.

Department of Education and Science (1999), *Statistical Report 1997-1998*, Dublin: Dublin Stationery Office.

Department of Education and Science (2000a), *Schools IT2000*, URL: http://www.irlgov.ie/educ/it2000/it2000.htm.

Department of Education and Science (2000b), *Statistical Report 1998-1999*, Dublin: Dublin Stationery Office.

Department of Education and Science (2000c), *Junior Certificate: Mathematics Syllabus*, Dublin: Dublin Stationery Office.

Department of Education and Science (2001), *Statistical Report 1999-2000*, Dublin: Dublin Stationery Office.

Desforges, C. and Cockburn, A. (1987), *Understanding the Mathematics Teacher*, Lewes: Falmer Press.

Devlin, B., Fineberg, S., Resnick, D.P. and Roeder, K. (eds.) (1997), *Intelligence, Genes and Success: Scientists Respond to 'The Bell Curve'*, New York: Springer-Verlag.

Dick, T.P. and Rallis, S.F. (1991), 'Factors and influences on high school student's career choices', *Journal for Research in Mathematics Education*, vol. 22, no. 4, pp. 281-292.

Dorn, S. (1996), *Creating the Dropout: An Institutional and Social History of School Failure*, London: Routledge and Kegan Paul.

Dossey, J. (1992), 'The Nature of Mathematics: Its role and influence', in D.A. Grouws (ed.), *Handbook of Research on Mathematics Teaching and Learning,* New York: Macmillan.

Douglas, J.W.B. (1964), *The Home and the School: A Study of Ability and Attainment in the Primary School,* London: MacGibbon, Kes

Drudy, S. and Uí Catháin, M. (1998), 'Gender differences in classroom interaction in a second level context', *Irish Educational Studies,* vol. 17, pp. 135-147.

Drudy, S. and Uí Catháin, M. (1999), *Gender Equality in Classroom Interaction,* Maynooth: Department of Education, NUI Maynooth.

Duffy, J., Warren, K. and Walsh, M. (2002), 'Classroom Interactions: Gender of Teacher, Gender of Student and Classroom Subject', *Sex Roles,* vol. 45, no. 9/10, pp. 579-593.

Dunne, M. (1994), *The Construction of Ability: A Critical Exploration of Mathematics Teachers' Accounts*, Unpublished PhD Thesis, University of Birmingham, UK.

Dunne, M. (1999), 'Positioned Neutrality: mathematics teachers and the cultural politics of their classrooms', Burton, L. (ed.), *Educational Review: The Culture of the Mathematics Classroom*, vol. 51, no. 2, pp. 117-128.

Dweck, C. S., Davidson, W., Nelson, S. and Enna, B. (1978), 'Sex Differences in learned helplessness: II The contingencies of evaluative feedback in the classroom: III An experimental analysis." *Developmental Psychology*, vol. 14, pp. 268-276.

Eagleton, T. (1983), *Literary Theory*, Oxford: Blackwell.

Eccles, J. (1989), 'Bringing young women to mathematics and science', in M. C. Crawford and M. Gentry (eds.), *Gender and Thought: Psychological Perspectives*, New York: Springer-Verlang.

Eisenstein, Z., (1979), *Capitalist Patriarchy and the Case for Socialist Feminism*, New York: The Monthly Review Press.

Entwisle, D. R., Alexander, K.L. and Olson, L.S. (1994), 'The Gender Gap in Math: Its Possible Origins in Neighborhood Effects', *American Sociological Review*, vol.59, no. 4, pp. 822-838.

Epstein, D. (ed.) (1994), *Challenging Lesbian and Gay Inequalities in Education*, Buckingham: Open University Press.

Epstein, D., Elwood, J., Hey, V. and Maw, J. (eds.) (1998), *Failing Boys? Issues in Gender and Achievement*, Buckingham: Open University Press.

Fanning, B., Veale, A. and O'Connor, D. (2001), *Beyond the Pale: Asylum-seeking children and Social Exclusion in Ireland*, Dublin: Irish Refugee Council and Combat Poverty Agency.

Fennema, E. (1980), 'Sex-related differences in mathematics achievement: Where and why', in L.H. Fox, L. Brody and D. Tobin (eds.), *Women and the Mathematical Mystique*, Baltimore: John Hopkins University Press.

Fennema, E., (1996a), 'Mathematics, gender and research', in G. Hanna (ed.), *Towards Gender Equity in Mathematics Education: An ICMI Study*, Dordrecht: Kluwer Academic Publishing.

Fennema, E. (1996b), 'Scholarship, gender and mathematics' in P.F. Murphy, and C.V. Gipps (eds.) *Equity in the Classroom: Towards Effective Pedagogy for Girls and Boys*, London: Falmer Press.

Fennema, E. and Tartre, L. A. (1985), 'The use of spatial visualization in mathematics by girls and boys', *Journal for Research in Mathematics Education*, vol. 16, no. 3, pp. 184-204.

Fennema, E. and Leder, G.C. (eds.) (1990), *Mathematics and Gender*, New York: Teachers College.

Fennema, E., Peterson, P. L., Carpenter, T.P. and Lubinski, C. (1990), 'Teachers' attributions and beliefs about girls, boys and mathematics', *Educational Studies in Mathematics*, vol. 21, no. 1, pp. 55-69.

Fennema, E., Nelson, B.S. (eds.) (1997), *Mathematics Teachers in Transition*, Mahwah, NJ: Erlbaum.

Fennema, E. and Romberg, T. (eds.) (1999), *Mathematics Classrooms that Promote Understanding: A Volume in the Studies in Mathematical Thinking and Learning Series*, London: Heinemann.

Fontes, P. and Kellaghan, T. (1983), 'Opinions of the Irish public on intelligence', *Irish Journal of Education*, vol. 17, no. 2, pp. 55-67.

Forgasz, H.J. and Leder, G.C. (2001), 'A+ for girls, B for boys: Changing perspectives on gender and equity' in B. Atweh, H.J Forgasz and B. Nebres (eds.), *Sociocultural Research on Mathematics Education: An International Perspective*, New Jersey: Lawrence Erlbaum Associates.

Foucault, M. (1977), *Discipline and Punish*, Harmondsworth: Penguin.

Francis, B. (1999), 'Lads, Lasses and (New) Labour: 14-16 year old students' responses to the 'laddish behaviour and boys' underachievement debate', *British Journal of Sociology of Education,* vol. 20, no. 3, pp. 355-371.

Francis, B. (2000), 'The gendered subject: students' subject preferences and discussion of gender and subject ability', *Oxford Review of Education,* vol. 26, no. 1, pp. 35-48.

Freire, P. (1972), *Pedagogy of the Oppressed,* New York: Penguin.

Gamoran, A. (1986), 'Instructional and Institutional Effect of Ability Grouping', *Sociology of Education,* vol. 59, pp. 185-98.

Gardner, H (1985), *Frames of Mind: The Theory of Multiple Intelligences*, 2nd edn, New York: Basic Books.

Gardner, H. (1993), *Multiple Intelligences: The Theory in Practice,* New York: Basic Books.

Gardner, H. (1999), *Intelligence Reframed: Multiple Intelligences for the 21st Century,* New York: Basic Books.

Gates, P. (ed.) (2001), *Issues in Mathematics Teaching*, London: RoutledgeFalmer,

Gellert, U. (2001), 'Research on attitudes in mathematics education: a discursive perspective' in M. van den Heuvel-Panhhizen (ed.), *Proceedings of the 25th Conference of the International Group for the Psychology of Mathematics Education*, The Netherlands: Freudenthal Institute, vol. 3, pp. 33-40.

Gewirtz, S., Ball, S. and Bowe, R. (1995), *Markets, Choice and Equity in Education*, Buckingham: Open University Press.

Gilligan, C. (1982), *In a Different Voice*, Cambridge, MA: Harvard University Press.

Giroux, Henry (1983), *Theory and Resistance in Education,* London: Heinemann.

Giroux, Henry (1997), *Pedagogy and the Politics of Hope,* Boulder, Col.: Westview Press.

Good, T. and Brophy, J. (2000), *Looking in Classrooms*, 8th edn., New York: Longman.

Gorard, S., Rees, G. and Salisbury, J. (2001), 'The differential attainment of boys and girls at school: Investigating the patterns and their determinants', *British Educational Research Journal* , vol. 27, no.2, pp. 125-139.

Gordon, Tuula (1996), 'Citizenship, difference and marginality in schools: Spatial and embodied aspects of gender construction' in P.F. Murphy, and C.V. Gipps (eds.), *Equity in the Classroom: Towards Effective Pedagogy for Girls and Boys,* London: Falmer Press.

Gravemeijer, K. and Kindt, M. (2001), '"Polar mathematics"- mathematics education in The Netherlands' in M. van den Heuvel-Panhhizen (ed.), *Proceedings of the 25th Conference of the International Group for the Psychology of Mathematics Education*, The Netherlands: Freudenthal Institute, vol. 1, pp. 89-91.

Greaney, V. and Close, S. (1976), 'Mathematics in Irish Primary Schools: A Review of Research', *Oideas*, vol. 38, pp. 41-61.

Gregg, J. (1995a), 'Discipline, control and the school mathematics curriculum', *Teaching and Teacher Education*, vol. 11, no. 6, pp. 579-593.

Gregg, J. (1995b), 'The tensions and contradictions of the school mathematics tradition', *Journal for Research in Mathematics Education*, vol. 26, no. 5, pp. 442-446.

Gregory, R.P. (1986), 'Mixed Ability Teaching – A Rod for the Teacher's Back?', *Journal of Applied Educational Studies*, vol. 15, no. 2, pp. 56-61.

Grouws, D.A. (ed.) (1992), *Handbook of Research on Mathematics Teaching and Learning*, New York: Macmillan.

Hacker, R. G., Rowe, M.J., Evans, R.D. (1991), 'The influences of ability grouping for secondary science lessons upon classroom processes: Part 1: homogeneous groupings', *School Science Review*, vol. 73, no. 262, pp. 125-129.

Hall, C. and Coles, M. (1997), 'Gendered Readings: Helping Boys Develop Critical Readers', *Gender and Education*, vol. 8, no. 3, pp. 311-321.

Hallam, S. and Toutounji, I. (1996), 'What do we know about grouping pupils by ability?', *Education Review*, vol. 10, no. 2, pp. 63-70.

Hammersley, M. (1992), 'On Feminist Methodology', *Sociology*, vol 26, no. 1, pp. 187-206.

Hammersley, M. (1995), *The Politics of Social Research*, London: Sage.

Hannan, D.F., Breen, R. Murray, B., Watson, D., Hardiman, K. and O'Higgins, K. (1983), *Schooling and Sex Roles: Sex Differences in Subject Provision and Student Choice in Irish Post-Primary Schools*, Dublin: ESRI.

Hannan, D.F. and Boyle, M. (1987), *Schooling Decisions: The Origins and Consequences of Selection and Streaming in Irish Post-Primary Schools*, Dublin: ESRI.

Hannan, D. F., Smyth, E., McCullagh, J., O'Leary, R. and McMahon, D. (1996), *Coeducation and Gender Equality: Exam Performance, Stress and Personal Development*, Dublin: Oak Tree Press.

Harding, S. (ed.) (1987), *Feminism and Methodology*, Milton Keynes: Open University Press.

Harding, S. (1991), *Whose Science? Whose Knowledge?: Thinking from Women's Lives*, Milton Keynes: Open University Press.

Hargreaves, A., Earl, L. and Ryan, J. (1996), *Schooling for Change: Revisiting Education for Early Adolescents*, London: Falmer Press.

Harker, R. (2000), 'Achievement, gender and the single-sex/coed debate', *British Journal of Sociology of Education*, vol. 21, no. 2, pp.203-218.

Harre, R. (1981), 'The Post-Empiricist Approach and its Alternative', in P. Reason and J. Rowan (eds.), *Human Inquiry: A Sourcebook of New Paradigm Research*, Chichester: John Wiley and Sons.

Hazin, I. and da Rocha-Falcao, J.T. (2001), 'Self-esteem and performance in school mathematics: A contribution to the debate about the relationship between cognition and affect', in M. van den Heuvel-Panhhizen (ed.), *Proceedings of the 25th Conference of the International Group for the Psychology of Mathematics Education*, The Netherlands: Freudenthal Institute, vol. 3, pp.121-128

Henningsen, M. and Stein, M.K. (1997), 'Mathematical tasks and student cognition: Classroom-based factors that support and inhibit high-level mathematical thinking and reasoning', *Journal for Research in Mathematics Education,* vol. 28, no. 5, pp. 524-549.

Heron, J. (1981), 'Philosophical basis for a new paradigm', in P. Reason, and J. Rowan (eds.), *Human Inquiry: A Sourcebook of New Paradigm Research,* Chichester: John Wiley and Sons.

Holland, D., Lachicotte, W., Skinner, D. and Cain, C. (1988), *Identity and Agency in Cultural Worlds,* Cambridge, MA: Harvard University Press.

Hooks, B. (1994), *Teaching to Transgress: Education as the Practice of Freedom,* New York: Routledge.

Howe, C. (1997), *Gender and Classroom Interaction; A Research Review,* Edinburgh: Scottish Council for Research in Education.

Humphries, B. and Truman, C. (eds.) (1994), *Rethinking Social Research*, Aldershot: Avebury.

Humphries, B. (1997), 'From Critical Thought to Emancipatory Action: Contradictory Research Goals', *Sociological Research Online,* URL: www.socresonline.org.uk/socresonline/2/1/3.html.

Jackson, C. and Warin, J. (2000), 'The importance of gender as an aspect of identity at key transition points in compulsory education', *British Educational Research Journal,* vol. 26, no. 3, pp. 375-391.

Johnston, S. (1994), 'Choosing mathematics: "You need it even if you don't want to do it"', *Australian Journal of Education,* vol. 38, no. 3, pp. 233-249.

Jones, J. (1990), 'Outcomes of girls' schooling: Unravelling some social differences', *Australian Journal of Education*, vol. 34, no. 2: 153-167.

Jones, L. and Smart, T. (1995a), 'The Confidence Factor – Intervention strategies designed to encourage positive attitudes to mathematics', in B. Grevholm, and G. Hanna (eds.), *Gender and Mathematics Education, an ICMI Study,* Lund: Lund University Press.

Jones, L. and Smart, T. (1995b), 'Confidence and mathematics: A gender issue?', *Gender and Education,* vol. 7, no. 2, pp. 157-166.

Jones, M. and Gerig, T. (1994), 'Silent sixth-grade students: characteristics, achievement and teacher expectations', *The Elementary School Journal,* vol. 95, no. 2, pp. 169-182.

Jovanovic, J. and King, S.S. (1998), 'Boys and Girls in the Performance-Based Science Classroom: Who's Doing the Performing?', *American Educational Research Journal,* vol. 35, no. 3, pp. 477-496.

Kahle, J.B. and Meece, J. (1994), 'Research on gender in the classroom', in D. Gabel (ed), *Handbook of Research in Science Teaching and Learning,* New York: Macmillan.

Kaiser, G and Rogers, P. (1995), 'Introduction: Equity in mathematics education', in P. Rogers and G. Kaiser (eds.), *Equity in Mathematics Education,* London: Falmer Press.

Karabenick, S.A. and Knapp, J.R. (1991), 'Relationship of academic help seeking to the use of learning strategies and other instrumental achievement behaviour in college students', *Journal of Educational Psychology,* vol. 83, no. 2, pp. 221-230.

Kawanaka, T., Stigler, J.W. and Hiebert, J., (1999), 'Studying Mathematics Classrooms in Germany, Japan and the United States: Lessons from TIMSS Videotape Study', in G. Kaiser, E. Luna and I. Huntley (eds.), *International Comparisons in Mathematics Education,* London: Falmer Press.

Keitel, C. and Kilpatrick, J. (1998), 'Rationality and irrationality of international comparative studies' in Kaiser, G., Luna, E. and Huntly, I. (eds.), *International Comparisons in Mathematical Education*, London: Falmer Press.

Kelleher, M. (ed) (2000), *Making it New: Essays on the Revised Leaving Certificate English Syllabus*, Dublin: The Lilliput Press.

Kelly, A. (1985a), 'Changing Schools and Changing Society: some reflections on the Girls Into Science and Technology Project', in M. Arnot (ed.), *Race and Gender: Equal Opportunities Policies in Education: A Reader,* Toronto: Pergamon Press.

Kelly, A. (1985b), 'The Construction of Masculine Science', *British Journal of Sociology of Education,* vol. 6, no.2, pp. 133-153.

Kelly, A. (1988), 'Gender differences in teacher-pupil interactions: a meta-analytic review', *Research in Education*, no. 39, pp. 1-23.

Kerry, T. (1982a), 'Mixed Ability Teaching in the Humanities' in M. Sands and T. Kerry (eds.), *Mixed Ability Teaching,* London: Croom Helm.

Kerry, T. (1982b), 'The demands made on pupils' thinking in mixed ability classes' in M. Sands and T. Kerry (eds.), *Mixed Ability Teaching,* London: Croom Helm.

Kilpatrick, J. (1992), 'A history of research in mathematics education', in D.A. Grouws (ed.), *Handbook of Research on Mathematics Teaching and Learning,* New York: Macmillan.

Kimmel, M.S. and Messner, M.A. (1997), *Men's Lives,* Boston/London: Allyn and Bacon.

Lakatos, I. (1976), *Proofs and Refutations*, Cambridge: Cambridge University Press.

Lareau, A. (1989), *Home Advantage: School Class and Parental Intervention in Elementary Schools*, London: Falmer Press.

Lareau, A. and Shumar, W. (1996), 'The Problem of Individualism in Family-School Policies', *Sociology of Education,* Special Issue, vol. 69, pp. 24-39.

Lave, J. and Wenger, E. (1991), *Situated Learning: Legitimate Peripheral Participation*, New York: Cambridge University Press.

Leder, G. (1980), 'Bright girls, Mathematics and the fear of success', *Educational Studies in Mathematics,* vol: 11, no: 4, pp. 411-422.

Leder, G. C. (1989), 'Do girls count in mathematics?' in G.C. Leder and S.N. Sampson (eds.), *Educating Girls: Practice and Research,* Sydney: Unwin Hyman.

Leder, G.C. (1992), 'Measuring attitudes to Mathematics' in W. Geeslin and K. Graham (eds.), *Proceedings of the 16th Conference of the International Group for the Psychology of Mathematics Education,* Durham, N.H.: University of New Hampshire, 2, pp. 33-39.

Leder, G.C. (1992b), 'Mathematics and gender: Changing perspectives', in D.A. Grouws (ed.), *Handbook of Research on Mathematics Teaching and Learning*, New York: Macmillan.

Leder, G.C. (2001), 'Pathways in mathematics towards equity: A 25 year journey', in M. van den Heuvel-Panhhizen (ed.), *Proceedings of the 25th Conference of the International Group for the Psychology of Mathematics Education*, The Netherlands: Freudenthal Institute, vol. 1, pp. 41-54.

Leder, G. C. and Fennema, E. (1990), 'Gender differences in mathematics: A synthesis', in E. Fennema and G. Leder (eds.), *Mathematics and Gender: Influences on Teachers and Students,* New York: Teachers College Press.

Leder, G.C. and Forgasz, H.J. (2000), 'Mathematics and gender: beliefs they are a changin', in J. Bana, and A. Chapman (eds.), *Mathematics Education Beyond 2000: Proceedings of the 23rd Annual Conference of the Mathematics Education Research Group of Australasia Inc.,* Perth: Executive Press, 370-376.

Lee, S. (1993), *Sugar and Spice: Sexuality and Adolescent Girls,* London: Penguin.

Lentin, R. (1993), 'Feminist research methodologies – A separate paradigm? Notes for a debate', *Irish Journal of Sociology,* vol. 3, pp. 119-138.

Lerman, S. (2000), 'The social turn in mathematics education research', in J. Boaler (ed.), *Multiple Perspectives on Mathematics Teaching and Learning,* Connecticut: Ablex Publishing.

Lindquist-Wong, P. (2000), 'New math, same old story: standards-based mathematics curriculum and English language learners', Paper presented at the Annual Meeting of the American Educational Research Association, New Orleans, April.

Lodge, A. (1998), *Gender Identity and Schooling: A Two Year Ethnographic Study of the Expression, Exploration and Development of Gender Identity in Seven to Nine Year Old Children in their School Environment,* Unpublished PhD Thesis, National University of Ireland, Maynooth.

Lortie, D.C. (1975), *Schoolteacher: A Sociological Study,* Illinois: Chicago University Press.

Lynch, K. (1987), 'Dominant Ideologies in Irish Educational Thought: Consensualism, Essentialism and Meritocratic Individualism', *Economic and Social Review,* vol. 18, no. 2, pp. 101-122.

Lynch, K. (1989), *The Hidden Curriculum: Reproduction in Education (A Reappraisal),* Lewes: Falmer Press.

Lynch, K. (1992), 'Intelligence, ability and education: Challenging traditional views', *Oideas.,* vol. 38, pp. 134-148.

Lynch, K. (1999), *Equality and Education,* Dublin: Gill and Macmillan.

Lynch, K. (2000), 'Research and Theory on Equality in Education' in M. Hallinan (ed.), *Handbook of Sociology of Education,* New York: Plenum Press.

Lynch, K. (2001), 'Creating a dialogue between sociological and egalitarian theory in the analysis of inequality in education', *International Studies in Sociology of Education,* vol. 11, no. 3, pp. 237-260.

Lynch, K. and O'Riordan, C. (1998), 'Inequality in Higher Education: A study of class barriers', *British Journal of Sociology of Education,* vol 19, no.4, pp. 445-478.

Lynch, K. and Lodge, A. (2002), *Equality and Power in Schools,* London: Routledge Falmer.

McCaslin, M. and Good, T.L. (1996), 'The Informal Curriculum', in D. Berliner and R. Calfee (eds.), *Handbook of Educational Psychology,* New York: Macmillan.

McDermott, K. (1985), 'Having an equal say: A study of classroom discourse', *The Irish Journal of Education,* vol. 19, no. 2, pp. 61-88.

McDonnell, A. (1995), *The Ethos of Catholic Voluntary Secondary Schools,* unpublished PhD Thesis, Education Department, University College Dublin.

McLaren (1986), 'Teacher education and the politics of engagement: The case for democratic schooling', *Harvard Educational Review,* vol.56, pp. 213-238.

McLaren, P. (1994), *Between Borders: Pedagogy and the Politics of Cultural Studies,* New York: Routledge.

McLeod, D.B. (1992), 'Research on effect in mathematics education: A reconceptualisation', in D.A. Grouws (ed.), *Handbook of Research on Mathematics Teaching and Learning,* New York: Macmillan.

McRobbie, A. (1978), 'Working class girls and the culture of femininity', in Women's Studies Group (eds.), *Women Take Issue: Aspects of Women's Subordination,* London: Hutchinson/CCCS.

Mac An Ghaill, M. (1994), *The Making of Men: Masculinities, Sexualities and Schooling,* Milton Keynes: Open University Press.

Ma, X. (1997), 'Reciprocal relationships between attitude toward mathematics and achievement in mathematics', *Journal of Educational Research,* vol. 90, no.4, pp. 221-229.

Ma, X. (1999), 'A meta-analysis of the relationship between anxiety toward mathematics and achievement in mathematics', *Journal for Research in Mathematics Education,* vol. 30, no. 5, pp. 520-540.

Mahony, P. (1983), 'How Alice's Chin Really Came to be Pressed Against her Foot: Sexist processes in interaction in mixed-sex classrooms', *Women's Studies Int. Forum,* vol. 6, no. 1, pp. 107-115.

Mahony, P. and Zmroczek, C. (eds.) (1997), *Class Matters: Working Class Women's Perspectives on Education,* London: Taylor and Francis.

Martin, J. R. (1996), 'A girls' pedagogy 'in relationship'' in P.F. Murphy and C.V. Gipps (eds.), *Equity in the Classroom: Towards Effective Pedagogy for Girls and Boys,* London: Falmer Press.

Martin, M.O., Hickey, B.L. and Murchan, D.P. (1992), 'The second international assessment of educational progress: Mathematics and science findings in Ireland', *Irish Journal of Education,* vol. 26 (Special Monograph Edition), pp. 3-146.

Martin, M.O., Mullis, I.V., Gregory, K.D., Hoyle, C. and Shen, C. (2000), *IEA's Third International Mathematics and Science Study: Effective Schools in Science and Mathematics,* Boston: TIMSS International Study Centre.

Meyer, J.W. and Rowan, B. (1988), 'The Structure of educational organisations' in A. Westoby (ed.), *Culture and Power in Educational Organisations,* Milton Keynes: Open University Press.

Miller, J. (1996), *School for Women,* London: Virago.

Moane, G. (1999), *Gender and Colonialism: A Psychological Analysis of Oppression and Liberation,* London: Macmillan.

Mura, R. (1987), 'Sex-related differences in expectations of success in undergraduate mathematics', *Journal for Research in Mathematics Education,* vol. 18, pp.15-24.

Murphy, P.F. and Gipps, C.V. (1996), *Equity in the Classroom: Towards Effective Pedagogy for Girls and Boys,* London: Falmer Press.

Murphy, R. and Torrance, H. (1988), *The Changing Face of Educational Assessment,* Milton Keynes: Open University Press.

Murray, C. and Hernstein, R.J. (1994), *The Bell Curve,* New York: Free Press.

Myhill, D. (1999), 'Boy Zones and Girl Power: Gender perceptions and preferences in English', *Curriculum,* vol. 10, no. 2, pp. 86-99.

Myhill, D. (2002), 'Bad Boys and Good Girls? Patterns of interaction and response in Whole Class Teaching', *British Educational Research Journal*, vol. 28, no. 3, pp. 339-352.

Nardi, E. and Steward, S. (2001), 'Observations on the nature of quiet disengagement in the mathematics classroom', in M. van den Heuvel-Panhhizen (ed.), *Proceedings of the 25th Conference of the International Group for the Psychology of Mathematics Education*, The Netherlands: Freudenthal Institute, vol. 3, pp. 407-414.

Nash, R. (2001), 'Class, "ability" and attainment: A problem for the sociology of education', *British Journal for the Sociology of Education*, vol. 22, no. 2, pp. 189-202.

National Council for Curriculum and Assessment (1999), *The Junior Cycle Review Progress Report: Issues and Options for Development*, Dublin: NCCA.

Nelson Le-Gall, S. (1981), 'Help Seeking: An understudied problem solving skill in children', *Developmental Review*, vol. 1, pp. 224-246.

Nickson, M. (1992), 'The culture of the mathematics classroom: An unknown Quantity?', in D.A. Grouws (ed.), *Handbook of Research on Mathematics Teaching and Learning*, New York: Macmillan.

Nussbaum, M. (1995), 'Emotions and women's capabilities' in M. Nussbaum and J. Glover (eds.), *Women, Culture and Development: A Study of Human Capabilities*, Oxford: Oxford University Press.

Oakes, J. (1985), *Keeping Track: How Schools Structure Inequality*, London: Yale University Press.

Oakes, J. (1990), 'Women and Minorities in mathematics and science', in E. Cazden (ed.), *Review of Research in Education*, vol. 16, pp. 135-222, Washington DC: American Educational Research Association.

OECD (1996), *Education at a Glance*, Paris: OECD, Centre for Educational Research and Innovation.

OECD (1997), *Parents as Partners in Schooling*, Paris: OECD, Centre for Educational Research and Innovation.

Oldham, E. (1993), 'Mathematics education: A review of recent research', *Studies in Education*, vol. 9, no. 2, pp. 67-90.

Oldham, E. (1996), 'Trends in mathematical education: Ireland in international perspective', *Studies in Education*, vol. 12, no. 2, pp. 37-51.

Oldham, E. (1997), *Mathematics at Second Level in the Republic of Ireland*, Unpublished Document.

Oldham, E. (2001), 'The Culture of mathematics education in the Republic of Ireland: Keeping the faith?', *Irish Educational Studies*, vol. 20, pp. 266-277.

Oliver, M. (1992), 'Changing the social relations of research production', *Disability,Handicap and Society*, vol. 7, pp. 101-114.

Omvig, C. (1989), *Teacher Student Classroom Interaction in Vocational Education*, Kentucky: University of Kentucky.

Oppenheim, A. N. (1966), *Questionnaire Design and Attitude Measurement*, London : Heinemann.

Pedro, J.D., Wolleat, P., Fennema, E. and Becker, A.D. (1981), 'Election of high school mathematics by females and males: Attributions and attitudes', *American Educational Research Journal*, vol. 18, no. 2, pp. 207-218.

Peterson, P. L. and Fennema, E. (1985), 'Effective teaching, student engagement of classroom activities and sex related differences in learning mathematics', *American Education Research Journal,* vol. 22, pp. 309-335.

Phillips, A. (1987), *Divided Loyalties: Dilemmas of Sex and Class,* London: Virago.

Picker, S.H. and Berry, J.S. (2001), 'Investigating pupils' images of mathematics' in M. van den Heuvel-Panhhizen, (ed.), *Proceedings of the 25th Conference of the International Group for the Psychology of Mathematics Education,* The Netherlands: Freudenthal Institute, vol. 4, pp. 49-56.

Points Commission (1999), *Commission on the Points System: Final Report and Recommendations,* Dublin: Dublin Stationery Office.

Ponte, J.P., Matos, J.F., Guimaraes, H.M., Cunha Leal, L. and Canavarro, A.P. (1992), 'Students' views and attitudes towards mathematics teaching and learning: A case study of a curriculum experience' in W. Geeslin, and K. Graham (eds.), *Proceedings of the 16th Conference of the International Group for the Psychology of Mathematics Education,* Durham, N.H.: University of New Hampshire, vol. 2, pp. 218-225.

Raymond, A.M. (1997), 'Inconsistency between a beginning elementary school teacher's mathematics beliefs and teaching practice', *Journal for Research in Mathematics Education,* vol. 28, no. 5, pp. 550-576.

Reason, P. (ed.) (1988), *Human Inquiry in Action: Developments in New Paradigm Research,* London: Sage.

Reason, P. and Rowan, J. (eds.) (1981), *Human Inquiry: A Sourcebook of New Paradigm Research,* Chichester: John Wiley and Sons.

Reay, D. (1996), 'Contextualising Choice: Social power and parental involvement', *British Educational Research Journal,* vol. 22, no. 5, pp. 581-596.

Reay, D. (1998), 'Rethinking Social Class: Qualitative perspectives on class and gender', *Sociology,* vol. 32, no. 2, pp. 259-275.

Reay, D. and Ball, S.J. (1998), 'Making their minds up': Family dynamics of school choice', *British Educational Research Journal,* vol. 24, no. 4, pp. 41-58.

Rees, D.I., Argys, L.M. and Brewer, D.J. (1996), 'Tracking in the United States: Descriptive statistics from the NELS', *Economics of Education Review,* vol. 15, no. 1, pp. 83-89.

Reid, M. E., Clunies-Ross, L. R., Goacher, B. and Vile, D. (1981), *Mixed Ability Teaching: Problems and Possibilities,* Windsor: NFER-Nelson.

Restivo, S. (1985), *The Social Relations of Physics, Mysticism and Mathematics: Studies in Social Structure, Interests and Ideas,* 2nd edn., Reidel: Dordrecht.

Restivo, S. (1992), *Mathematics in Society and History: Sociological Inquiries,* Dordrecht: Kluwer Academic Publishers.

Reynolds, A.J. and Walberg, H.J. (1992), 'A process model of mathematics achievement and attitude', *Journal for Research in Mathematics Education,* vol. 23, no. 4, pp. 306-328.

Reynolds, T. (1995), 'Boys and English – So what's the problem?', *English and Media Magazine,* vol. 33, pp.15-18.

Robinson, K. (1992), 'Class-room discipline: Power, resistance and gender. A look at teacher perspectives', *Gender and Education,* vol. 4, no. 3, pp. 273-287.

Romberg, T. A., Zarinnia, E. A. and Collis, K. F. (1990), 'A new world view of assessment in mathematics', in G. Kulm (ed.), *Assessing Higher Order Thinking in*

Mathematics, Washington DC: American Association for the Advancement of Science.

Romberg, T. (2001), 'Mathematics goals and achievement in the United States' in M. van den Heuvel-Panhhizen (ed.), *Proceedings of the 25th Conference of the International Group for the Psychology of Mathematics Education,* The Netherlands: Freudenthal Institute, vol. 1, pp. 180-185.

Romberg, T., and Kaput, J. (1999), 'Mathematics worth teaching, mathematics worth understanding' in Fennema, E. and Romberg, T. (eds.), *Mathematics Classrooms that Promote Understanding,* Mahwah, NJ: Lawrence Erlbaum Associates.

Rosenbaum, J.E. (1976), *Making Inequality: The Hidden Curriculum of High School Tracking,* New York: John Wiley & Sons.

Ruffell, M., Mason, J. and Allen, B. (1998), 'Studying attitude to mathematics', *Educational Studies in Mathematics,* vol. 35, no. 1, pp. 1-18.

Ryan, A. M., Gheen, M. H. and Midgley, C. (1998), 'Why do some students avoid asking for help? An examination of the interplay among students' academic efficacy, teachers' social-emotional role, and the classroom goal structure', *Journal of Educational Psychology,* vol. 90, no. 3, pp. 528-535.

Sadker, M. and Sadker, D. (1985), 'Sexism in the schoolroom of the '80s', *Psychology Today,* vol. 19, no. 3, pp.54-57.

Schoenfeld, A.S. (1992), 'Learning to think mathematically: Problem solving, metacognition and sense making in mathematics', in D.A. Grouws (ed.), *Handbook of Research on Mathematics Teaching and Learning,* New York: Macmillan.

Seale,C. (ed.) (1998), *Researching Society and Culture,* Sage: London.

Secada, W.G. (1992), 'Race, ethnicity, social class, language and achievement in mathematics' in D.A. Grouws (ed.), *Handbook of Research on Mathematics Teaching and Learning,* New York: Macmillan.

Secada, W.G. (1995), 'Social and critical dimensions for equity in mathematics education', in W.G. Secada, E. Fennema and L.B. Adajian (eds.), *New Directions for Equity in Mathematics Education,* Cambridge: Cambridge University Press.

Seegers, G. and Boekaerts, M. (1996), 'Gender-related differences in self-referenced cognitions in relation to mathematics', *Journal for Research in Mathematics Education,* vol. 27, no. 2, pp. 215-240.

Shavelson, R. J. and Stern, P. (1981), 'Research on teachers' pedagogical thoughts, judgements, decisions and behaviour', *Review of Educational Research,* vol. 51, no. 4, pp. 455-498.

She, Hsiao-Ching (2000), 'The interplay of a biology teacher's beliefs, teaching practices and gender-based student-teacher classroom interaction', *Educational Research,* vol. 42, no. 1, pp. 100-111.

Shiel, G., Cosgrove, J., Sofroniou, N. and Kelly, A. (2001), *Ready for Life? The Literacy Achievements of Irish 15-Year Olds with Comparative International Data,* Dublin: Educational Research Centre.

Simon, B. (1978), *Intelligence, Psychology and Education,* 2nd edn, London: Lawrence Wishart.

Sirotnik, K. (1983), 'What you see is what you get – consistency, persistence and mediocrity in classrooms', *Harvard Educational Review,* vol. 53, no. 1, pp. 16-31.

Skeggs, B. (1994), 'Refusing to be civilised: "Race", sexuality and power', in H. Afshar and M. Maynard (eds.), *The Dynamics of Race and Gender*, London: Taylor and Francis.

Skeggs, B. (1997), *Formations of Class and Gender*, London: Sage Publications.

Skilbeck, M. (1998), *Education in the OECD, 1990-2010,* Paris: OECD, Mimeo.

Skilbeck, M. (2001), *The University Challenged: A Review of International Trends and Issues with Particular Reference to Ireland*, Dublin: Higher Education Authority, Government Publications Office.

Smith, A. and Glynn, T. (1990), 'Contexts for boys and girls learning mathematics: Teacher interactions and student behaviour in two classrooms', *New Zealand Journal of Psychology,* vol. 19, pp. 9-16.

Smith, D. (1987), *The Everyday World as Problematic,* Buckingham: Open University Press.

Sorenson, A.B. and Hallinan, M.T. (1986), 'Effects of ability grouping on growth in academic achievement', *American Educational Research Journal,* vol. 23, no. 4, pp. 519-542.

Stanley, L. and Wise, S. (1983), *Breaking Out: Feminist Consciousness and Feminist Research*, London: Routledge and Kegan Paul.

Steinbring, H. (2001), 'Analysis of mathematical interaction in teaching processes' in van den Heuvel-Panhhizen, M. (ed.), *Proceedings of the 25th Conference of the International Group for the Psychology of Mathematics Education*, The Netherlands: Freudenthal Institute, vol. 1, pp. 211-215.

Sternberg, R.J. (1998), 'How intelligent is intelligence testing?', *Scientific American*, vol. 9, no. 4, pp. 12-17.

Stigler, J.W. and J. Hiebert (1999), 'Understanding and improving classroom mathematics instruction: An overview of the TIMSS video study' in B. Jaworski and D. Phillips (eds.), *Comparing Standards Internationally: Research and Practice in Mathematics and Beyond,* Oxford Studies in Comparative Education, Wallingford : Symposium.

Sukhnandan, L. and Lee, B. (1998), *Streaming, Setting and Grouping by Ability: A Review of the Literature,* Slough: National Foundation for Educational Research (NFER).

Taber, K. S. (1992), 'Girls' interactions with teachers in mixed physics classes – results of classroom observations', *International Journal of Science Education,* vol. 14, pp. 163-180.

Taole, J.K., Zonneveld, M. and Letsie-Taole, L. (1995), 'Gender Interaction in Mathematics Classrooms: Reflection and Transformation', *Educational Studies in Mathematics*, vol. 28, no. 3, pp.263-274.

Taylor, N. (1993), 'Ability grouping and its effect on pupil behaviour: A case study of a Midlands comprehensive school', *Education Today,* vol. 43, no. 2, pp. 14–17.

Thomas, Kim (1990), *Gender and Subject in Higher Education,* UK: SRHE and Open University Press.

Thompson, A.G. (1992), 'Teachers' beliefs and conceptions: A synthesis of the research' in D.A. Grouws (ed.), *Handbook of Research on Mathematics Teaching and Learning*, New York: Macmillan.

Tobin, K. (1988), 'Target students involvement in high school science', *International Journal of Science Education,* vol. 10, no. 3, pp. 317-330.

Tobin, K. (1993), 'Target Students' in B. Fraser (ed.), *Research Implications for Science and Mathematics Teachers,* vol. 1, Perth, Australia: Curtin University of Technology, National Key Centre for School Science and Mathematics.

Tolmie, A. and Warden, D. (eds.) (1994), *Group and Interactive Learning,* Southampton: Computational Mechanics.

Travers, C.J. and Cooper, C. (1996), *Teachers Under Pressure: Stress in the Teaching Profession,* London: Routledge.

Useem, E. L. (1992), 'Middle schools and math groups: Parents' involvement in children's placement', *Sociology of Education,* vol. 65, pp. 263-279.

van Veen, K., Sleegers, P., Bergen, T. and Klaasen, C. (2001), 'Professional orientations of schoolteachers towards their work', *Teaching and Teacher Education,* vol. 17, pp. 175-194.

Volman, M. and ten Dam, G. (1998), 'Equal but different: Contradictions in the development of gender identity in the 1990s', *British Journal of Sociology of Education,* vol. 19, no. 4, pp. 529-546.

Walkerdine, V. and Lucey, H. (1989), *Democracy in the Kitchen: Regulating Mothers and Socialising Daughters,* London: Virago.

Wang, M.C. and Haertal, G.D. (1995), 'Educational resilience' in M.C. Wang, M.C. Reynolds and H.J. Walberg (eds), *Handbook of Special and Remedial Education Research and Practice,* Oxford: Pergamon.

Warrington, M., Younger, M. and Williams, J. (2000), 'Student attitudes, image and the gender gap' *British Educational Research Journal,* vol. 26, no. 3, pp.393-407.

Watson, A. (1998), 'Potential sources of inequity in teachers' informal judgements about pupils' mathematics', paper presented at *Mathematics Education and Society: An International Conference,* Nottingham, September.

Weiler, K., (1988), *Women Teaching For Change; Gender Class and Power,* Massachusetts: Bergin and Garvey.

Weiler, K. (1991), 'Freire and a Feminist Pedagogy of Difference', *Harvard Educational Review,* vol.61, no.4, pp. 449-474.

Wells, A.S. and Oakes, J. (1996), 'Potential pitfalls of systematic reform: Early lessons from research on detracking', *Sociology of Education,* Special Issue, vol. 69, pp. 135-143.

Wells, A. S. and Serna, I. (1996), 'The politics of culture: Understanding local political resistance to detracking in racially mixed schools', *Harvard Educational Review,* vol. 66, no. 1, pp. 93-118.

Wenger, E. (1998), *Communities of Practice: Learning, Meaning and Identity,* Cambridge: Cambridge University Press.

West, A., Noden, P., Edge, A. and David, M. (1998), 'Parental involvement in education in and out of school', *British Educational Research Association,* vol. 24, no. 4, pp. 461-484.

White, J. (1996), 'Research on English and the teaching of girls' in P.F. Murphy and C.V. Gipps (eds.), *Equity in the Classroom: Towards Effective Pedagogy for Girls and Boys,* London: Falmer Press.

Widmer, C.C.,Goulding, M. and Oldham, E. (1998), 'Problem solving in mathematics: Curriculum and assessment in Ireland, the USA and England and Wales', *Studies in Education, A Journal of Educational Research,* vol. 14, no. 1, pp. 45-54.

Willis, P. (1977), *Learning to Labour: How Working Class Kids get Working Class Jobs*, Fanbrough, Hants: Saxon House.

Younger, Michael, Molly Warrington and Jacquetta Williams (1999), 'The gender gap and classroom interactions: reality and rhetoric', *British Journal of Sociology of Education,* vol. 20, no. 3, pp. 325-341.

Zevenbergen, R. (2000), 'Boys, mathematics and classroom interactions: The construction of masculinity in working-class mathematics classrooms' in O. Zalavsky (ed.), *Proceedings of the 23rd Conference of the International Group for the Psychology of Mathematics Education*, Haifa: PME, vol. 4, pp. 177-184.

Znaniecki, F. (1947), *The Polish Peasant in Europe and America*, Boston: Richard G. Badger.

Index